SOME PROBLEMS

OF

GEODYNAMICS

Dean D. Duffy

SOME PROBLEMS
OF
GEODYNAMICS

BEING AN ESSAY TO WHICH
THE ADAMS PRIZE
IN THE UNIVERSITY OF CAMBRIDGE
WAS ADJUDGED IN 1911

BY

A. E. H. LOVE, M.A., D.Sc., F.R.S.
FORMERLY FELLOW OF ST JOHN'S COLLEGE, CAMBRIDGE
HONORARY FELLOW OF QUEEN'S COLLEGE, OXFORD
SEDLEIAN PROFESSOR OF NATURAL PHILOSOPHY
IN THE UNIVERSITY OF OXFORD

DOVER PUBLICATIONS, INC.
NEW YORK

Published in Canada by General Publishing Company, Ltd., 30 Lesmill Road, Don Mills, Toronto, Ontario.

Published in the United Kingdom by Constable and Company, Ltd., 10 Orange Street, London WC 2.

This Dover edition, first published in 1967, is an unabridged and unaltered republication of the work originally published in 1911 by the Cambridge Unversity Press. It is reprinted by permission of the Cambridge University Press.

Library of Congress Catalog Card Number: 66-30009

Manufactured in the United States of America
Dover Publications, Inc.
180 Varick Street
New York, N.Y. 10014

PREFACE

THE subject selected for the Adams' Prize of 1910 was "Some investigation connected with the physical constitution or motion of the earth." A number of questions on which it is desirable to obtain further knowledge were mentioned; among them were "The stresses in continents and mountains, when the supposition of the existence of the isostatic layer is accepted; the propagation of seismic waves." At the time when this announcement was made, March 1909, I had found that modification of previous theories concerning the effects produced by compressibility in a body of planetary dimensions which forms the basis of the investigations in Chapters VII—X of this Essay, and had sketched a programme of work dealing with the special subject cited above from the announcement. The investigations concerning the effects of the earth's rotation on earth tides did not arise as part of the original programme, but were undertaken after a discussion of the subject at the Winnipeg Meeting of the British Association for the Advancement of Science.

As the analytical investigations in the Essay are rather intricate, it has been thought advisable to prefix an Abstract, stating the special hypotheses and limitations in accordance with which the various problems are discussed, and describing the conclusions which have been reached.

My best thanks are due to the authorities of the Cambridge University Press for the readiness with which they have met all my wishes in regard to the printing.

A. E. H. L.

April, 1911.

TABLE OF CONTENTS

CHAPTER IV

PAGE

GENERAL THEORY OF EARTH TIDES

CHAPTER V

EFFECT OF INERTIA ON EARTH TIDES

CHAPTER VI

EFFECT OF THE SPHEROIDAL FIGURE OF THE EARTH ON EARTH TIDES

CHAPTER VII

GENERAL THEORY OF A GRAVITATING COMPRESSIBLE PLANET

CHAPTER VIII

EFFECT OF COMPRESSIBILITY ON EARTH TIDES

CHAPTER IX

PAGE

THE PROBLEM OF GRAVITATIONAL INSTABILITY

CHAPTER X

VIBRATIONS OF A GRAVITATING COMPRESSIBLE PLANET

CHAPTER XI

THEORY OF THE PROPAGATION OF SEISMIC WAVES

ABSTRACT

THE first three Chapters deal with the problem of determining the Stress produced in the Interior of the Earth by the Weight of Continents and Mountains. Chapter I contains a brief discussion of the distribution of land and water on the surface of the globe. This discussion is designed to evaluate roughly the amplitudes of those spherical harmonic inequalities which are most prominent in the shape of the lithosphere. By the lithosphere is here meant the surface of the land in places where there is land, and the surface at the bottom of the sea in places where there is sea. The most important deviation of this surface from a spherical form is the inequality specified by the ellipticity of the meridians; but this inequality is without influence upon the distribution of land and water, for the lithosphere and the surface of the sea both have elliptic meridians, and the difference of their ellipticities is trifling. After the ellipticity of the meridians the most prominent inequalities are those which are manifested in the existence of a single continental block, embracing all the continents, and surrounding two great areas of depression, the basin of the Pacific Ocean and the basin of the Atlantic and Indian Oceans, the portions of the Southern Ocean which lie to the south of these oceans respectively being counted as parts of them. The inequalities manifested in mountain ranges and deeps have not nearly so much importance in regard to the figure of the Earth as a whole.

In Chapter I it is explained how the shape of the lithosphere could, if the elevation or depression of every point above or below a mean level were known accurately, be expressed by equating the radius vector, which joins the centre of gravity and a point of assigned latitude and longitude, to a sum of spherical surface harmonics, which are definite functions of the latitude and longitude, each provided with a suitable coefficient. Further it is shown, on the basis of previous work by the writer, that the inequalities manifested in the continental block and ocean basins may be represented roughly by restricting the sum in question to harmonics of the first, second, and third degrees. It appears that the elevations and depressions answering to the first and third harmonics are nearly equal, the third slightly the greater, and greater than those answering to the second harmonic; and that an amplitude of 2 km., implying, in the case of the uneven harmonics, a range of 4 km. from greatest elevation to greatest depression, and, in the case of the second harmonic, a range of 3 km., would be amply sufficient to express the elevation of the actual mean surface of the land above the bottom of the sea.

Such deviations from the spherical figure as are manifested in the continental block and the ocean basins, and in mountains and deeps, imply the existence within the earth of tangential stresses. They could not be maintained if the stress at every point across every plane passing through the point were normal to the plane. The maintenance of the ellipticity due to the rotation does not require any tangential stress. In Chapter II it is explained that the problem of finding the stress required for the support of continents and mountains is strictly indeterminate, as it would admit of an infinite number of solutions founded on different hypotheses; and a solution is sought on the basis of isostasy. Even when this hypothesis is adopted the problem is still indeterminate, and that in two ways. In the first place the hypothesis, as developed by previous writers, lacks precision. In the second place the equations of equilibrium of a solid body, subjected to its own gravitation, do not suffice for the determination of the stress within it until some relation between stress and strain is introduced; and, in the present problem, the notion of strain is inappropriate, because the earth is not strained from a state without continents and mountains to a state possessing these features. It becomes necessary to make two assumptions. The first assumption amounts to assigning a special form to the hypothesis of isostasy. According to the hypothesis, the inequalities of the earth's figure (apart from the ellipticity due to the rotation) are associated with inequalities of density in a superficial layer, the thickness of which is about one-fiftieth of the radius, in such a way that the stress in the interior parts is hydrostatic pressure which is not affected by the inequalities of density. This condition could be satisfied by an infinite number of laws of density in the layer, and the special law which is chosen is dictated by analytical convenience. It proves to be convenient to assign a form to the inequalities of potential that are due to the inequalities of density, and to deduce a law of density which, it must be admitted, appears to be rather artificial. This is effected by taking the inner surface of the superficial layer, or "layer of compensation," to be a spherical surface of radius b, and the mean outer surface to be a concentric spherical surface of radius a, and supposing that the terms which are contributed to the potential at any point within the layer by the inequalities of density contain as factors the expressions $(a-r)$ and $(r-b)^2$, where r denotes the distance of the point from the centre of the spherical surfaces. The rotation is neglected. The factor $(a-r)$ secures that, in spite of the inequalities, the mean outer surface is an equipotential surface, a condition which must be fulfilled, at least approximately, if the theory is to be brought into accord with geodetic observations. The factor $(r-b)$ must occur, and be repeated, if, as is laid down in the hypothesis, the stress at every point within the inner surface of the layer across every plane passing through the point is normal to the plane. Clearly the function by which the potential due to the inequalities is expressed is not determined by the condition of possessing the two factors $(a-r)$ and $(r-b)^2$. To any spherical harmonic inequality of the surface there must answer a term of this potential which contains also, as another factor, the spherical surface harmonic expressing the inequality. This term may, without affecting the hypothesis, be multiplied by any function of r. By choosing this function in various ways we could arrive at an infinite number of laws of density in the layer, all of them equally compatible with the hypothesis of isostasy. The law actually chosen is obtained by taking this function to be the lowest power of r for which the equations of the problem can be integrated without introducing any logarithmic terms. The corresponding inequalities of density are deduced from the inequalities of potential by Poisson's rule. Apart from these inequalities, the density of the layer of compensation is taken to be uniform. No assumption is made in regard to the distribution of density of the matter within the inner surface of the layer, except that it is symmetrical about the centre. Even when the law of density is settled, in the sense described above, the problem of determining the stress remains indeterminate, and it is necessary to make another assumption in order to render it determinate. The second assumption relates to the subsidiary equations which take the place occupied by stress-strain relations in the ordinary theory of elasticity. It is assumed that, apart from a hydrostatic pressure, the stress at any point in the layer is related to a vector quantity, called the "fictitious displacement," in the same way as the stress in an isotropic elastic solid body, which is slightly strained, is related to the displacement of the body, and further that the divergence of this vector vanishes, as it would do if the vector denoted an actual displacement in an incompressible solid. This assumption must be distinguished from the assumption that the earth behaves as an incompressible solid body which undergoes a slight strain.

On the basis of the two assumptions described above the equations of equilibrium of the earth are formed, and the solution corresponding to any spherical harmonic inequality is obtained. The strength which the material of the layer must have in order to support an inequality of assigned amplitude, and specified by an assigned spherical surface harmonic, is to be determined by calculating the "stress-difference," which is the difference between the algebraically greatest and least principal stresses at a point. Formulae for calculating the stress-difference answering to any zonal harmonic inequality are obtained. The solution of the equations of equilibrium is expressed in terms of a number of definite integrals, and these are not at first evaluated analytically, but the solution is completed in an approximate fashion for inequalities which are expressed by zonal harmonics of low degrees. The work is simplified by taking the mean density of the matter within the inner surface of the layer of compensation to be twice the mean density of the matter of the layer, in accordance with the known fact that the mean density of the earth is about twice the mean density of surface rocks. The stress-difference which is calculated, in accordance with the assumptions described above, as that necessary to support an inequality, specified by a spherical harmonic inequality of the first, second or third degree, and having an amplitude of 2 km., is much smaller than the tenacity, or the crushing strength, of any ordinary solid material. In particular, in the case of the harmonic of the third degree, it is less than $\frac{1}{88}$ of a metric tonne per square cm. For the support of similar inequalities of the first and second degrees smaller tenacities would be required. Further it appears that, for harmonic inequalities of the first degree, the maximum stress-difference occurs at a depth equal to one-third of the thickness of the layer of compensation, and beneath places where the gradient of the superficial inequality is steepest. For harmonics of the second and third degrees, it occurs at a slightly smaller depth, and beneath places intermediate between those where the height of the superficial inequality is greatest and those where the gradient is steepest. As the crushing strengths of various kinds of granite have been measured as $\frac{2}{5}$ of a metric tonne per square cm. and upwards, it may be concluded that no exceptional strength is needed in the materials of the layer in order to support a continental block and ocean basins, of such dimensions as those which actually exist on the earth, but these could be maintained easily by any ordinary solid material. The theory gives no support to the doctrine that the earth is a "failing structure."

In Chapter III the analysis developed in the previous Chapter is adapted to the problem of determining a stress-system by which inequalities that may be taken to represent mountains could be supported. Such inequalities may be taken to be expressed by zonal spherical harmonics of rather high degrees. The solution of the equations of equilibrium obtained in Chapter II is completed by an analytical evaluation of the definite integrals that occur in it, and by a numerical calculation of their values in the special case where the degree of the spherical harmonic concerned is 50, which is the assumed ratio of the mean radius of the earth to the mean thickness of the layer of compensation. The corresponding stress-difference is calculated approximately. It appears that it is greatest at the mean surface, and beneath places where the height of the superficial inequality is greatest. The solution is adapted to the special case of a series of parallel mountain-ranges at distances apart equal to about 400 km., and with crests at a height of about 4 km. above the valley bottoms; and, as in the previous Chapter, the work is simplified by taking the mean density of the matter within the inner surface of the layer of compensation to be twice the mean density of the matter composing the layer. The stress-difference which is calculated, in accordance with the assumptions described above, as that necessary to support such mountains is about the tenacity of sheet-lead, or a little greater than half the crushing strength of moderately strong granite. From this theory it would appear that much stronger materials are required to support existing mountains than to support existing continents. The theory is however imperfect, because existing mountains are much less well represented by means of a few zonal harmonic inequalities than existing continents.

The next three Chapters of the Essay, Chapters IV—VI, deal with the problem of Earth Tides. In Chapter IV there is given a *résumé* of the work of previous writers. As this Chapter is explanatory, and does not contain any intricate analysis, it may suffice here to state that it is designed to bring out the points which have not been elucidated in previous discussions of the problem. One of these points is the fact, disclosed by Dr Hecker's observations, that the force which disturbs a horizontal pendulum at Potsdam is a larger fraction of the tide-generating force when it acts east or west than when it acts north or south. The suggestion, made by Sir George Darwin, that this phenomenon may be due to the rotation of the earth, seemed to demand that the effect of rotation should be investigated. An investigation of this effect is undertaken and carried out in the two following Chapters. This investigation is based upon certain simplifying assumptions which may be stated here. The first assumption is that the earth may be treated as a homogeneous solid body, the material of which is absolutely incompressible, but possesses a finite degree of rigidity. The second assumption is that, apart from the action of tide-generating forces, this body is in a state of initial stress, by which its own gravitation is balanced throughout its mass, while the body rotates uniformly about an axis passing through its centre of gravity. The third assumption is that the figure of the body, when undisturbed, is an ellipsoid of revolution about this axis, the ellipticity, supposed small, being connected with the angular velocity in the same way as it would be if the material were homogeneous incompressible fluid. This involves the further assumption that the initial stress is hydrostatic pressure. These assumptions involve the hypothesis that, when the body is disturbed, the stress at any point is compounded of the initial hydrostatic pressure and an additional stress, which depends upon the displacement produced by the disturbing forces in the same way as the stress in an incompressible solid body, which is slightly strained from a state of zero stress, depends upon the relative displacements of the parts of the body. In the problem in hand the disturbing force may be taken to be the tide-generating force of the moon; and, according to a well-known analysis, this force is derived from a potential, which can be expressed as a sum of terms, every term being the product of a spherical solid harmonic of the second degree, a simple harmonic function of the time, and a constant coefficient. The most important term of this sum is the term which answers to the principal lunar semi-diurnal tide, and the period of that simple harmonic function of the time which is a factor of this term is half a lunar day. The investigation is restricted to determining those effects which are simple harmonic functions of the time and have this period, that is to say it is conducted as if the corresponding term of the tide-generating potential were the only one.

In Chapter V it is explained how the problem may be treated approximately, in accordance with the assumptions stated above, as that of finding a correction to the known solution of the problem of determining the displacement that would be produced in a homogeneous incompressible solid sphere by constant forces, these forces being derived from a potential which is proportional to a spherical solid harmonic of the second degree. It is shown that the desired correction must consist of two parts, one depending upon the inertia of the body, and the other upon the ellipticity of its figure. These are described as the "correction for inertia" and the "correction for ellipticity." The rest of Chapter V is occupied with the working out of the correction for inertia. It is shown that the problem can be reduced to the statical problem of determining the displacement that would be produced in a homogeneous, incompressible solid sphere by a certain system of body forces. The ordinary solution of this problem cannot, however, be adapted to the question in hand, and the solution necessarily introduces new features. For the various questions which arise, and the methods adopted for dealing with them, the reader must be referred to the Chapter itself. The result which is obtained may be stated as follows:—In addition to the inequality determined by the ordinary known theory, the periodic tide-generating force raises two inequalities in the surface, one expressed by a constant multiple of the tide-generating potential, and the other expressed by a certain spherical harmonic of the fourth degree. The potential of the forces which can disturb a horizontal pendulum contains additional terms proportional to the same two spherical harmonics. The first does not alter the ratio of the forces which act in the east-west and north-south directions, but, in consequence of the presence of the second term, there is a force acting on the pendulum against the moon's force in the north-south direction, but not in the east-west direction. The sense of the correction is therefore precisely that required by Hecker's result, as, indeed, it is obvious beforehand that it should be. The magnitude of the correction is calculated on the assumption that the rigidity is about that of steel. It turns out to be so small as to be quite outside the limits of error of observation. Without any analysis it could be expected that the correction would be proportional to the quantity $a\omega^2/g$, where a denotes the mean radius of the earth, ω the angular velocity of rotation, g the mean value of gravity at the surface; but this quantity might have been multiplied by a rather large coefficient. The result found is that it is multiplied by a rather small coefficient. No probable value of the rigidity will make the coefficient large.

Chapter VI contains an investigation on similar lines of the correction for ellipticity. It is explained how the problem may be reduced to that of expressing the boundary-conditions which hold at the surface of the disturbed ellipsoid of revolution to boundary-conditions which hold at the surface of a sphere of equal volume. This reduction requires a considerable amount of rather intricate analysis, for which the reader must be referred to the Chapter itself. The result which comes out is that, in addition to the inequality produced by tide-generating forces in a homogeneous incompressible solid *sphere*, these forces raise two inequalities in the surface of the ellipsoid of revolution, one proportional to the tide-generating potential, and the other expressed by a spherical harmonic of the fourth degree. The potential of the forces which can disturb a horizontal pendulum contains two additional terms which are proportional to the same two spherical harmonics. The correction for ellipticity affects the forces which can disturb a horizontal pendulum in two ways. In the first place the additional terms in the potential must be taken into account. In the second place the forces must be derived from the potential by forming derivatives in the directions of meridians and parallels drawn on the ellipsoid of revolution, not on the sphere of equal volume. It appears that the forces in both directions, east-west as well as north-south, are subject to correction, and both are altered by amounts which are multiples of the ellipticity. The corrections are calculated for the latitude of Potsdam on the supposition that the rigidity is about that of steel. It is found that both forces are increased, the east-west component less than the north-south component. Thus the sense of the correction is opposite to that required by Hecker's result. It is obvious beforehand that the magnitude of the correction should be proportional to the ellipticity, but, without investigation, the sense of the correction could not be guessed, and its magnitude might have been such that the ellipticity would have to be multiplied by a rather large coefficient. The coefficient by which it is actually multiplied differs but little from unity, and therefore the correction falls almost outside the limits of error of the observations.

From these investigations it appears to be unlikely that the effect observed by Hecker is due to the rotation of the earth. Although simplifying assumptions are introduced, it is improbable that they can affect the sense or that they can affect very much the order of magnitude of the corrections which should be made on account of the rotation. By making similar assumptions, and taking account of deviations from the spherical figure other than the ellipticity, and expressed by spherical harmonics of low degrees, it would be possible to work out similar corrections in order to express the effects which might be due to the distribution of land and water; but, after what has been done, it would seem to be very improbable that such effects would be large enough to be observed. But, if the cause of the observed effect is not to be sought either in the rotation of the earth or in the distribution of land and water, it may be suggested that it is possibly due to the attraction of the tide-wave in the North Atlantic and its pressure on the bed of the ocean. A rough calculation sketched at the end of Chapter VI indicates that these causes may be of about the right order of magnitude to produce the observed result if they are timed properly.

After the Essay was in type my attention was called to an investigation of Earth Tides which had been conducted by A. Orloff* at Yurief (Dorpat). He used two horizontal pendulums, hung in the meridian plane and the plane of the prime vertical, and supported in a different way from those used by Hecker, and he adopted a different method of reducing his observations. The results which he found are similar to those found by Hecker. The lunar semi-diurnal parts of the observed effects show a close agreement of phase with the corresponding part of the tide-generating force, the observed deflexions of the pendulums are on the average a little less than two-thirds of what they would be if the earth were absolutely rigid, and the force that deflects a horizontal pendulum at Dorpat is a larger fraction of the tide-generating force when it acts east or west than when it acts north or south. If the results were expressed by a diagram, as on p. 55, the inner curve would be flatter than the outer in the same direction as in that diagram, but not nearly so much, the ratio of the major axes of the inner and outer curves at Dorpat being about 0·65, and that of the minor axes about 0·55. These results appear to be in accordance with the above explanation of the phenomenon observed by Hecker; for a horizontal pendulum at Dorpat (Lat. about 60° N., Long. about 27° E.) would be much less affected by the tide-wave in the North Atlantic Ocean than a similar instrument at Potsdam (Lat. about 53° N., Long. about 13° E.).

The next four Chapters of the Essay, Chapters VII—X, are devoted to the Dynamics of a Gravitating Compressible Body of Planetary Dimensions. In the classical solutions of the problems of corporeal tides and the vibrations of the earth, considered as a spherical solid body, the assumption was made that the substance could be treated as incompressible. The remarkable effects that could be caused by compressibility were first brought to light by Jeans, but he found it necessary to regard the self-gravitation of the body as balanced in the undisturbed state by external body forces, instead of being balanced, as it must be, by internal stress. A theory of the balancing of the self-gravitation by "initial" stress, which was worked out in detail by the author, is now found to stand in need of modification. In that theory it was assumed that the stress at any point of the body when disturbed consists

* A. Orloff, "Beobachtungen über die Deformation des Erdkörpers unter dem Attraktionseinfluss des Mondes an Zöllnerschen Horizontalpendeln." *Astr. Nachrichten*, Nr. 4446, Bd. 186 (October, 1910).

of two stress-systems:—the *initial* stress and the *additional* stress. The initial stress was taken to be hydrostatic pressure; and the additional stress was taken to be related to the strain, by which the body passes from the undisturbed state to the disturbed state, by the same formulae as hold in an isotropic elastic solid body which is slightly strained from a state of zero stress. The modification which it is now proposed to make in the theory consists in a different way of assigning the value of the hydrostatic pressure (constituting the initial stress) at a point of the disturbed body. When a small portion of the undisturbed body around a geometrical point P is displaced so as to become a small portion of the disturbed body around a neighbouring geometrical point Q, it suffers dilatation and distortion. In the Essay it is regarded as carrying its initial pressure with it and acquiring an additional stress which depends upon the dilatation and distortion. Thus the stress at Q in the disturbed body is here regarded as compounded of the hydrostatic pressure at P in the undisturbed body and a stress correlated in the usual way with the displacement. In my previous theory the hydrostatic pressure at the geometrical point Q in the disturbed body was taken to be the same as the hydrostatic pressure at the same geometrical point Q (not P) in the undisturbed body. In Chapter VII this modification of the theory is explained in detail, and the equations of vibratory motion are formed in accordance with it. For simplicity it is assumed that the body in the undisturbed state is homogeneous. A typical solution of the equations is found. The typical solution contains a single spherical solid harmonic, and more general solutions can be obtained by a synthesis of typical solutions. It appears that the functions of the radius that are involved in the typical solutions are already well-known, but the parameters, by which, in these functions, the radius is multiplied, are the roots of a quadratic equation, the coefficients in which involve the frequency of vibration, the elastic constants, and the density of the body. The special equations which express the condition that the bounding surface is free from traction are obtained. A short discussion is given of the special formulae which hold when the displacement is purely radial.

The first application of the general theory of Chapter VII is to determine the Effect of Compressibility on Earth Tides. This is discussed in Chapter VIII. Solutions of this problem have been obtained by various writers, but in none of them is proper account taken of the initial stress. It was, as a matter of fact, by an attempt to apply my previous theory of initial stress to the problem that I found that that theory needed modification; for it led to the surprising result that the (compressible) earth should yield less to tide-generating forces than it would do if it were incompressible. A new solution of the problem is here obtained on the basis of the modified theory developed in Chapter VII, and the results that are obtained are entirely in accordance with what might be expected. The problem is treated as a statical one. The earth is treated as an elastic solid body, which, in the undisturbed state, is homogeneous and bounded by a spherical surface, and it is assumed that, in the undisturbed state, the gravitation of the body is balanced throughout its mass by hydrostatic pressure. The rigidity of the material composing the body is taken to be about that of steel, and it is found that, if the Poisson's ratio of the material is $\frac{1}{3}$, the height of the corporeal tide is increased, on account of the compressibility, by about 10 per cent. of itself, while, if the Poisson's ratio of the material is $\frac{1}{4}$, the increase is about 20 per cent. It is known that the earth actually yields less to tide-generating forces than it would do if it were homogeneous and incompressible, the rigidity being supposed to be adjusted in accordance with the assumptions of homogeneity and incompressibility and the results of horizontal pendulum observations. It is also known that the effect of heterogeneity (the density increasing from surface to centre) is to diminish the yielding, while the effect of compressibility is now found to be an increase of the yielding, as could be expected beforehand. It appears therefore that heterogeneity of density produces more important effects in modifying the resistance which the earth offers to disturbing forces than does the compressibility of the substance.

The next application of the general theory of Chapter VII is to the problem of Gravitational Instability. The problem arises from the fact that gravitating matter tends to condense towards any part where the density is in excess of the average. In a body of ordinary size this tendency is checked by the elastic resistance of the body, but in a body of planetary dimensions the resistance may be insufficient to hold the tendency in check. For example, it might be impossible for a body of the size and mass of the earth to exist in a homogeneous state. If such a body existed for an instant it might be unstable, and then the slightest change of density in any part would be followed by a large progressive change which would only come to an end when equilibrium in a new configuration, differing appreciably from the original one, was reached. To investigate the question for a body of given constitution in a given configuration, we have to begin by forming the equations of vibration of the body, supposed to be slightly disturbed from that configuration, and then to seek the conditions that must be satisfied if there can be a vibration of zero frequency. For the sake of simplicity we may begin by considering a body of the same size and mass as the earth to be formed of homogeneous material, and seek the conditions that that body may be gravitationally stable. A first solution of this problem was given some years ago by J. H. Jeans. He avoided all questions of initial stress by assuming that, in the undisturbed state, the self-gravitation of the body was balanced by an external system of body forces. He found that when the body is disturbed, so that the radial displacement at a point is proportional to a spherical harmonic of an assigned degree, the condition for the existence of a vibration of zero frequency became a transcendental equation to determine a certain modulus of elasticity of the material as a multiple of $g\rho_0 a$, where g denotes the mean value of gravity at the surface, ρ_0 the density in the undisturbed state, and a the mean radius. The equation in question contained also, as a parameter, the ratio of the rigidity to the incompressibility. It was found that the elastic resistance necessary to render the body stable in regard to disturbances specified by spherical harmonics of the first degree would be sufficient to render it stable in regard to disturbances specified by spherical harmonics of any higher degree. The conditions necessary to secure stability in regard to radial disturbances were not discussed. It was taken as probable that, if a homogeneous body with certain elastic constants is unstable in respect of disturbances specified by spherical harmonics of any degree, a heterogeneous body, with not very different values of the *average* elastic resistances to compression and distortion, would be unstable in respect of the same type of disturbances. It was found that in accordance with the assumptions here described the earth would be gravitationally stable if it were homogeneous, the average rigidity and incompressibility of its substance being those deduced from the theory of seismic waves; but it was suggested that, if the earth was once in such a condition as regards elastic resistance to compression and distortion that, if homogeneous, it would have been gravitationally unstable, it should now exhibit some traces of this past state, and that such traces might be found in the existing distribution of land and water on the surface of the globe. In particular, it was pointed out that the geographical fact of the land and water hemispheres was in accordance with the result that the instability would manifest itself in respect of disturbances specified by spherical harmonics of the first degree.

A second solution of the problem was afterwards given by the present writer on the basis of that theory of initial stress which has already been mentioned. In its main results this solution did not differ very much from that given by Jeans, but one result that was found was that if the body, supposed homogeneous, was unstable at all it would be unstable as regards radial displacements. On this theory therefore, if the land and water hemispheres could be traces of a past state, in which the earth would have been unstable unless the mass of one hemisphere had been greater than that of the other, it would be necessary that the argument stated above as to the average values of the elastic resistances in a heterogeneous body should be sound. At the same time it was shown how the rotation could be taken into account. The modes of vibration of a rotating body in the form of a planetary ellipsoid can be correlated with those of a sphere at rest; and it was proved that to such modes of the sphere as are specified by spherical harmonics of the first degree there would answer, in the ellipsoid, modes specified by harmonics of the first, second, and third degrees properly superposed. It was pointed out that the earth does exhibit prominent inequalities of these degrees. The idea that the main features in the shape of the earth might be due to its having once been in such a state that, if its mass had been arranged symmetrically around its centre, it would have been unstable, seemed to be of sufficient interest to make it desirable to obtain a fresh solution on the basis of the new theory of initial stress. This is given in Chapter IX of this Essay. The new results throw some further light upon the question. It remains true, in so far as the problem has been examined, that elastic resistances which are sufficient to secure stability in respect of disturbances specified by spherical harmonics of the first degree are also sufficient to secure stability in respect of disturbances specified by spherical harmonics of any higher degree; and it also remains true that, if the ratio of the elastic resistances to compression and distortion is neither large nor small compared with the values which it has for ordinary solid materials, subjected to experiment at the earth's surface, then elastic resistances which are sufficient to secure stability in respect of radial displacements are amply sufficient to secure stability in respect of displacements specified by spherical harmonics of the first or any higher degree. But the interesting result is found that, if the rigidity is rather small compared with the resistance to compression, the body may be unstable in respect of displacements specified by spherical harmonics of the first degree although stable as regards radial displacements. This result is distinctly favourable to the hypothesis that the division of the earth's surface into a land hemisphere and a water hemisphere may be a survival from a past state in which a symmetrical arrangement of the matter about the centre would have been unstable. The superficial displacements which occur in any mode of vibration of the body, whether of zero frequency or not, are associated with inequalities in the density, and these are of the same spherical harmonic type as the radial inequality of figure, so that, if the actual inequalities of the figure of the earth, or any large part of them, can be traced to the cause under consideration, the elevations and depressions of the surface should be compensated by defects or excesses of density in the underlying material, as is assumed in the theory of isostasy. It seemed therefore to be worth while to examine the distribution of density which a sphere would take up if it were unstable when homogeneous, with no tendency to condense towards the centre (stability as regards radial displacements), but with a tendency to sway to one side, so that one hemisphere would have a preponderant mass (instability as regards displacements specified by spherical harmonics of the first degree). The result is not very favourable to the hypothesis. It is found that the inequalities of density would be deep-seated, instead of being practically confined to a superficial layer, as the doctrine of isostasy lays it down that they should be. It must, however, be understood that the results have been obtained by making several simplifying assumptions. The body of which the gravitational stability is examined is assumed to have the same size and mass as the earth, it is assumed to be homogeneous as regards the distribution of its density and as regards its elastic resistances to compression and distortion, it is assumed that, in the undisturbed state, the initial stress by which the self-gravitation of the body is balanced throughout its mass is simply hydrostatic pressure. It is possible that the result might be different if the problem could be solved for a body of which the density increases from surface to centre and the elastic resistances to compression and distortion are different at different depths. It is also possible that the part of the earth's volume within which there is compensation of the superficial inequalities of figure by inequalities of density may now be more restricted than it was once, or, in other words, that in the course of long ages an inequality which was once appreciable at great depths may have been progressively diminishing, and diminishing faster near the centre than near the surface. This suggestion is, however, rather speculative. In Chapter IX the problem of gravitational instability is solved for an initially homogeneous sphere, the material of which is supposed to possess resistances to compression and distortion which are in one or other of certain definite ratios, and the displacements of which, with their accompanying inequalities of density, are taken to be either symmetrical about the centre or specified by spherical harmonics of the first, second, or third degree.

Chapter X is devoted to a determination of the Normal Modes of Vibration of a Gravitating Compressible Sphere. The sphere is taken to be homogeneous in the undisturbed state, and to be of sufficient rigidity to secure gravitational stability. The modes fall into two classes in exactly the same way as those of a sphere which is free from gravitation; and the modes of the first class, characterized by the absence of radial displacement, are unaffected by gravitation. If the rigidity is small enough, the modes of the second class are of two kinds, which may be described roughly as vibrations governed mainly by elasticity and vibrations governed mainly by gravity. The latter have the smaller frequencies, and the two kinds of modes are described in the Essay as being of "quick types" and "slow types" respectively. If the rigidity has one or other of a certain determinate set of values, there may be vibrations of intermediate types. The particular case of vibrations specified by spherical harmonics of the second degree is worked out in detail, and it is found that, for a body of the size and mass of the earth, there are no vibrations in modes of this degree, which are of slow or intermediate types, if the Poisson's ratio of the material is $\frac{1}{4}$, and the rigidity is great enough to secure stability in respect of radial displacements. It is known that, for a homogeneous sphere which is free from gravitation, the gravest of all the normal modes of vibration is of a type in which the sphere becomes an harmonic spheroid of the second degree, and that, if the sphere has the same size and mass as the earth, and the material is incompressible and as rigid as steel, the period of these vibrations is about 66 minutes. It is known also that, if gravitation is taken into account, but the other conditions, including that of incompressibility, are maintained, the period is reduced to about 55 minutes. It is now found that, when account is taken of compressibility as well as gravitation, the period is almost exactly one hour, the Poisson's ratio of the material being taken to be $\frac{1}{4}$.

The theory of the vibrations of a body of planetary dimensions leads naturally to a discussion of the theory of Seismic Waves. This theory is considered in Chapter XI. The Chapter begins with a description of the most important steps that have been taken in the interpretation of seismic records, accompanied by a statement of the chief points in respect of which the existing theory seems to require extension. These relate to the oscillatory character of the recorded movements and the nature of the Large Waves. To elucidate these matters a series of problems are solved. The first of these problems is to determine the laws of transmission of waves through a gravitating compressible planet. On the basis of the dynamical theory developed in Chapter VII it is shown that, if the planet in the undisturbed state is spherical and homogeneous, waves of pure distortion, characterized by rotation of the elementary portions without change of volume, can be transmitted in precisely the same way as if the body were free from gravitation, but that the law of propagation of dilatational waves is affected by gravitation. In the first place the waves cannot be purely dilatational, but there must be a small rotation accompanying the change of volume. In the second place the velocity of propagation is not constant, but it depends partly on the locality and partly on the wave-length, the shorter waves travelling faster than the longer ones. This result indicates dispersion, and suggests that the displacement observed at any place during the preliminary tremors should be oscillatory, with gradually increasing intervals between successive maxima. Both these characters are in accordance with observation.

The second problem discussed in Chapter XI is that of the limiting form to which the frequency equation, obtained in Chapter X for a vibrating sphere, tends when the degree of the spherical harmonic involved is high. The result gives the wave-velocity with which a train of simple harmonic straight-crested waves can be transmitted over the surface without penetrating far into the interior. The sphere being assumed to be homogeneous when undisturbed, the waves must, except for a small correction depending on gravity, belong to the type discovered by Lord Rayleigh, and since known as "Rayleigh-waves." The correction has the effect of introducing a slight amount of dispersion, and if, as is probable, the average Poisson's ratio of surface rocks is not less than $\frac{1}{4}$, the wave-velocity increases slightly as the wave-length increases.

The observed fact that, in the earlier phases of the large seismic waves, the motion of the ground is mainly in a direction at right angles to the direction of propagation of the waves, cannot be brought under any theory by which the Large Waves are identified with Rayleigh-waves; and, so long as the earth is treated as homogeneous, it is theoretically impossible for waves of any other type to be transmitted over the surface without penetrating far into the interior. To introduce the possibility of waves which shall have the two characters: (1) transverse horizontal movement, (2) superficial transmission, it has been proposed by more than one writer to assume that the body of the earth is covered by a rather thin layer of matter having different mechanical properties from the matter beneath it; but the conditions necessary to secure these characters in the transmitted waves appear not to have been investigated hitherto. The third problem discussed in Chapter XI is that of the transmission of transverse waves through a superficial layer, such waves to be practically confined to the layer, the motion in the subjacent material diminishing rapidly as the depth increases. The problem is discussed under the simplifying assumptions that the surface may be treated as plane and the waves as straight-crested; and it is proved that the essential condition for the existence of waves having the desired characters is that the velocity of simple distortional waves in the layer should be decidedly less than that in the subjacent material. It is proved further that the wave-velocity of a simple harmonic wave-train cannot be less than the velocity of simple distortional waves in the layer, and that it increases with the wave-length, approaching the velocity of simple distortional waves in the subjacent material as a limit. The analogy of waves on deep water, the only example of waves subject to dispersion which has been worked out fully, suggests that, on account of the relation between wave-velocity and wave-length, the disturbance received at a place should be oscillatory, and the intervals between successive maxima should diminish as time goes on. This result is in accordance with observation of the earlier phases of the Large Waves.

If we invoke a superficial layer, or crust of the earth, to help us to explain the phenomena presented by the earlier phases of the Large Waves, we must not neglect to consider the effect of such a layer in modifying the laws of transmission of those superficial waves in which the horizontal displacement is parallel to the direction of propagation. The problem of the transmission of such waves through a superficial layer is the fourth problem considered in Chapter XI. The surface is treated as plane, the material as incompressible, and the waves as straight-crested. It is proved that there necessarily must be a class of waves similar in type to Rayleigh-waves, and that simple harmonic waves of this class have a wave-velocity which, for very short waves, is the velocity of Rayleigh-waves, but increases as the wave-length increases, approaching the velocity of simple distortional waves in the layer as a limit. A result of some theoretical interest is that these waves, analogous to Rayleigh-waves, may not be the only type of waves which, while they do not penetrate far beneath the layer, have their horizontal displacements parallel to the direction of propagation. Under suitable conditions there may be a second type. The condition that waves of the second type may exist is found to be that the difference between the velocities of simple distortional waves in the two media should be small. As this condition is opposed to the condition which was found to be essential if waves with transverse horizontal displacement are to be transmitted through the layer without penetrating far into the subjacent material, the possible existence of the new type of waves under suitable conditions would seem to have no bearing on the interpretation of seismic records. The waves in the layer which are analogous to Rayleigh-waves are subject to slight dispersion, both on account of gravity, as was seen in the solution of the second problem, and on account of the change of mechanical properties at the under surface of the layer, and, on both accounts, the wave-velocity of a simple harmonic wave-train increases as the wave-length increases. The analogy of waves on deep water leads us to expect that the movement which can be observed at any place should be oscillatory, and that the intervals between successive maxima should diminish as time goes on. These results are in accordance with observations of the central phases of the Large Waves.

The view as to the nature of the Large Waves which is put forward in the Essay is that these waves are of two distinct types. The motion of either type is regarded as an aggregate of motions corresponding to standing simple harmonic waves, which combine to form progressive waves, or, what comes to the same thing, as an aggregate of motions transmitted by simple harmonic wave-trains, the period of any simple harmonic wave depending upon the wave-length according to rather complex laws. The waves of the first type are waves of transverse displacement, transmitted through a superficial layer, and not penetrating far into the matter beneath it. The second type of waves are analogues of Rayleigh-waves, and differ from these only by the modifications that are necessary on account of gravity and the change of mechanical properties at the under surface of the layer. The wave-velocities of simple harmonic waves of both types increase as the wave-lengths increase, and there is for each type a maximum and a minimum wave-velocity, but the minimum of the first type is identical with the maximum of the second. Since the propagation is practically two-dimensional, minima of wave-velocity are less important than maxima, for it is known that waves propagated in two dimensions are prolonged in a sort of "tail," even in the simplest case, that in which all simple harmonic wave-trains travel with the same velocity. If the above-stated view as to the nature of the Large Waves is correct, we should expect that there would be a marked change of type in the observed movement, and that this change would occur at different places at such times as would correspond to the passage over the surface of a phase travelling with the velocity of simple distortional waves in the layer, the horizontal displacement before the change being mainly transverse to the direction of propagation, and after the change mainly parallel to this direction. The existence of such a marked change of type is well established by observation. The proposed view would also account for the facts in regard to the gradual changes in the observed "periods." It suggests, in fact, that these so-called periods are not genuine periods of simple harmonic wave-trains, but intervals of time separating successive instants at which the displacement attains a maximum, the displacement being an aggregate of simple harmonic displacements. This suggestion also furnishes a possible explanation of the apparent discrepancy between theory and observation which arises from the fact that, whereas in Rayleigh-waves the vertical displacement is larger than the horizontal, the vertical displacements observed by seismologists are always smaller than the horizontal. In an aggregate of standing simple harmonic waves, in each of which the theoretical relation between the two components of displacement holds, but the periods are not proportional to the wave-lengths, the relative magnitudes of the maxima of the two components may depend upon the initial circumstances.

The results obtained in Chapter XI, like those obtained in Chapters II and III, suggest that there is a veritable "crust of the earth," or superficial layer, the mechanical properties of which differ from those of the matter composing the interior portions. The results are, in fact, obtained by assuming that such a layer exists. But a little consideration shows that the results could not be very different if the constitution were such that all the quantities, density, rigidity, and so on, by which it is specified, were expressed by continuous functions of the depth, or, more generally, by continuous functions of the position of a point within the earth. Heterogeneity there certainly is, and the simplest heterogeneous constitution that can be imagined is that specified by a nucleus and a superficial layer; but a constitution specified by continuously varying quantities might very well be quite as consistent with the results of observations made at the surface as this discontinuous structure, especially if the quantities should vary rather rapidly near the surface and more gradually at greater depths.

SOME PROBLEMS

OF

GEODYNAMICS

CHAPTER I

THE DISTRIBUTION OF LAND AND WATER

1. The purpose of this Chapter is to explain how the surface of the earth may be represented by means of spherical harmonics, and to estimate the amplitudes of those harmonics which are concerned in the representation of the most important features.

If we wish to discuss the distribution of land and water with greater precision than is customary in books on Geography we may adopt either of two points of view:—those of Mathematical Geography and Geophysics. In Mathematical Geography the object aimed at is a precise geometrical or analytical description of the actual shape of the earth's surface. In Geophysics we seek the causes which have led to the shape being what it is. Before we can make any progress with the geophysical enquiry we must know what the shape of the earth's surface really is. To know this is to know the equation of the surface referred to some assigned axes and origin. But here it is necessary to distinguish one from another various surfaces which are all equally regarded as being "the surface of the earth" when different matters are discussed. The *visible* surface is that surface on which the atmosphere rests, the matter of which it is the bounding surface being land in some parts and water in others. The surface of the ocean is disturbed by tidal and other waves, but the mean surface of the ocean, which is a level surface of the earth's attraction (the rotation being taken into account), enables us to define the surface which is called the *geoid*. This is a closed surface which is everywhere a level surface of the earth's gravity modified by the rotation, and coincides with the mean undisturbed surface of the ocean wherever there is ocean. In treatises on the "Figure of the Earth" the problem to which most attention is paid is the problem of determining the geoid. The height of any place above the geoid is its "height above sea-level," and the depth of the bottom of the sea at a spot "below sea-level" is the depth below the geoid. The geoid is the surface that is always used as a zero in determining levels. But when we speak of the surface of the earth we may, and often do, mean a surface which is neither the visible surface nor the geoid, but the surface of the land, in places where there is land, and the surface at the bottom of the sea, in places where there is sea. A name sometimes used for this surface is the *lithosphere*, and this name will be adopted here*. We regard the question that is posed when precise information as to the shape of the earth is sought as the question of determining the shape of the lithosphere. To know the shape of the lithosphere we must first find the shape of the geoid, next find the height of every spot of land above sea-level, and then find the depth of the sea at every locality in the sea (determined by latitude and longitude). This is the course that is necessary in practice, but an abstract geometrical description need not introduce the sea at all, it would be concerned only with determining the shape of the somewhat irregular round body on which the ocean and the atmosphere rest. The result of the enquiry, if it could be obtained, would be expressed by writing down the equation of the lithosphere, which is the surface of this somewhat irregular round body.

2. The shape of the geoid is known with considerable exactness. It is very nearly an oblate ellipsoid of revolution of ellipticity 1/297, the axis of revolution being the polar axis of the earth. For determining the lithosphere the best origin is the centre of this ellipsoid, and the most appropriate coordinates are polar coordinates, the co-latitude and longitude of a point. Let these be denoted by r, θ, ϕ. The equation of the lithosphere would express r as a function of θ and ϕ.

Let the equation of the nearly spherical harmonic spheroid of the second degree which most nearly coincides with the geoid be

$$r = a_0 - \tfrac{2}{3} a_0 \epsilon_0 P_2(\cos\theta),$$

where a_0 denotes the mean radius ($6{\cdot}37 \times 10^8$ cm.), ϵ_0 the ellipticity of the meridians ($\frac{1}{297}$), and P_2 the zonal surface harmonic of the second degree given by the formula

$$P_2(\cos\theta) = \tfrac{3}{2}\cos^2\theta - \tfrac{1}{2}.$$

The actual surface of the geoid must be expressible by an equation of the form

$$r = a_0 - \tfrac{2}{3} a_0 \epsilon_0 P_2(\cos\theta) + F_0(\theta, \phi),$$

in which $F_0(\theta, \phi)$ could be expanded, if it were known, in a series of surface harmonics, and the series would contain no term in $P_2(\cos\theta)$. In other words $F_0(\theta, \phi)$ must be such that the equation

$$\int_0^{2\pi} d\phi \int_0^{\pi} P_2(\cos\theta) F_0(\theta, \phi) \sin\theta \, d\theta = 0$$

is satisfied. The function $F_0(\theta, \phi)$ is small compared with a_0 for all values of θ and ϕ. What is more important is that it is small compared with $a_0\epsilon_0$. The deviations of the geoid from an harmonic spheroid of the second degree

* The word "lithosphere" is sometimes used as a synonym for the "crust of the earth," whatever that may be.

are everywhere quite trivial compared with the deviations of the harmonic spheroid (of the second degree) of closest fit from a sphere of equal volume.

3. In like manner the equation of the lithosphere must be of the form

$$r = a - \tfrac{2}{3} a_0 \epsilon_0 P_2 (\cos\theta) + F(\theta, \phi),$$

in which a denotes the mean radius of the lithosphere. It is known that $a < a_0$, for the volume within the lithosphere is slightly smaller than that within the geoid. The distance denoted by $a_0 - a$ is between 3 and 4 km., and the level at depth $a_0 - a$ below the level of the sea is known as "mean sphere level." The elevation, or depression, of the lithosphere above, or below, the geoid is expressed by the formula

$$F(\theta, \phi) - F_0(\theta, \phi) - (a_0 - a),$$

and we may say that where this expression is positive there is land, and where it is negative there is sea. But this statement needs qualification if there is land below sea-level; the land around the shores of the Caspian Sea may serve as an example. Since all the values of $F_0(\theta, \phi)$ are small compared with $a_0 - a$, the main features of the distribution of land and water are seen to be expressed by the function $F(\theta, \phi)$, which represents the elevation of a point on the lithosphere above mean sphere level (depression when the function is negative). Since, however, $F(\theta, \phi)$ may be positive without being so great as $a_0 - a$, large tracts of the lithosphere which ought to be regarded as places of elevation, because they are above mean sphere level, are actually submerged. This description applies not only to the whole of the continental shelf but also to the beds of nearly land-locked seas, such as the Mediterranean, and even to some parts of the open ocean.

4. The elevated portions of the lithosphere, the portions that are above mean sphere level, form the "continental block*," and the remaining parts the "ocean basins." The lithosphere protrudes beyond the mean sphere $r = a$ in some parts and lies inside it in others, but the characteristic property of the mean sphere is that the volume contained between the sphere and the protruding part of the lithosphere is equal to the volume contained between the sphere and the parts of the lithosphere which lie inside it. The continental block is believed to form a single continuous region† of elevation, the great continents being all connected together beneath the sea at depths which do not much exceed 3 km. at any place. A map of the world at mean

* The name is often given to the portions of the lithosphere which are actually land or continental shelf (within the hundred-fathom line). The usage adopted in the text seems more appropriate to the present discussion.

† This was not the case in the map of the world at mean sphere level drawn by H. R. Mill in *The Scottish Geographical Magazine* (Edinburgh), vol. VI. 1890, p. 184, where the Antarctic land is shown separated from the rest of the block; but the writer has been informed by Dr Mill that the depth of mean sphere level below sea-level was underestimated in 1890.

sphere level, with merely local irregularities smoothed out, shows an extremely simple plan. The contour line at this depth gives a very good indication of those features of the shape of the lithosphere which must be regarded as the most important. It seems to the writer that a geometrical plan of the earth, to be acceptable, must show a contour line actually or nearly coinciding with this line. In other words the function denoted above by $F(\theta, \phi)$ must vanish at all points of a curve which lies everywhere close to this curve, and it must be positive on the side towards the continental block, and negative on the side towards the two great ocean basins.

5. Now whatever the function $F(\theta, \phi)$ may be, it can be expanded in a series of surface harmonics, and the most important features of the shape ought to be represented by the first few terms of the series. We should expect therefore that an expression, consisting of surface harmonics of the first three or four degrees, could be constructed to vanish along a curve which nearly coincides with the outline of the continental block, and to be positive within the block. It has been shown that the first three degrees suffice for the purpose*. Thus a first approximation to the shape of the lithosphere is given by a formula of the type

$$r = a + S_1 + S_2 + S_3,$$

where S_1, S_2, S_3 denote surface harmonics of degrees indicated by the suffixes.

6. According to the paper cited above we may take

$$S_1 = \{(16{\cdot}5)\cos\phi + (9{\cdot}5)\sin\phi\}\sin\theta + 8\cos\theta,$$

$$S_2 = \{(1{\cdot}5)\cos\phi + (2{\cdot}5)\sin\phi\}\sin 2\theta + \{(-7)\cos 2\phi + (-4)\sin 2\phi\}\sin^2\theta + \{3\cos 2\theta + 1\},$$

$$S_3 = (-5)\{\cos 3\theta + (0{\cdot}6)\cos\theta\} + \{(-1{\cdot}25)\cos\phi + (-0{\cdot}5)\sin\phi\}(\sin\theta + 5\sin 3\theta) + (6{\cdot}5)\sin 2\phi(\cos\theta - \cos 3\theta) + \{(-0{\cdot}25)\cos 3\phi + (3{\cdot}5)\sin 3\phi\}(3\sin\theta - \sin 3\theta).$$

S_1 is a zonal harmonic with a maximum value (about 20·5) near to the point $\theta = 67°$, $\phi = 30°$. S_2 is not exactly a zonal harmonic, but is very nearly a zonal harmonic having a maximum numerical value (about 10) near to $\theta = 105°$, $\phi = 15°$. At this point, and at its antipodes, S_2 is negative. S_3 is not exactly a zonal harmonic, but does not differ much from a zonal harmonic having its pole near to $\theta = 75°$, $\phi = 35°$; the maximum value (at the pole) is about 25. The actual values of the coefficients in the expressions for S_1, S_2, S_3 do not express any fact about the shape, as the scale of the inequalities was arbitrary in the paper cited. The ratios of the coefficients are alone significant. It appears that the harmonics of the first and third degrees are much more important than those of the second degree, the

* A. E. H. Love, *Proc. R. Soc. Lond.* (Ser. A), vol. 80, 1908, p. 555.

harmonics of the third degree slightly more important than those of the first degree. The greatest elevations and depressions corresponding to harmonics of the first and third degrees occur near the same places (Northern Africa and its antipodes in the Pacific Ocean). Now the average depth of the ocean may be taken roughly to be about 4 km.*, and the average height of the continents above sea-level is less than $\frac{1}{2}$ km., so that, if we allow that a large part of the continental elevations and the oceanic depressions can be represented by harmonics of the first three degrees, it would seem that an amplitude of 2 km. would be more than sufficient for any one harmonic, since this gives an elevation of 4 km. for the highest point above the lowest point in the case of any harmonic of uneven degree.

It is proper to observe that, although the formulae given in the paper cited above furnish a fair representation of the *outline* of the continental block, they do not adequately represent the amount of elevation or depression at a place. In particular, they make the Pacific Ocean much deeper than any other ocean, and they make the northern part of the continent of Africa much higher than any other land. This defect does not seem to render them ineffective as approximations to the first three terms of the series by which the radius of the lithosphere would be expressed if it were known accurately.

* A more exact estimate is not needed for the purpose in hand.

CHAPTER II

THE PROBLEM OF THE ISOSTATIC SUPPORT OF THE CONTINENTS

7. The existence of the continental elevations and oceanic depressions proves decisively that the earth as a whole cannot be in a state of fluid equilibrium, that is to say a state such that the stress at any point, across any plane passing through the point, is normal to the plane. For, if this were so, the stress at any point would be the same in all directions round the point, or it would have the character of hydrostatic pressure; and then the surfaces of equal pressure would coincide with the equipotential surfaces, and, in particular, the surface of the earth would be an equipotential surface, everywhere at right angles to the direction of gravity. To an observer anywhere on the earth's surface the ground would appear to be a level plain. Since this is not the case, it is certain that the stress at a point within the body of the earth cannot have the character of hydrostatic pressure; there must be tangential tractions as well as normal tractions.

8. The question to be discussed is: How are the great inequalities, the continental elevations and the oceanic depressions, supported? The idea which one naturally forms is something like this: one imagines a perfectly spherical or spheroidal solid model of the earth to be deformed by paring away material from the parts that are to form the oceanic depressions and heaping it up to form the continental elevations. In fact, one naturally thinks of the continental block as if it were stuck on to the earth like a postage-stamp on an envelope. But this notion is quite erroneous. In the first place the attraction of the block would probably be so great that the sea would be drawn up over it and it would be almost submerged*. In the second place it is doubtful if the material of which the earth is composed could be strong enough to stand the strain†. But the decisive reason for rejecting this notion is that the values of gravity, as observed at places in the interior of the continents and in the open ocean, or on oceanic islands, cannot be reconciled with the values that would be deduced by assuming the notion to be correct‡.

* This is the result obtained by F. R. Helmert, *Math. u. phys. Theorien d. höheren Geodäsie*, Teil 2, Kap. 4 (Leipzig, 1884).

† This is the general result of the calculation made by G. H. Darwin, "On the stresses caused in the interior of the earth by the weight of continents and mountains," *Phil. Trans. R. S.* vol. 173 (1882), revised in *Scientific Papers*, vol. II. p. 457 (Cambridge, 1908).

‡ See § 38 of Teil 2 of the treatise by Helmert cited above, and also his article "Die Schwerkraft u. d. Massenverteilung d. Erde" in *Ency. d. math. Wissenschaften*, Bd. VI. Teil I. Nr. 7 (Leipzig, 1910).

Most writers who have rejected the idea above described have supposed that the superficial inequalities of shape are correlated with internal inequalities of density, so that the elevated portions are, as it were, floated up and kept in position by hydrostatic pressure. This hypothesis under various forms is known as the "hypothesis of compensation" or the "hypothesis of isostasy," and is ascribed to J. H. Pratt. Certain anomalies observed in the measurements of gravity in Northern India were interpreted by him as pointing to a compensation of the mass of the Himalaya by a comparatively light layer of matter beneath them; and he also pointed out that the geographical fact of the land and water hemispheres indicated a displacement of the centre of gravity of the earth from the centre of the geoid towards the middle of the Pacific Ocean*. The hypothesis was adopted by Helmert in 1884 for the reason already stated as decisive against older notions. In recent times it has been revived and developed very much in America by C. E. Dutton† and by O. H. Tittmann and J. F. Hayford‡. It has also been tested by Helmert§ in discussions of various series of geodetic observations. The forms of the hypothesis which have proved to be adequate for Geodesy seem to be not quite sufficiently precise for the purpose of determining a system of stresses by which the inequalities can be supported, and a rather special form will presently be proposed. It must, however, be understood that the special form is introduced for the sake of analytical simplicity rather than physical appropriateness.

Special form of the hypothesis of isostasy.

9. According to the hypothesis of isostasy, as developed by Hayford, the earth consists of a central core coated over with a rocky crust. Within the core it is assumed that there are no tangential stresses, but the matter is in a state of fluid equilibrium; the tangential stresses necessary to maintain the continents and mountains are supposed to be confined to the crust. Within the thickness of the crust the mass is assumed to be so distributed as not to affect the hydrostatic equilibrium of the core. This condition would imply the same amount of mass in every vertical column of the crust,

* J. H. Pratt, "On the deflection of the plumb-line...," *Phil. Trans. R. S.*, vol. 149 (1859), p. 745; and "A treatise on...the Figure of the Earth," 3rd edition, 1865, pp. 135, 159.

† C. E. Dutton, "Some of the greater problems of physical geology," *Bull. Phil. Soc. Washington*, vol. XI. 1892.

‡ Tittmann and Hayford, "United States geodetic operations in the years 1903—1906," *Comptes Rendus de la 15me. conférence générale de l'association géodésique internationale*, 1908. See also J. F. Hayford, "The figure of the earth and isostasy from measurements in the United States," Washington, 1909.

§ F. R. Helmert, "Die Schwerkraft in Hochgebirge," *Veröff. k. preuss. geodät. Inst.* Berlin, 1890; see also L. Haasemann, "Bestimmung d. Intensität d. Schwerkraft im Harze," *Veröff. k. preuss. geodät. Inst.* Berlin, 1905, and F. R. Helmert, "Die Tiefe d. Ausgleichsfläche..." *Berlin Sitzungsberichte*, 1909.

if the thickness of the crust could be neglected, and the core were truly spherical; for a layer of uniform surface-density on a sphere gives rise to no attraction at an internal point. The height of the elevated parts of the crust is thus assumed to be compensated by defect of density. For this reason the crust is described as the "layer of compensation." When account is taken of the thickness of the layer it appears that the law of density stated above is only a first approximation. The thickness of the layer is estimated by Hayford to be about 120 km., and this estimate is supported by Helmert. As this is not far from $\frac{1}{50}$ of the radius of the earth, the numerical work in this Chapter and the following will be performed on the supposition that the mean thickness of the layer is $\frac{1}{50}$ of the earth's radius.

10. Among the considerations which led to the hypothesis of isostasy one of the most important was the fact, established by geodetic observation, that the actual forms of the equipotential surfaces near the surface of the earth are very approximately oblate spheroids, as they would be if the whole earth were in a state of fluid equilibrium under gravitation and rotation. This result implies that the inequalities of potential which are due to the inequalities of density in the crust, and to the deviations of the outer surface of the crust from an equipotential surface, are very small in the neighbourhood of this outer surface. With a view to a precise formulation of the hypothesis of isostasy, it is convenient to assume that these inequalities of potential actually vanish at the mean outer surface of the crust. It is part of the hypothesis that they vanish within the core. We shall therefore take them to vanish at both the mean outer and the inner surfaces of the layer of compensation. Further the gravitational attraction within the earth varies continuously from point to point. Within the core it must be independent of the inequalities of density which occur in the layer of compensation. At any point within the layer of compensation the gravitational attraction depends partly on the inequalities of density. To secure continuity at the internal surface of the layer it is necessary that those terms in the expression for the attraction which arise from these inequalities should vanish at this surface.

11. In order to formulate this theory analytically it will be sufficient to neglect the rotation of the earth. If a body of the size and mass of the earth, at rest, could support assigned continental elevations and oceanic depressions without requiring an improbable degree of tenacity in its materials, a body of similar constitution rotating once in a day could almost certainly support similar elevations and depressions. We shall therefore take the core to be spherical, and the outer surface of the layer of compensation to be a nearly spherical surface concentric with the surface of the core, and shall suppose the radial elevation of the outer surface to be expanded in a series of spherical surface harmonics, and we shall write the equations of these two surfaces in the forms:

$$\text{for the core} \quad r = b,$$

$$\text{for the crust} \quad r = a + \Sigma \epsilon_n S_n,$$

where the suffix n denotes the degree of the surface harmonic S_n, and ϵ_n is a small constant indicating the magnitude of the inequality. In general it will be sufficient to discuss the case where $\Sigma \epsilon_n S_n$ reduces to a single term. The inequalities of density within the layer of compensation are then to be correlated with this term.

12. The density at any point within the core will be a quantity which can be expressed as a function of r only. The expression for the density at any point within the layer of compensation will consist of two terms, the first term being a function of r, and the second term the product of a function of r and the spherical surface harmonic S_n. The potential at any point in the core will be a function of r only. The potential at any point within the layer of compensation will be the sum of two terms, one of them a function of r only, and the other the product of a function of r and S_n. The second term is the inequality of potential above mentioned; we shall denote it by V'. It is convenient to assume a form for V' and deduce a form for the density. To give effect to the considerations already adduced in regard to the form of V' we must suppose that the r-factor of V' contains $(a - r)$ and $(r - b)^2$ as factors. The factor $(a - r)$ secures that the mean surface is an equipotential, the factor $(r - b)^2$ secures that the inequality of potential and the corresponding inequality of attraction shall both vanish at the surface of the core. Accordingly we assume for V' an expression of the form

$$(r - a)(r - b)^2 f(r)\, r^n \epsilon_n S_n.$$

The factor r^n has been introduced in order that we may have to deal with a spherical solid harmonic $r^n S_n$. The factor $f(r)$ is in our power; all forms for it except such as become infinite at a, or b, or at an intermediate value of r, are equally compatible with the hypothesis of isostasy, according to the statement of this hypothesis made above. It might be possible to choose it so as to diminish the amounts of the calculated tangential stresses, but, for the present, it is better to choose it with a view to analytical simplicity. It turns out to be convenient to assume that $f(r)$ is simply proportional to r^4. See p. 18 *infra*, ftn. As the outcome of this discussion we put

$$V' = A_n (r - a)(r - b)^2 r^4 W_n \quad \text{.......................(1)},$$

where W_n is written for the spherical solid harmonic $r^n S_n$, and A_n is a constant to be determined in terms of ϵ_n.

13. To simplify the problem to the utmost we are going to assume that the mean density of the layer of compensation is independent of r. Within the layer of compensation the density ρ is assumed to be given by

$$\rho = \rho_1 + \rho' \quad \text{.............................(2)},$$

where ρ_1 is a constant, and ρ' is the inequality of density mentioned above. Then the potential V' is that due to (i) a volume distribution of density ρ' in the region $a > r > b$, (ii) a surface distribution of density $\rho_1 \epsilon_n S_n$ on the surface $r = a$. The potential V_0 at any point within the core is a function of r only. The potential V at any point within the layer of compensation is expressed by the equation

$$V = V_1 + V',$$

where $$V_1 = \tfrac{4}{3}\pi\gamma(\rho_0 - \rho_1)\frac{b^3}{r} + \tfrac{2}{3}\pi\gamma\rho_1(3a^2 - r^2) \quad \text{..................(3)},$$

γ denotes the constant of gravitation, and ρ_0 is the mean density of the core.

To determine ρ' we have the equation

$$\nabla^2 V' = -4\pi\gamma\rho' \quad \text{...........................(4)},$$

and in accordance with (1) this gives

$$-4\pi\gamma\rho' = A_n[7(2n+8)r^5 - 6(2n+7)r^4(a+2b)$$
$$+ 5(2n+6)r^3 b(2a+b) - 4(2n+5)r^2ab^2]\,W_n \quad \text{...(5)}.$$

V' is the potential of a certain volume density and a certain surface density, as explained above. V' vanishes at $r = a$, and therefore the potential at any point outside the surface $r = a$, due to the same volume density and surface density, is zero. The surface characteristic equation for the potential at the surface $r = a$ therefore becomes

$$\left(\frac{\partial V'}{\partial r}\right)_{r=a} = 4\pi\gamma\rho_1\epsilon_n S_n,$$

and this gives $$A_n(a-b)^2 a^{n+4} = 4\pi\gamma\rho_1\epsilon_n \quad \text{......................(6)}.$$

14. Corresponding to the superficial inequality expressed by $\epsilon_n S_n$ we have the inequalities of potential and density expressed by

$$V' = \frac{(r-a)(r-b)^2}{(a-b)^2}\,\frac{r^4}{a^{n+4}}\,4\pi\gamma\rho_1\epsilon_n W_n \quad \text{.................(7)}$$

and $$\rho' = -\rho_1[7(2n+8)r^5 - 6(2n+7)(a+2b)r^4$$
$$+ 5(2n+6)b(2a+b)r^3 - 4(2n+5)ab^2r^2]\,\frac{\epsilon_n W_n}{a^{n+4}(a-b)^2} \quad \text{...(8)}.$$

It may be shown without much difficulty that this somewhat complicated law of density accords with the suggestion that, in the layer of compensation, the product of density and thickness should be constant. If the thickness is small compared with the radius, this relation holds to a first approximation.

It is to be observed that this law of density appears to be needlessly complicated. It has been adopted to simplify the expression for the potential, and is, as has been explained, only one of an infinite set of laws which are all equally consistent with the general hypothesis of isostasy. It may be shown in regard to this particular law that the excess density ρ', corresponding to a single spherical harmonic, changes sign within the layer of compensation, so that, if a single harmonic were involved, the portion of the layer where there is superficial elevation would consist of a double layer, lighter outside and heavier inside; and in like manner the portion of the layer where there is superficial depression would consist of a double layer, lighter inside and heavier outside. The simple phrase "heavier matter under the oceans," by which the hypothesis is sometimes popularly expressed, would be misleading. Immediately beneath the oceans the matter is made out to be heavier than the average surface rock, but beneath this heavier matter there would also be some matter of less density than the average density appropriate to its depth. It can be shown without much difficulty that this peculiarity is not restricted to the assumed law of density, but is a necessary consequence of the two assumptions: (1) that within the internal boundary of the layer of compensation the stress is hydrostatic pressure, (2) that the mean surface is an equipotential surface.

Equations of equilibrium.

15. The theory by which the stress is to be determined is a modified theory of elasticity. The ordinary theory is not applicable because the interior of the earth must be in a state of initial stress. In other words, if gravitation could cease to act, or if a body force equal and opposite to the local value of gravity could be brought to act at every point within the earth, changes of such magnitude would be produced in the shape and size of the earth, and in the distribution of its mass, that the corresponding displacement could not be calculated by the ordinary theory of elasticity, in which it is assumed that the stress-strain relation is linear. Another way of expressing this idea is furnished by the observation that in the ordinary theory we contemplate a body in two states, the strained state, in which it is held by forces, and the unstrained state in which it would be if the forces ceased to act. If the (gravitational) forces by which the earth is held in its actual shape, with its actual distribution of density, were to cease to act, the earth would pass into a new state; and if this state is regarded as the unstrained state, and the actual state is regarded as the strained state, then it is certain that the strains involved are not small quantities, as they would have to be if the ordinary theory were applicable, and the unstrained state, which would need to be known if the ordinary theory were to be applied, would be quite unknown.

Our problem really is to determine a stress-system by which gravitation can be balanced in a body of known size, shape and mass. The problem admits of an infinite number of solutions even if the distribution of the mass is known, for there are six components of stress at a point, and they are connected with the known body forces by three differential equations; they must also satisfy the conditions that the surface is free from traction. These equations and conditions are insufficient. In the ordinary theory of elasticity they are supplemented by the stress-strain relation, and by the equations expressing the components of strain in terms of a vector quantity—the displacement by which the body passes from the unstrained to the strained state. Thus the number of unknowns is reduced from six to three—the number of independent quantities that determine a vector. Now we have seen that the notions of strain and displacement are not appropriate to the problem in hand, and we may not therefore have recourse to the methods of the ordinary theory. The problem must remain indeterminate, and all we can do is to obtain explicitly one or more of the infinitely numerous solutions.

One solution of the problem was obtained by Sir G. Darwin* by assuming that the stress is connected with a displacement by the same equations as hold in the ordinary theory of an elastic *incompressible* solid, but that this displacement is not one by which the body could pass from a spherically symmetrical configuration to the actual configuration. For simplicity the density was taken to be uniform. The results showed that the tangential stresses required, according to this solution, to support the continental inequalities would be rather large, and that great tenacity in the materials that compose the earth would be required if the inequalities were really supported in this way.

16. A different solution of the problem will be obtained here by adopting the hypothesis of isostasy, in the special form already explained, and supplementing it by assumptions which shall simplify the problem and render it determinate. The general idea underlying these assumptions was introduced by Lord Rayleigh†, and may be expressed in the statement that the stress at a point consists of two superposed stress-systems: one, a state of hydrostatic pressure by which the gravitation of a spherically symmetrical earth would be balanced throughout its interior; this is the *initial stress.* The second stress-system is taken to be correlated with a displacement, as in the ordinary theory; this is the *additional stress.* In the problem in hand the notion of displacement is not very appropriate. We may introduce a vector quantity connected with the additional stress by the usual equations, and

* *Loc. cit. ante*, p. 6.

† Lord Rayleigh, "On the dilatational stability of the earth," *Proc. R. S. London*, A, vol. 77, 1906.

call it a "displacement," but we must not regard it as the displacement by which the body would pass from the unstrained state to the actual state. This being the case, we may simplify the problem by assuming that the divergence of the vector vanishes, as it would do if the vector were the actual displacement of an incompressible solid; and then we shall have to introduce into the expressions for the additional stress terms that represent an additional hydrostatic pressure as well as the terms that contain differential coefficients of the components of the fictitious displacement*. This procedure is simpler than that of taking the fictitious displacement to involve dilatation.

17. According to the hypothesis explained above, the stress at a point in the core is hydrostatic pressure p_0, expressible as a function of r only by means of the equation

$$\frac{\partial V_0}{\partial r} - \frac{1}{\rho_0}\frac{\partial p_0}{\partial r} = 0 \quad \text{.............................(9).}$$

Within the layer of compensation the stress will be taken to consist of two stress-systems: (i) a hydrostatic pressure p_1, expressible as a function of r only, (ii) an additional stress. The pressure p_1 will be taken to be given by the equation

$$\frac{\partial V_1}{\partial r} - \frac{1}{\rho_1}\frac{\partial p_1}{\partial r} = 0 \quad \text{.............................(10).}$$

To express this idea we introduce six components of stress denoted by

$$X_x,\ Y_y,\ Z_z,\ Y_z,\ Z_x,\ X_y,$$

and put

in the core $\qquad X_x = Y_y = Z_z = -p_0, \quad Y_z = Z_x = X_y = 0$ ....(11),

in the layer $X_x = -p_1 + X_x', \quad Y_y = -p_1 + Y_y', \quad Z_z = -p_1 + Z_z'$......(12),

but Y_z, Z_x, X_y do not vanish in the layer.

18. For the determination of the stress at any point within the layer of compensation we have the three equations of equilibrium of the type

$$\frac{\partial X_x}{\partial x} + \frac{\partial X_y}{\partial y} + \frac{\partial Z_x}{\partial z} + \rho\frac{\partial V}{\partial x} = 0 \quad \text{.....................(13)}$$

and the special conditions which hold at the inner and outer bounding surfaces of the layer. At the inner surface $r = b$ there must be continuity of stress; and therefore the normal traction on this surface must be a pressure, equal to the value assumed by p_0 when r is put equal to b, and the tangential traction on this surface must vanish. The outer surface $r = a + \epsilon_n S_n$ must be free from traction. These conditions are manifestly not sufficient to determine the six components of stress, and the problem is strictly indeterminate. We therefore set ourselves the task of finding

* The ordinary formula $X_x = \lambda\Delta + 2\mu\,\partial u/\partial x$ becomes $X_x = -p + 2\mu\,\partial u/\partial x$, where p denotes a hydrostatic pressure, if the material is incompressible.

a stress-system which shall satisfy the conditions above stated, and, as was explained above, we render the problem determinate by imposing additional conditions. These conditions amount to assuming that there exists a vector (u, v, w) which is such that the stress expressed by the six components $(X_x', Y_y', Z_z', Y_z, Z_x, X_y)$ is related to it in the same way as if u, v, w were the components of displacement in an isotropic incompressible elastic solid body slightly strained from a state of zero stress. It is particularly to be noticed that we do not assume the material of the sphere to be actually incompressible. The "displacement" (u, v, w) is not any actual displacement suffered by the material of the sphere in passing from a state which it has at one time to a state which it has at another time. It is only a subsidiary quantity arbitrarily introduced for the purpose of making the problem determinate.

19. This assumption implies the equations

$$\left.\begin{aligned} &X_x' = -p' + 2\mu\frac{\partial u}{\partial x}, \quad Y_y' = -p' + 2\mu\frac{\partial v}{\partial y}, \quad Z_z' = -p' + 2\mu\frac{\partial w}{\partial z} \\ &Y_z = \mu\left(\frac{\partial w}{\partial y} + \frac{\partial v}{\partial z}\right), \quad Z_x = \mu\left(\frac{\partial u}{\partial z} + \frac{\partial w}{\partial x}\right), \quad X_y = \mu\left(\frac{\partial v}{\partial x} + \frac{\partial u}{\partial y}\right) \\ &\qquad\qquad \frac{\partial u}{\partial x} + \frac{\partial v}{\partial y} + \frac{\partial w}{\partial z} = 0 \end{aligned}\right\} \quad \ldots(14),$$

in which p' denotes an additional pressure.

The equations of equilibrium then take the form

$$\left.\begin{aligned} -\frac{\partial p_1}{\partial x} - \frac{\partial p'}{\partial x} + \mu\nabla^2 u + \rho\frac{\partial V}{\partial x} = 0 \\ -\frac{\partial p_1}{\partial y} - \frac{\partial p'}{\partial y} + \mu\nabla^2 v + \rho\frac{\partial V}{\partial y} = 0 \\ -\frac{\partial p_1}{\partial z} - \frac{\partial p'}{\partial z} + \mu\nabla^2 w + \rho\frac{\partial V}{\partial z} = 0 \end{aligned}\right\} \quad \ldots\ldots\ldots\ldots\ldots\ldots(15).$$

On substituting $\rho_1 + \rho'$ for ρ and $V_1 + V'$ for V, and neglecting the product $\rho' V'$, these equations become three of the type

$$-\frac{\partial p_1}{\partial x} - \frac{\partial p'}{\partial x} + \mu\nabla^2 u + \rho_1\frac{\partial V_1}{\partial x} + \rho_1\frac{\partial V'}{\partial x} + \rho'\frac{\partial V_1}{\partial x} = 0.$$

By putting, in accordance with (10),

$$p_1 = \rho_1 V_1 + \text{const.}$$

we reduce these equations to three of the type

$$-\frac{\partial p'}{\partial x} + \mu\nabla^2 u + \rho_1\frac{\partial V'}{\partial x} + \rho'\frac{\partial V_1}{\partial x} = 0 \quad \ldots\ldots\ldots\ldots\ldots\ldots(16).$$

In these equations V_1, V', and ρ' have the forms given in the equations (3), (7) and (8).

Solution of the equations.

20. We shall now proceed to a solution of the equations. They are three of the type

$$-\frac{\partial p'}{\partial x}+\mu\nabla^2 u+4\pi\gamma\rho_1^2\frac{\epsilon_n}{a^{n+4}(a-b)^2}\left[r^4(r-a)(r-b)^2\frac{\partial W_n}{\partial x}\right.$$
$$\left.+\{7r^5-6(a+2b)r^4+5b(2a+b)r^3-4ab^2r^2\}\,xW_n\right]$$
$$+\tfrac{4}{3}\pi\gamma\rho_1^2\left(\frac{\rho_0-\rho_1}{\rho_1}\frac{b^3}{r^3}+1\right)\frac{\epsilon_n}{a^{n+4}(a-b)^2}[7(2n+8)r^5-6(2n+7)(a+2b)r^4$$
$$+5(2n+6)b(2a+b)r^3-4(2n+5)ab^2r^2]\,xW_n=0\ldots(17),$$

with
$$\frac{\partial u}{\partial x}+\frac{\partial v}{\partial y}+\frac{\partial w}{\partial z}=0\ldots\ldots\ldots\ldots(18).$$

To solve them we put
$$p'=f_nW_n\ldots\ldots\ldots\ldots(19),$$

$$u=F_n\frac{\partial W_n}{\partial x}+G_nxW_n,\quad v=F_n\frac{\partial W_n}{\partial y}+G_nyW_n,\quad w=F_n\frac{\partial W_n}{\partial z}+G_nzW_n\ldots(20),$$

where f_n, F_n, G_n denote functions of r. To satisfy (18) we must have

$$\frac{n}{r}\frac{dF_n}{dr}+r\frac{dG_n}{dr}+(n+3)G_n=0\ldots\ldots\ldots\ldots(21).$$

Now
$$\frac{\partial p'}{\partial x}=f_n\frac{\partial W_n}{\partial x}+\frac{1}{r}\frac{df_n}{dr}xW_n,$$

and
$$\nabla^2u=\left(\frac{d^2F_n}{dr^2}+\frac{2n}{r}\frac{dF_n}{dr}+2G_n\right)\frac{\partial W_n}{\partial x}+\left(\frac{d^2G_n}{dr^2}+\frac{2(n+2)}{r}\frac{dG_n}{dr}\right)xW_n.$$

Hence we get

$$-f_n+\mu\left(\frac{d^2F_n}{dr^2}+\frac{2n}{r}\frac{dF_n}{dr}+2G_n\right)+4\pi\gamma\rho_1^2\frac{\epsilon_n}{a^{n+4}(a-b)^2}(r-a)(r-b)^2r^4=0$$
$$\ldots\ldots(22),$$

and

$$-\frac{1}{r}\frac{df_n}{dr}+\mu\left(\frac{d^2G_n}{dr^2}+\frac{2(n+2)}{r}\frac{dG_n}{dr}\right)+4\pi\gamma\rho_1^2\frac{\epsilon_n}{a^{n+4}(a-b)^2}\frac{1}{r}\frac{d}{dr}\{(r-a)(r-b)^2r^4\}$$
$$+\tfrac{4}{3}\pi\gamma\rho_1^2\left(\frac{\rho_0-\rho_1}{\rho_1}\frac{b^3}{r^3}+1\right)\frac{\epsilon_n}{a^{n+4}(a-b)^2}[7(2n+8)r^5-6(2n+7)(a+2b)r^4$$
$$+5(2n+6)b(2a+b)r^3-4(2n+5)ab^2r^2]=0\ldots(23).$$

Since
$$\frac{1}{r}\frac{d}{dr}\left(\frac{d^2F_n}{dr^2}+\frac{2n}{r}\frac{dF_n}{dr}\right)=\left(\frac{d^2}{dr^2}+\frac{2(n+1)}{r}\frac{d}{dr}\right)\left(\frac{1}{r}\frac{dF_n}{dr}\right),$$

we get on eliminating f_n from (22) and (23)

$$\mu\left\{\frac{d^2G_n}{dr^2}+\frac{2(n+1)}{r}\frac{dG_n}{dr}\right\}-\mu\left\{\frac{d^2}{dr^2}+\frac{2(n+1)}{r}\frac{d}{dr}\right\}\left(\frac{1}{r}\frac{dF_n}{dr}\right)$$
$$+\tfrac{4}{3}\pi\gamma\rho_1^2\left(\frac{\rho_0-\rho_1}{\rho_1}\frac{b^3}{r^3}+1\right)\frac{\epsilon_n}{a^{n+4}(a-b)^2}\{7(2n+8)r^5-6(2n+7)(a+2b)r^4$$
$$+5(2n+6)b(2a+b)r^3-4(2n+5)ab^2r^2\}=0,$$

or, by (21),

$$\mu\left\{\frac{d^2}{dr^2}+\frac{2(n+1)}{r}\frac{d}{dr}\right\}\left\{r\frac{dG_n}{dr}+(2n+3)G_n\right\}$$
$$+\tfrac{4}{3}n\pi\gamma\rho_1^2\left(\frac{\rho_0-\rho_1}{\rho_1}\frac{b^3}{r^3}+1\right)\frac{\epsilon_n}{a^{n+4}(a-b)^2}\{7(2n+8)r^5-\dots\}=0$$

or
$$\mu\frac{1}{r^{2n+2}}\frac{d}{dr}\left[r^{2n+2}\frac{d}{dr}\left\{\frac{1}{r^{2n+2}}\frac{d}{dr}(r^{2n+3}G_n)\right\}\right]$$
$$+\tfrac{4}{3}n\pi\gamma\rho_1^2\frac{\rho_0-\rho_1}{\rho_1}b^3\frac{\epsilon_n}{a^{n+4}(a-b)^2}\left\{7(2n+8)r^2-6(2n+7)(a+2b)r\right.$$
$$\left.+5(2n+6)b(2a+b)-4(2n+5)ab^2\frac{1}{r}\right\}$$
$$+\tfrac{4}{3}n\pi\gamma\rho_1^2\frac{\epsilon_n}{a^{n+4}(a-b)^2}\{7(2n+8)r^5-6(2n+7)(a+2b)r^4$$
$$+5(2n+6)b(2a+b)r^3-4(2n+5)ab^2r^2\}=0.$$

Thus G_n satisfies the equation

$$-\mu\frac{d}{dr}\left[r^{2n+2}\frac{d}{dr}\left\{\frac{1}{r^{2n+2}}\frac{d}{dr}(r^{2n+3}G_n)\right\}\right]$$
$$=\frac{\tfrac{4}{3}\pi\gamma\rho_1^2\epsilon_n}{a^{n+4}(a-b)^2}n\left[\frac{\rho_0-\rho_1}{\rho_1}b^3\{7(2n+8)r^{2n+4}-6(2n+7)(a+2b)r^{2n+3}\right.$$
$$+5(2n+6)b(2a+b)r^{2n+2}-4(2n+5)ab^2r^{2n+1}\}$$
$$+7(2n+8)r^{2n+7}-6(2n+7)(a+2b)r^{2n+6}+5(2n+6)b(2a+b)r^{2n+5}$$
$$\left.-4(2n+5)ab^2r^{2n+4}\right]\quad\dots\dots\dots(24).$$

When G_n is found from this equation f_n and F_n can be deduced.

21. On integrating both members of equation (24) with respect to r we get

$$-\mu r^{2n+2}\frac{d}{dr}\left\{\frac{1}{r^{2n+2}}\frac{d}{dr}(r^{2n+3}G_n)\right\}$$
$$=\frac{\tfrac{4}{3}\pi\gamma\rho_1^2\epsilon_n}{a^{n+4}(a-b)^2}n\left[\frac{\rho_0-\rho_1}{\rho_1}b^3\int\frac{1}{r^3}\frac{d}{dr}\{7r^{2n+8}-6(a+2b)r^{2n+7}+5b(2a+b)r^{2n+6}\right.$$
$$-4ab^2r^{2n+5}\}\,dr$$
$$\left.+\{7r^{2n+8}-6(a+2b)r^{2n+7}+5b(2a+b)r^{2n+6}-4ab^2r^{2n+5}\}\right]$$
$$+A,$$

where A is constant, or we have

$$-\mu\frac{d}{dr}\left\{\frac{1}{r^{2n+2}}\frac{d}{dr}(r^{2n+3}G_n)\right\}$$

$$=\tfrac{4}{3}\frac{\pi\gamma\rho_1^2\epsilon_n}{a^{n+4}(a-b)^2}n\left[\frac{\rho_0-\rho_1}{\rho_1}\frac{b^3}{r^{2n+5}}\{7r^{2n+8}-6(a+2b)r^{2n+7}+5b(2a+b)r^{2n+6}-4ab^2r^{2n+5}\}\right.$$

$$\left.+\frac{\rho_0-\rho_1}{\rho_1}\frac{b^3}{r^{2n+2}}3\int(7r^{2n+8}-\ldots)\frac{dr}{r^4}+\frac{d}{dr}\{r^4(r-a)(r-b)^2\}\right]$$

$$+\frac{A}{r^{2n+2}},$$

or

$$-\mu\frac{d}{dr}\left\{\frac{1}{r^{2n+2}}\frac{d}{dr}(r^{2n+3}G_n)\right\}$$

$$=\frac{\tfrac{4}{3}\pi\gamma\rho_1^2\epsilon_n}{a^{n+4}(a-b)^2}n\left[\frac{\rho_0-\rho_1}{\rho_1}\frac{b^3}{r^3}\frac{d}{dr}\{r^4(r-a)(r-b)^2\}\right.$$

$$+3\frac{\rho_0-\rho_1}{\rho_1}\frac{b^3}{r^{2n+2}}\int_b^r r^{2n-2}\frac{d}{dr}\{r^4(r-a)(r-b)^2\}\,dr$$

$$\left.+\frac{d}{dr}\{r^4(r-a)(r-b)^2\}\right]+\frac{A}{r^{2n+2}}$$

or

$$-\mu\frac{d}{dr}\left\{\frac{1}{r^{2n+2}}\frac{d}{dr}(r^{2n+3}G_n)\right\}$$

$$=\frac{\tfrac{4}{3}\pi\gamma\rho_1^2\epsilon_n}{a^{n+4}(a-b)^2}n\left[\frac{\rho_0-\rho_1}{\rho_1}\left\{\frac{b^3}{r^3}\frac{d}{dr}\{r^4(r-a)(r-b)^2\}+3b^3(r-a)(r-b)^2\right.\right.$$

$$\left.-\frac{6(n-1)b^3}{r^{2n+2}}\int_b^r r^{2n+1}(r-a)(r-b)^2dr\right\}$$

$$\left.+\frac{d}{dr}\{r^4(r-a)(r-b)^2\}\right]+\frac{A}{r^{2n+2}}$$

$$=\frac{\tfrac{4}{3}\pi\gamma\rho_1^2\epsilon_n}{a^{n+4}(a-b)^2}n\left[\frac{\rho_0-\rho_1}{\rho_1}b^3\left\{7(r-a)(r-b)^2+r\frac{d}{dr}\{(r-a)(r-b)^2\}\right\}\right.$$

$$-\frac{6(n-1)b^3}{r^{2n+2}}\frac{\rho_0-\rho_1}{\rho_1}\int_b^r r^{2n+1}(r-a)(r-b)^2\,dr$$

$$\left.+\frac{d}{dr}\{r^4(r-a)(r-b)^2\}\right]+\frac{A}{r^{2n+2}}$$

$$=\frac{\tfrac{4}{3}\pi\gamma\rho_1^2\epsilon_n}{a^{n+4}(a-b)^2}n\left[\frac{\rho_0-\rho_1}{\rho_1}\frac{b^3}{r^6}\frac{d}{dr}\{r^7(r-a)(r-b)^2\}\right.$$

$$-\frac{\rho_0-\rho_1}{\rho_1}\frac{6(n-1)b^3}{r^{2n+2}}\int_b^r r^{2n+1}(r-a)(r-b)^2\,dr$$

$$\left.+\frac{d}{dr}\{r^4(r-a)(r-b)^2\}\right]+\frac{A}{r^{2n+2}}.$$

Hence

$$-\frac{\mu}{r^{2n+2}}\frac{d}{dr}(r^{2n+3}G_n)$$

$$=\frac{\frac{4}{3}\pi\gamma\rho_1{}^2\epsilon_n}{a^{n+4}(a-b)^2}n\left[\frac{\rho_0-\rho_1}{\rho_1}b^3\left\{r(r-a)(r-b)^2+6\int_b^r(r-a)(r-b)^2dr\right\}\right.$$

$$-\frac{\rho_0-\rho_1}{\rho_1}6(n-1)b^3\int_b^r\frac{1}{r^{2n+2}}\left\{\int_b^r r^{2n+1}(r-a)(r-b)^2dr\right\}dr$$

$$\left.+r^4(r-a)(r-b)^2\right]-\frac{A}{(2n+1)r^{2n+1}}+B,$$

where B is constant, or we have

$$-\mu\frac{d}{dr}(r^{2n+3}G_n)$$

$$=\frac{\frac{4}{3}\pi\gamma\rho_1{}^2\epsilon_n}{a^{n+4}(a-b)^2}n\left[\frac{\rho_0-\rho_1}{\rho_1}b^3\left\{r^{2n+3}(r-a)(r-b)^2+6r^{2n+2}\int_b^r(r-a)(r-b)^2dr\right\}\right.$$

$$-\frac{\rho_0-\rho_1}{\rho_1}6(n-1)b^3r^{2n+2}\int_b^r\frac{1}{r^{2n+2}}\left\{\int_b^r r^{2n+1}(r-a)(r-b)^2dr\right\}dr$$

$$\left.+r^{2n+6}(r-a)(r-b)^2\right]-\frac{Ar}{(2n+1)}+Br^{2n+2}.$$

Hence we find*

$$-\mu r^{2n+3}G_n$$

$$=\frac{\frac{4}{3}\pi\gamma\rho_1{}^2\epsilon_n}{a^{n+4}(a-b)^2}n\left[\frac{\rho_0-\rho_1}{\rho_1}b^3\int_b^r r^{2n+3}(r-a)(r-b)^2dr\right.$$

$$+6\frac{\rho_0-\rho_1}{\rho_1}b^3\int_b^r r^{2n+2}\int_b^r(r-a)(r-b)^2dr\,.\,dr$$

$$-\frac{\rho_0-\rho_1}{\rho_1}6(n-1)b^3\int_b^r r^{2n+2}\int_b^r\frac{1}{r^{2n+2}}\int_b^r r^{2n+1}(r-a)(r-b)^2dr\,.\,dr\,.\,dr$$

$$\left.+\int_b^r r^{2n+6}(r-a)(r-b)^2dr\right]$$

$$-\frac{Ar^2}{2(2n+1)}+\frac{Br^{2n+3}}{2n+3}+C,$$

or $-\mu G_n$

$$=-\frac{A}{2(2n+1)r^{2n+1}}+\frac{B}{2n+3}+\frac{C}{r^{2n+3}}$$

$$+\frac{\frac{4}{3}\pi\gamma\rho_1{}^2\epsilon_n}{a^{n+4}(a-b)^2}n\left[\frac{\rho_0-\rho_1}{\rho_1}\frac{b^3}{r^{2n+3}}\int_b^r r^{2n+3}(r-a)(r-b)^2dr\right.$$

* It is in the determination of the form of G_n that we get a simplification by assuming that V' contains r^4 as a factor (see p. 9, *ante*). If we assumed that the function $f(r)$ there introduced is of the form r^k where k is any integer, then at some stage of the integration a logarithm would be introduced if k were less than 4. The simplest formula for V' which will not introduce a logarithm is obtained by taking $f(r)$ to be proportional to r^4.

$$+ 6\frac{\rho_0-\rho_1}{\rho_1}\frac{b^3}{r^{2n+3}}\int_b^r r^{2n+2}\int_b^r (r-a)(r-b)^2\,dr\,.\,dr$$

$$-6(n-1)\frac{\rho_0-\rho_1}{\rho_1}\frac{b^3}{r^{2n+3}}\int_b^r r^{2n+2}\int_b^r\frac{1}{r^{2n+2}}\int_b^r r^{2n+1}(r-a)(r-b)^2\,dr\,.\,dr\,.\,dr$$

$$\left.+\frac{1}{r^{2n+3}}\int_b^r r^{2n+6}(r-a)(r-b)^2\,dr\right].$$

The expression $(r-a)$ under the signs of integration can be replaced by $(r-b)-(a-b)$, and thus each of the integrals can be expressed as the difference of two integrals one of which contains $(a-b)$ as a factor. Thus we may write

$$-\mu G_n = -\frac{A}{2(2n+1)r^{2n+1}}+\frac{B}{2n+3}+\frac{C}{r^{2n+3}}+\gamma_n \qquad \text{............(25)},$$

where

$$\gamma_n=\frac{\frac{4}{3}\pi\gamma\rho_1{}^2\epsilon_n}{a^{n+4}(a-b)^2}\,n\left[\frac{\rho_0-\rho_1}{\rho_1}\frac{b^3}{r^{2n+3}}\int_b^r r^{2n+3}(r-b)^3\,dr\right.$$

$$+\frac{6(\rho_0-\rho_1)}{\rho_1}\frac{b^3}{r^{2n+3}}\int_b^r r^{2n+2}\int_b^r (r-b)^3\,dr\,.\,dr$$

$$-6(n-1)\frac{\rho_0-\rho_1}{\rho_1}\frac{b^3}{r^{2n+3}}\int_b^r r^{2n+2}\int_b^r\frac{1}{r^{2n+2}}\int_b^r r^{2n+1}(r-b)^3\,dr\,.\,dr\,.\,dr$$

$$\left.+\frac{1}{r^{2n+3}}\int_b^r r^{2n+6}(r-b)^3\,dr\right]$$

$$-\frac{\frac{4}{3}\pi\gamma\rho_1{}^2\epsilon_n}{a^{n+4}(a-b)}\,n\left[\frac{\rho_0-\rho_1}{\rho_1}\frac{b^3}{r^{2n+3}}\int_b^r r^{2n+3}(r-b)^2\,dr\right.$$

$$+6\frac{\rho_0-\rho_1}{\rho_1}\frac{b^3}{r^{2n+3}}\int_b^r r^{2n+2}\int_b^r (r-b)^2\,dr\,.\,dr$$

$$-6(n-1)\frac{\rho_0-\rho_1}{\rho_1}\frac{b^3}{r^{2n+3}}\int_b^r r^{2n+2}\int_b^r\frac{1}{r^{2n+2}}\int_b^r r^{2n+1}(r-b)^2\,dr\,.\,dr\,.\,dr$$

$$\left.+\frac{1}{r^{2n+3}}\int_b^r r^{2n+6}(r-b)^2\,dr\right] \qquad \text{......................................(26)}.$$

It will be convenient hereafter to note that we have

$$\frac{d}{dr}(r^{2n+3}\gamma_n)$$

$$=\frac{\frac{4}{3}\pi\gamma\rho_1{}^2\epsilon_n}{a^{n+4}(a-b)^2}\,n\left[\frac{\rho_0-\rho_1}{\rho_1}b^3r^{2n+3}(r-a)(r-b)^2+6\frac{\rho_0-\rho_1}{\rho_1}b^3r^{2n+2}\frac{(r-b)^4}{4}\right.$$

$$\left.+r^{2n+6}(r-a)(r-b)^2-\frac{\rho_0-\rho_1}{\rho_1}6(n-1)b^3r^{2n+2}\int_b^r\frac{1}{r^{2n+2}}\int_b^r r^{2n+1}(r-b)^3\,dr\,.\,dr\right]$$

$$-\frac{\frac{4}{3}\pi\gamma\rho_1{}^2\epsilon_n}{a^{n+4}(a-b)}\,n\left[6\frac{\rho_0-\rho_1}{\rho_1}b^3r^{2n+2}\frac{(r-b)^3}{3}\right.$$

$$\left.-6(n-1)\frac{\rho_0-\rho_1}{\rho_1}b^3r^{2n+2}\int_b^r\frac{1}{r^{2n+2}}\int_b^r r^{2n+1}(r-b)^2\,dr\,.\,dr\right] \qquad \text{......(27)}.$$

22. To find the forms of F_n and f_n we begin by noting the equation (21), which is

$$\frac{dF_n}{dr} = -\frac{1}{n}\left\{r^2\frac{dG_n}{dr} + (n+3)\,rG_n\right\}.$$

Therefore $$\frac{d^2F_n}{dr^2} = -\frac{1}{n}\left\{r^2\frac{d^2G_n}{dr^2} + (n+5)\,r\frac{dG_n}{dr} + (n+3)\,G_n\right\},$$

and

$$2G_n + \frac{d^2F_n}{dr^2} + \frac{2n}{r}\frac{dF_n}{dr}$$

$$= -\frac{1}{n}\left\{r^2\frac{d^2G_n}{dr^2} + (3n+5)\,r\frac{dG_n}{dr} + (n+3)(2n+1)\,G_n - 2nG_n\right\}$$

$$= -\frac{1}{n}\left\{r^2\frac{d^2G_n}{dr^2} + 2(n+2)\,r\frac{dG_n}{dr} + (n+1)\,r\frac{dG_n}{dr} + (2n^2+5n+3)\,G_n\right\}$$

$$= -\frac{r}{n}\left\{r\frac{d^2G_n}{dr^2} + 2(n+2)\frac{dG_n}{dr}\right\} - \frac{n+1}{n}\left\{r\frac{dG_n}{dr} + (2n+3)\,G_n\right\}$$

$$= -\frac{r}{n}\frac{d}{dr}\left\{r\frac{dG_n}{dr} + (2n+3)\,G_n\right\} - \frac{n+1}{n}\left\{r\frac{dG_n}{dr} + (2n+3)\,G_n\right\}$$

$$= -\frac{r}{n}\frac{d}{dr}\left\{\frac{1}{r^{2n+2}}\frac{d}{dr}(r^{2n+3}G_n)\right\} - \frac{n+1}{n}\left\{\frac{1}{r^{2n+2}}\frac{d}{dr}(r^{2n+3}G_n)\right\}.$$

Hence by (22)

$$f_n = \frac{4\pi\gamma\rho_1^2\epsilon_n r^4}{a^{n+4}(a-b)^2}(r-a)(r-b)^2$$

$$+ \frac{\frac{4}{3}\pi\gamma\rho_1^2\epsilon_n}{a^{n+4}(a-b)^2}\left[\frac{\rho_0-\rho_1}{\rho_1}\frac{b^3}{r^5}\frac{d}{dr}\{r^7(r-a)(r-b)^2\}\right.$$

$$- 6(n-1)\frac{\rho_0-\rho_1}{\rho_1}\frac{b^3}{r^{2n+1}}\int_b^r r^{2n+1}(r-a)(r-b)^2\,dr$$

$$\left. + r\frac{d}{dr}\{r^4(r-a)(r-b)^2\}\right] + \frac{A}{nr^{2n+1}}$$

$$+ \frac{\frac{4}{3}\pi\gamma\rho_1^2\epsilon_n}{a^{n+4}(a-b)^2}(n+1)\left[\frac{\rho_0-\rho_1}{\rho_1}b^3r(r-a)(r-b)^2\right.$$

$$+ 6\frac{\rho_0-\rho_1}{\rho_1}b^3\int_b^r (r-a)(r-b)^2\,dr$$

$$- 6(n-1)\frac{\rho_0-\rho_1}{\rho_1}b^3\int_b^r\frac{1}{r^{2n+2}}\int_b^r r^{2n+1}(r-a)(r-b)^2\,dr\,.\,dr$$

$$\left. + r^4(r-a)(r-b)^2\right] - \frac{n+1}{n}\frac{A}{(2n+1)\,r^{2n+1}} + \frac{n+1}{n}B,$$

where the terms in A and B come to

$$\frac{A}{(2n+1)\,r^{2n+1}} + \frac{n+1}{n} B,$$

so that we have

$$f_n = \frac{A}{(2n+1)\,r^{2n+1}} + \frac{n+1}{n} B + \frac{\frac{4}{3}\pi\gamma\rho_1{}^2\epsilon_n}{a^{n+4}(a-b)^2}\left(\frac{\rho_0-\rho_1}{\rho_1} b^3 r^2 + r^5\right)(r-b)^2$$

$$+ \frac{4\pi\gamma\rho_1{}^2\epsilon_n r^4}{a^{n+4}(a-b)^2}(r-a)(r-b)^2$$

$$+ \frac{\frac{4}{3}\pi\gamma\rho_1{}^2\epsilon_n}{a^{n+4}(a-b)^2}\left[\frac{\rho_0-\rho_1}{\rho_1}\frac{b^3}{r^5}(r-a)\frac{d}{dr}\{r^7(r-b)^2\} + r(r-a)\frac{d}{dr}\{r^4(r-b)^2\}\right]$$

$$+ \frac{\frac{4}{3}\pi\gamma\rho_1{}^2\epsilon_n}{a^{n+4}(a-b)^2}(n+1)\left[\frac{\rho_0-\rho_1}{\rho_1} b^3 r(r-a)(r-b)^2 + r^4(r-a)(r-b)^2\right] + \phi_n \qquad \text{.........(28)},$$

where

$$\phi_n = \frac{\frac{4}{3}\pi\gamma\rho_1{}^2\epsilon_n}{a^{n+4}(a-b)^2}\left[6(n+1)\frac{\rho_0-\rho_1}{\rho_1} b^3 \int_b^r (r-b)^3\,dr\right.$$

$$- 6(n-1)\frac{\rho_0-\rho_1}{\rho_1}\frac{b^3}{r^{2n+1}}\int_b^r r^{2n+1}(r-b)^3\,dr$$

$$\left.- 6(n^2-1)\frac{\rho_0-\rho_1}{\rho_1} b^3 \int_b^r \frac{1}{r^{2n+2}}\int_b^r r^{2n+1}(r-b)^3\,dr\,.\,dr\right]$$

$$- \frac{\frac{4}{3}\pi\gamma\rho_1{}^2\epsilon_n}{a^{n+4}(a-b)}\left[6(n+1)\frac{\rho_0-\rho_1}{\rho_1} b^3 \int_b^r (r-b)^2\,dr\right.$$

$$- 6(n-1)\frac{\rho_0-\rho_1}{\rho_1}\frac{b^3}{r^{2n+1}}\int_b^r r^{2n+1}(r-b)^2\,dr$$

$$\left.- 6(n^2-1)\frac{\rho_0-\rho_1}{\rho_1} b^3 \int_b^r \frac{1}{r^{2n+2}}\int_b^r r^{2n+1}(r-b)^2\,dr\,.\,dr\right] \qquad \text{......(29)}.$$

23. Again to find F_n we have the equation (21), viz.

$$\frac{dF_n}{dr} = -\frac{r}{n}\left\{r\frac{dG_n}{dr} + (n+3)\,G_n\right\}$$

$$= -\frac{r}{n}\frac{1}{r^{2n+2}}\frac{d}{dr}(r^{2n+3}G_n) + rG_n$$

$$= -\frac{1}{n}\frac{1}{r^{2n+1}}\frac{d}{dr}(r^{2n+3}G_n) + rG_n.$$

Hence

$$\mu\frac{dF_n}{dr} = -\frac{A}{n(2n+1)\,r^{2n}} + \frac{B}{n} r + \frac{A}{2(2n+1)\,r^{2n}} - \frac{B}{2n+3} r - \frac{C}{r^{2n+2}}$$

$$+ \frac{\frac{4}{3}\pi\gamma\rho_1{}^2\epsilon_n}{a^{n+4}(a-b)^2}\left[\frac{\rho_0-\rho_1}{\rho_1} b^3 r^2 (r-a)(r-b)^2 + 6\frac{\rho_0-\rho_1}{\rho_1} b^3 r \int^r (r-a)(r-b)^2\,dr\right.$$

$$-6(n-1)\frac{\rho_0-\rho_1}{\rho_1}b^3r\int_b^r\frac{1}{r^{2n+2}}\int_b^r r^{2n+1}(r-a)(r-b)^2\,dr\,.\,dr$$

$$+r^5(r-a)(r-b)^2\Big]$$

$$-\frac{\frac{4}{3}\pi\gamma\rho_1{}^2\epsilon_n}{a^{n+4}(a-b)^2}n\left[\frac{\rho_0-\rho_1}{\rho_1}b^3\frac{1}{r^{2n+2}}\int_b^r r^{2n+3}(r-a)(r-b)^2\,dr\right.$$

$$+6\frac{\rho_0-\rho_1}{\rho_1}b^3\frac{1}{r^{2n+2}}\int_b^r r^{2n+2}\int_b^r(r-a)(r-b)^2\,dr\,.\,dr$$

$$-6(n-1)\frac{\rho_0-\rho_1}{\rho_1}b^3\frac{1}{r^{2n+2}}\int_b^r r^{2n+2}\int_b^r\frac{1}{r^{2n+2}}\int_b^r r^{2n+1}(r-a)(r-b)^2\,dr\ldots$$

$$\left.+\frac{1}{r^{2n+2}}\int_b^r r^{2n+6}(r-a)(r-b)^2\,dr\right],$$

where the terms in A, B, C are

$$\frac{A(n-2)}{2n(2n+1)r^{2n}}+\frac{B(n+3)}{n(2n+3)}r-\frac{C}{r^{2n+2}}.$$

This gives on integration with respect to r

$$\mu F_n=-\frac{A(n-2)}{(2n-1)2n(2n+1)r^{2n-1}}+\frac{n+3}{2n(2n+3)}Br^2+\frac{C}{(2n+1)r^{2n+1}}+D+\Phi_n \qquad \ldots\ldots\ldots(30),$$

where

$$\Phi_n=\frac{\frac{4}{3}\pi\gamma\rho_1{}^2\epsilon_n}{a^{n+4}(a-b)^2}\left[\frac{\rho_0-\rho_1}{\rho_1}b^3\int_b^r r^2(r-a)(r-b)^2\,dr\right.$$

$$+6\frac{\rho_0-\rho_1}{\rho_1}b^3\int_b^r r\int_b^r(r-a)(r-b)^2\,dr\,.\,dr$$

$$-6(n-1)\frac{\rho_0-\rho_1}{\rho_1}b^3\int_b^r r\int_b^r\frac{1}{r^{2n+2}}\int_b^r r^{2n+1}(r-a)(r-b)^2\,dr\,.\,dr\,.\,dr$$

$$\left.+\int_b^r r^5(r-a)(r-b)^2\,dr\right]$$

$$-\frac{\frac{4}{3}\pi\gamma\rho_1{}^2\epsilon_n}{a^{n+4}(a-b)^2}n\left[\frac{\rho_0-\rho_1}{\rho_1}b^3\int_b^r\frac{1}{r^{2n+2}}\int_b^r r^{2n+3}(r-a)(r-b)^2\,dr\,.\,dr\right.$$

$$+6\frac{\rho_0-\rho_1}{\rho_1}b^3\int_b^r\frac{1}{r^{2n+2}}\int_b^r r^{2n+2}\int_b^r(r-a)(r-b)^2\,dr\,.\,dr\,.\,dr$$

$$-6(n-1)\frac{\rho_0-\rho_1}{\rho_1}b^3\int_b^r\frac{1}{r^{2n+2}}\int_b^r r^{2n+2}\int_b^r\frac{1}{r^{2n+2}}\int_b^r r^{2n+1}(r-a)(r-b)^2\,dr\ldots$$

$$\left.+\int_b^r\frac{1}{r^{2n+2}}\int_b^r r^{2n+6}(r-a)(r-b)^2\,dr\,.\,dr\right],$$

or, as it may be written,

$$\Phi_n = \frac{\frac{4}{3}\pi\gamma\rho_1^2\epsilon_n}{a^{n+4}(a-b)^2}\left[\frac{\rho_0-\rho_1}{\rho_1}b^3\int_b^r r^2(r-b)^3\,dr + 6\frac{\rho_0-\rho_1}{\rho_1}b^3\int_b^r r\int_b^r (r-b)^3\,dr\,.\,dr\right.$$

$$\left.-6(n-1)\frac{\rho_0-\rho_1}{\rho_1}b^3\int_b^r r\int_b^r \frac{1}{r^{2n+2}}\int_b^r r^{2n+1}(r-b)^3\,dr.dr.dr + \int_b^r r^5(r-b)^3\,dr\right]$$

$$-\frac{\frac{4}{3}\pi\gamma\rho_1^2\epsilon_n}{a^{n+4}(a-b)}\left[\frac{\rho_0-\rho_1}{\rho_1}b^3\int_b^r r^2(r-b)^2\,dr + 6\frac{\rho_0-\rho_1}{\rho_1}b^3\int_b^r r\int_b^r (r-b)^2\,dr\,.\,dr\right.$$

$$\left.-6(n-1)\frac{\rho_0-\rho_1}{\rho_1}b^3\int_b^r r\int_b^r \frac{1}{r^{2n+2}}\int_b^r r^{2n+1}(r-b)^2\,dr.dr.dr + \int_b^r r^5(r-b)^2\,dr\right]$$

$$-\frac{\frac{4}{3}\pi\gamma\rho_1^2\epsilon_n}{a^{n+4}(a-b)^2}\,n\left[\frac{\rho_0-\rho_1}{\rho_1}b^3\int_b^r \frac{1}{r^{2n+2}}\int_b^r r^{2n+3}(r-b)^3\,dr\,.\,dr\right.$$

$$+6\frac{\rho_0-\rho_1}{\rho_1}b^3\int_b^r \frac{1}{r^{2n+2}}\int_b^r r^{2n+2}\int_b^r (r-b)^3\,dr\,.\,dr\,.\,dr$$

$$-6(n-1)\frac{\rho_0-\rho_1}{\rho_1}b^3\int_b^r \frac{1}{r^{2n+2}}\int_b^r r^{2n+2}\int_b^r \frac{1}{r^{2n+2}}\int_b^r r^{2n+1}(r-b)^3\,dr\,.\,dr\,.\,dr\,.\,dr$$

$$\left.+\int_b^r \frac{1}{r^{2n+2}}\int_b^r r^{2n+6}(r-b)^3\,dr\,.\,dr\right]$$

$$+\frac{\frac{4}{3}\pi\gamma\rho_1^2\epsilon_n}{a^{n+4}(a-b)}\,n\left[\frac{\rho_0-\rho_1}{\rho_1}b^3\int_b^r \frac{1}{r^{2n+2}}\int_b^r r^{2n+3}(r-b)^2\,dr\,.\,dr\right.$$

$$+6\frac{\rho_0-\rho_1}{\rho_1}b^3\int_b^r \frac{1}{r^{2n+2}}\int_b^r r^{2n+2}\int_b^r (r-b)^2\,dr\,.\,dr\,.\,dr$$

$$-6(n-1)\frac{\rho_0-\rho_1}{\rho_1}b^3\int_b^r \frac{1}{r^{2n+2}}\int_b^r r^{2n+2}\int_b^r \frac{1}{r^{2n+2}}\int_b^r r^{2n+1}(r-b)^2\,dr\,.\,dr\,.\,dr\,.\,dr$$

$$\left.+\int_b^r \frac{1}{r^{2n+2}}\int_b^r r^{2n+6}(r-b)^2\,dr\,.\,dr\right]\ldots(31).$$

We have now expressed the functions G_n, F_n, f_n in terms of integrals all of which can be evaluated without much difficulty, and therewith have obtained the solution of the equations (17) of p. 15. The result gives formulae for the "displacement" (u, v, w) and the additional pressure p' in terms of the spherical harmonic W_n, the distance r, and four constants A, B, C, D. The constants are to be determined by means of the boundary conditions, and when this is done the stress can be calculated.

24. The initial pressure (p_0 in the core, and p_1 in the layer of compensation) is determined by the equations (9) and (10) of p. 13 and the conditions that $p_0 = p_1$ at $r = b$ and $p_1 = 0$ at $r = a$. The actual values of p_0 and p_1 are not required in the problem of determining the tangential stresses. Manifestly p_0 depends upon the distribution of mass in the core, about which no assumption has been made beyond that of spherical symmetry.

Boundary Conditions.

25. We proceed to investigate the boundary conditions by which the constants A, ... are to be determined.

The traction across any spherical surface within the layer of compensation has components X_r, Y_r, Z_r which are expressed by equations of the type

$$X_r = -\frac{x}{r}(p_1+p') + \frac{\mu}{r}\left(\frac{\partial \zeta}{\partial x} + r\frac{\partial u}{\partial r} - u\right) \quad \text{..................(32)},$$

in which

$$\zeta = xu + yv + zw \quad \text{....................................(33)}.$$

The corresponding expressions within the core are given by

$$X_r = -\frac{x}{r} p_0.$$

Now we have

$$\zeta = (nF_n + r^2G_n) W_n,$$

so that

$$\frac{\partial \zeta}{\partial x} = (nF_n + r^2G_n)\frac{\partial W_n}{\partial x} + \frac{1}{r}\frac{d}{dr}(nF_n + r^2G_n)\, x W_n.$$

Also we have

$$r\frac{\partial u}{\partial r} - u = \left\{r\frac{dF_n}{dr} + (n-2)F_n\right\}\frac{\partial W_n}{\partial x} + \left(r\frac{dG_n}{dr} + nG_n\right) x W_n.$$

Hence the expression for X_r in the layer becomes

$$-\frac{x}{r}(p_1+p') + \frac{\mu}{r}\left[\left\{r\frac{dF_n}{dr} + 2(n-1)F_n + r^2G_n\right\}\frac{\partial W_n}{\partial x} + \left\{\frac{n}{r}\frac{dF_n}{dr} + 2r\frac{dG_n}{dr} + (n+2)G_n\right\} x W_n\right].$$

It follows that the normal component of traction across the spherical surface, which is $(xX_r + yY_r + zZ_r)/r$, is given by

$$\frac{xX_r + yY_r + zZ_r}{r} = -(p_1+p') + \frac{\mu}{r}\left[2n\frac{dF_n}{dr} + 2\frac{n(n-1)}{r}F_n + 2r^2\frac{dG_n}{dr} + 2(n+1)rG_n\right] W_n \quad \text{...(34)}.$$

The tangential traction across the spherical surface can be resolved into components parallel to the axes, the x-component being

$$X_r - \frac{x}{r}\frac{xX_r + yY_r + zZ_r}{r},$$

and we find for this the value

$$\frac{\mu}{r}\left[\left\{r\frac{dF_n}{dr} + 2(n-1)F_n + r^2G_n\right\}\frac{\partial W_n}{\partial x} + \left\{-nG_n - 2n(n-1)\frac{F_n}{r^2} - \frac{n}{r}\frac{dF_n}{dr}\right\} x W_n\right] \quad \text{...(35)}.$$

26. The conditions of continuity of stress at the surface $r=b$ are that the normal component of traction is equal to $-p_0$ and the tangential traction vanishes. Since $p_0=p_1$ at $r=b$ these conditions give the two equations

$$-f_n+\frac{\mu}{r}\left[2n\frac{dF_n}{dr}+2\frac{n(n-1)}{r}F_n+2r^2\frac{dG_n}{dr}+2(n+1)rG_n\right]=0,$$

and
$$r\frac{dF_n}{dr}+2(n-1)F_n+r^2G_n=0 \qquad (36).$$

These two equations hold at $r=b$. The first of them can, by using (21), be reduced to

$$-f_n+2\frac{\mu}{r}\left[\frac{n(n-1)}{r}F_n-2rG_n\right]=0 \qquad (37).$$

27. The conditions that the surface $r=a+\epsilon_n S_n$ may be free from traction are three equations of the type

$$-l(p_1+p')_{r=a+\epsilon_n S_n}+\frac{\mu}{r}\left(\frac{\partial\zeta}{\partial x}+r\frac{\partial u}{\partial r}-u\right)=0 \qquad (38),$$

where l is the cosine of the angle which the normal to the surface drawn outwards makes with the axis of x. Since p_1 vanishes at $r=a$ its value at $r=a+\epsilon_n S_n$ can be taken with sufficient approximation to be $\epsilon_n S_n \dfrac{\partial p_1}{\partial r}$, and the above equation can be reduced to

$$-\frac{x}{a}(-g\rho_1\epsilon_n S_n+p')+\frac{\mu}{a}\left(\frac{\partial\zeta}{\partial x}+r\frac{\partial u}{\partial r}-u\right)=0 \qquad (39),$$

where $-g$ is written for $(\partial V_1/\partial r)_a$, which is the same as $(\rho_1^{-1}\partial p_1/\partial r)_a$, so that

$$g=\tfrac{4}{3}\pi\gamma\rho_1\left\{\frac{\rho_0-\rho_1}{\rho_1}\frac{b^3}{a^2}+a\right\} \qquad (40).$$

On reducing the equations of this type in the same way as before it will be found that they become

$$-f_n+\frac{2\mu}{r^2}\{n(n-1)F_n-2r^2G_n\}=-\frac{g\rho_1\epsilon_n}{r^n} \qquad (41),$$

and
$$r\frac{dF_n}{dr}+2(n-1)F_n+r^2G_n=0 \qquad (42).$$

These two equations hold at $r=a$. The first of them really expresses the result that the normal traction on the mean sphere $r=a$ is a pressure equal to the weight of the harmonic inequality. The second of them expresses the condition that the tangential traction on the mean sphere vanishes.

28. With a view to the determination of the four constants A, B, C, D we write the results obtained in §§ 21—23 in the form

$$-\mu G_n = -\frac{A}{2(2n+1)r^{2n+1}} + \frac{B}{2n+3} + \frac{C}{r^{2n+3}} + \gamma_n \qquad \text{.........(43)},$$

$$-\mu\frac{d}{dr}(r^{2n+3}G_n) = -\frac{Ar}{2n+1} + Br^{2n+2} + \frac{d}{dr}(r^{2n+3}\gamma_n) \qquad \text{.........(44)},$$

$$\mu F_n = -\frac{A(n-2)}{(2n-1)(2n)(2n+1)r^{2n-1}} + \frac{n+3}{2n(2n+3)}Br^2 + \frac{C}{(2n+1)r^{2n+1}} + D + \Phi_n \qquad \text{.........(45)},$$

$$f_n = \frac{A}{(2n+1)r^{2n+1}} + \frac{n+1}{n}B + \frac{\frac{4}{3}\pi\gamma\rho_1^2\epsilon_n}{a^{n+4}(a-b)^2}\left(\frac{\rho_0-\rho_1}{\rho_1}b^3r^2 + r^5\right)(r-b)^2 + \psi_n + \phi_n \qquad \text{.........(46)},$$

where ψ_n vanishes both when $r=a$ and when $r=b$, and γ_n, $\frac{d}{dr}(r^{2n+3}\gamma_n)$, Φ_n, ϕ_n all vanish when $r=b$.

The normal stress-condition at $r=b$ is

$$-\frac{A}{(2n+1)b^{2n+1}} - \frac{n+1}{n}B$$

$$-\frac{A(n-1)(n-2)}{(2n-1)(2n+1)b^{2n+1}} + \frac{(n-1)(n+3)}{2n+3}B + \frac{2n(n-1)C}{(2n+1)b^{2n+3}} + 2n(n-1)\frac{D}{b^2}$$

$$-\frac{2A}{(2n+1)b^{2n+1}} + \frac{4B}{2n+3} + \frac{4C}{b^{2n+3}} = 0,$$

which is

$$-\frac{n^2+3n-1}{(2n-1)(2n+1)}\frac{A}{b^{2n-1}} + \frac{(n+1)(n^2-n-3)}{n(2n+3)}Bb^2$$

$$+\frac{2(n+1)(n+2)}{2n+1}\frac{C}{b^{2n+1}} + 2n(n-1)D = 0.$$

The tangential stress-condition at $r=b$ is

$$-\frac{(n-1)(n-2)}{n(2n-1)(2n+1)}\frac{A}{b^{2n-1}} + \frac{(n-1)(n+3)}{n(2n+3)}Bb^2 + \frac{2(n-1)}{2n+1}\frac{C}{b^{2n+1}} + 2(n-1)D$$

$$-\frac{1}{n(2n+1)}\frac{A}{b^{2n-1}} + \frac{1}{n}Bb^2$$

$$+\frac{1}{2n+1}\frac{A}{b^{2n-1}} - \frac{2Bb^2}{2n+3} - \frac{2C}{b^{2n+1}} = 0,$$

which is

$$\frac{n^2-1}{n(2n-1)(2n+1)}\frac{A}{b^{2n-1}} + \frac{n+2}{2n+3}Bb^2 - \frac{2(n+2)}{2n+1}\frac{C}{b^{2n+1}} + 2(n-1)D = 0.$$

These give
$$C=\frac{Ab^2}{2(2n+1)}+\frac{2n^2+4n+3}{2n(n+2)(2n+3)}Bb^{2n+3} \quad \text{.........(47)},$$

$$2(n-1)D=\frac{2n^2+1}{n(2n-1)(2n+1)^2}\frac{A}{b^{2n-1}}-\frac{n^2-1}{n(2n+1)}Bb^2 \quad \text{......(48)}.$$

29. The tangential stress-condition at $r=a$ is

$$\frac{n^2-1}{n(2n-1)(2n+1)}\frac{A}{a^{2n-1}}+\frac{n+2}{2n+3}Ba^2-\frac{2(n+2)}{2n+1}\frac{C}{a^{2n+1}}+2(n-1)D$$
$$+2(n-1)\Phi_n(a)+\frac{1}{na^{2n}}\frac{d}{dr}(r^{2n+3}\gamma_n)_a-2a^2\gamma_n(a)=0,$$

which is

$$-\frac{(n+2)}{(2n+1)^2}\left(\frac{b^2}{a^{2n+1}}-\frac{1}{a^{2n-1}}\right)A+\frac{2n^2+1}{n(2n-1)(2n+1)^2}\left(\frac{1}{b^{2n-1}}-\frac{1}{a^{2n-1}}\right)A$$
$$-\frac{(2n^2+4n+3)}{n(2n+1)(2n+3)}\left(\frac{b^{2n+3}}{a^{2n+1}}-a^2\right)B-\frac{n^2-1}{n(2n+1)}(b^2-a^2)B$$
$$+2(n-1)\Phi_n(a)+\frac{1}{na^{2n}}\frac{d}{dr}(r^{2n+3}\gamma_n)_a-2a^2\gamma_n(a)=0,$$

or

$$\left[+\frac{2n^2+1}{n(2n-1)(2n+1)^2}\frac{a^{2n-1}-b^{2n-1}}{a^{2n-1}b^{2n-1}}+\frac{n+2}{(2n+1)^2}\frac{a^2-b^2}{a^{2n+1}}\right]A$$
$$+\left[\frac{2n^2+4n+3}{n(2n+1)(2n+3)}\frac{a^{2n+3}-b^{2n+3}}{a^{2n+1}}+\frac{n^2-1}{n(2n+1)}(a^2-b^2)\right]B$$
$$+2(n-1)\Phi_n(a)+\frac{1}{na^{2n}}\frac{d}{dr}(r^{2n+3}\gamma_n)_a-2a^2\gamma_n(a)=0 \quad \text{......(49)}.$$

The normal stress-condition at $r=a$ is

$$-\frac{n^2+3n-1}{(2n-1)(2n+1)}\frac{A}{a^{2n+1}}+\frac{(n+1)(n^2-n-3)}{n(2n+3)}B$$
$$+\frac{2(n+1)(n+2)}{2n+1}\frac{C}{a^{2n+3}}+2n(n-1)\frac{D}{a^2}$$
$$+\frac{2n(n-1)}{a^2}\Phi_n(a)-\phi_n(a)+4\gamma_n(a)=0,$$

which is

$$\left[\frac{(n+1)(n+2)}{(2n+1)^2}\left(\frac{b^2}{a^{2n+3}}-\frac{1}{a^{2n+1}}\right)+\frac{2n^2+1}{(2n-1)(2n+1)^2}\left(\frac{1}{a^2b^{2n-1}}-\frac{1}{a^{2n+1}}\right)\right]A$$
$$+\left[\frac{(n+1)(2n^2+4n+3)}{n(2n+1)(2n+3)}\left(\frac{b^{2n+3}}{a^{2n+3}}-1\right)-\frac{n^2-1}{2n+1}\left(\frac{b^2}{a^2}-1\right)\right]B$$
$$+\frac{2n(n-1)}{a^2}\Phi_n(a)-\phi_n(a)+4\gamma_n(a)=0,$$

or
$$\left[\frac{2n^2+1}{(2n-1)(2n+1)^2}\frac{a^{2n-1}-b^{2n-1}}{a^{2n+1}b^{2n-1}}-\frac{(n+1)(n+2)}{(2n+1)^2}\frac{a^2-b^2}{a^{2n+3}}\right]A$$
$$+\left[\frac{n^2-1}{2n+1}\frac{a^2-b^2}{a^2}-\frac{(n+1)(2n^2+4n+3)}{n(2n+1)(2n+3)}\frac{a^{2n+3}-b^{2n+3}}{a^{2n+3}}\right]B$$
$$+\frac{2n(n-1)}{a^2}\Phi_n(a)-\phi_n(a)+4\gamma_n(a)=0 \text{ .... (50).}$$

Put $$a-b=t \text{ .... (51),}$$
so that t is the mean thickness of the layer of compensation. Then the equations (49) and (50) can be written
$$\left[\frac{2n^2+1}{(2n-1)(2n+1)^2}\left\{\left(1-\frac{t}{a}\right)^{-(2n-1)}-1\right\}+\frac{n(n+2)}{(2n+1)^2}\left(\frac{2t}{a}-\frac{t^2}{a^2}\right)\right]\frac{A}{a^{2n-1}}$$
$$+\left[\frac{2n^2+4n+3}{(2n+1)(2n+3)}\left\{1-\left(1-\frac{t}{a}\right)^{2n+3}\right\}+\frac{n^2-1}{2n+1}\left(\frac{2t}{a}-\frac{t^2}{a^2}\right)\right]Ba^2$$
$$+2n(n-1)\Phi_n(a)+\frac{1}{a^{2n}}\frac{d}{dr}(r^{2n+3}\gamma_n)_a-2na^2\gamma_n(a)=0 \text{ .... (52),}$$
and
$$\left[\frac{2n^2+1}{(2n-1)(2n+1)^2}\left\{\left(1-\frac{t}{a}\right)^{-(2n-1)}-1\right\}-\frac{(n+1)(n+2)}{(2n+1)^2}\left(\frac{2t}{a}-\frac{t^2}{a^2}\right)\right]\frac{A}{a^{2n-1}}$$
$$+\left[-\frac{(n+1)(2n^2+4n+3)}{n(2n+1)(2n+3)}\left\{1-\left(1-\frac{t}{a}\right)^{2n+3}\right\}+\frac{n^2-1}{2n+1}\left(\frac{2t}{a}-\frac{t^2}{a^2}\right)\right]Ba^2$$
$$+2n(n-1)\Phi_n(a)-a^2\phi_n(a)+4a^2\gamma_n(a)=0 \text{ .... (53).}$$

These equations can be solved for A and B and then C and D can be found from equations (47) and (48).

30. Instead of proceeding with a general algebraic solution it appears to be more convenient to solve the equations approximately in two cases. In the first case n is a small integer, one or two or three, and t/a is a small fraction. In the second case n is a large integer, so that nt/a is of the order unity.

THE STRESS-DIFFERENCE.

31. Before working out these solutions we consider the formulae relating to the conditions that must be satisfied in order that the material may be strong enough to support the inequalities.

Several recent writers on the strength of materials have drawn from experiment the conclusion that rupture is produced when the greatest shearing stress developed in a material exceeds a definite limit. The stress at a point can always be expressed by means of three principal stresses, which are the tractions across three particular planes that cut each other at right angles, and the greatest shearing stress developed in the material is half the absolute value of the difference between the algebraically greatest and least of the principal stresses. This difference has been called the *stress-difference.* According to this view, rupture is produced if the stress-difference exceeds the tenacity of the material. Alternative views, which now receive less support, are to the effect that rupture takes place when the absolutely greatest stress, provided it is not a pressure, or the absolutely greatest strain, exceed definite limits. Such views are inapplicable to our problem because on the one hand the greatest stress is certainly a pressure, and on the other hand there is no question of strain; for the earth is not strained from a state without continents and mountains to a state presenting these features. In this problem therefore our procedure must be to evaluate the stress-difference required to support continents and mountains of such dimensions as actually occur, and compare it with the tenacities of various materials, or with the crushing strengths of these materials.

We observe that the stress-difference is unaltered if with the actual stress we compound any hydrostatic pressure. Thus the only part of the stress that need be considered is the part that is correlated with the "displacement" (u, v, w).

32. To simplify the problem we shall assume that the spherical harmonics by which the inequalities of the surface are expressed are zonal.

We shall use polar coordinates referred to the axis of the zonal harmonics. Let these be r, θ, ϕ. Then the direction $d\phi$ is that of one of the principal stresses.

Let P, Q, R denote the relevant parts of the normal component tractions across the surfaces $\theta = \text{const.}$, $\phi = \text{const.}$, $r = \text{const.}$, which pass through any point, S the shearing stress consisting of two equal tangential tractions, one acting in the direction $d\theta$ across the surface $r = \text{const.}$, the other acting in the direction dr across the surface $\theta = \text{const.}$ The stress-system expressed by P, Q, R, S is the same as that expressed by $X_x' + p'$, $Y_y' + p'$, $Z_z' + p'$, Y_z, Z_x, X_y. Let N_1, N_2, N_3 denote the principal stresses. Then

$$N_2 = Q,$$

and N_1, N_3 are given by the equations

$$N_1 + N_3 = P + R, \quad N_1 N_3 = PR - S^2,$$

so that we have

$$N_1 = \tfrac{1}{2}\left[(P+R) + \sqrt{\{(P-R)^2 + 4S^2\}}\right],$$

$$N_3 = \tfrac{1}{2}\left[(P+R) - \sqrt{\{(P-R)^2 + 4S^2\}}\right].$$

Also, since the mean pressure corresponding to this stress-system vanishes, we have

$$P + Q + R = 0,$$

or

$$P + R = -N_2.$$

The stress-difference is the absolute value of the numerically greatest of the three expressions

$$\left.\begin{array}{r}\tfrac{1}{2}[-3Q+\sqrt{\{(P-R)^2+4S^2\}}]\\ \tfrac{1}{2}[-3Q-\sqrt{\{(P-R)^2+4S^2\}}]\\ \sqrt{\{(P-R)^2+4S^2\}}\end{array}\right\} \qquad\qquad(54).$$

33. Again let u_1, u_2, u_3 denote the components in the directions $d\theta$, $d\phi$, dr of the "displacement" (u, v, w). Then, according to the usual formulae for strain components referred to polar coordinates, we have

$$\left.\begin{array}{l}P=2\mu\left(\dfrac{1}{r}\dfrac{\partial u_1}{\partial\theta}+\dfrac{u_3}{r}\right),\quad Q=2\mu\left(\dfrac{u_1}{r}\cot\theta+\dfrac{u_3}{r}\right),\quad R=2\mu\dfrac{\partial u_3}{\partial r}\\ S=\mu\left(\dfrac{\partial u_1}{\partial r}-\dfrac{u_1}{r}+\dfrac{1}{r}\dfrac{\partial u_3}{\partial\theta}\right)\end{array}\right\} \quad\ldots(55).$$

Also by (20) of p. 15, since W_n is independent of ϕ,

$$u_1=\frac{1}{r}F_n\frac{\partial W_n}{\partial\theta},\quad u_2=0,\quad u_3=\left(\frac{n}{r}F_n+rG_n\right)W_n,$$

or

$$u_1=r^{n-1}F_n\frac{dS_n}{d\theta},\quad u_2=0,\quad u_3=(nr^{n-1}F_n+r^{n+1}G_n)S_n.$$

Hence

$$P=2\mu\left[r^{n-2}F_n\frac{d^2S_n}{d\theta^2}+(nr^{n-2}F_n+r^nG_n)S_n\right],$$

$$Q=2\mu\left[r^{n-2}F_n\cot\theta\frac{dS_n}{d\theta}+(nr^{n-2}F_n+r^nG_n)S_n\right],$$

$$R=2\mu\left[nr^{n-1}\frac{dF_n}{dr}+n(n-1)r^{n-2}F_n+r^{n+1}\frac{dG_n}{dr}+(n+1)r^nG_n\right]S_n,$$

$$S=\mu\left[r^{n-1}\frac{dF_n}{dr}+2(n-1)r^{n-2}F_n+r^nG_n\right]\frac{dS_n}{d\theta}.$$

The expression for S accords with the values found on p. 24 for the tangential traction on a spherical surface. The expression for P can be simplified by means of the equation

$$\frac{d^2S_n}{d\theta^2}+\cot\theta\frac{dS_n}{d\theta}+n(n+1)S_n=0,$$

and the expressions for R and S can be simplified by means of the equation

$$\frac{n}{r}\frac{dF_n}{dr}+r\frac{dG_n}{dr}+(n+3)G_n=0.$$

Thus we find

$$P = 2\mu\left[(r^n G_n - n^2 r^{n-2} F_n) S_n - r^{n-2} F_n \cot\theta \frac{dS_n}{d\theta}\right] \quad\ldots\ldots(56),$$

$$Q = 2\mu\left[(r^n G_n + n r^{n-2} F_n) S_n + r^{n-2} F_n \cot\theta \frac{dS_n}{d\theta}\right] \quad\ldots\ldots(57),$$

$$R = 2\mu\left[\{-2r^n G_n + n(n-1) r^{n-2} F_n\} S_n\right] \quad\ldots\ldots(58),$$

$$S = \mu\left[\left\{2r^n G_n - \frac{1}{n r^{n+2}} \frac{d}{dr}(r^{2n+3} G_n) + 2(n-1) r^{n-2} F_n\right\} \frac{dS_n}{d\theta}\right] \quad\ldots\ldots(59),$$

and

$$P - R = 2\mu\left[\{3r^n G_n - n(2n-1) r^{n-2} F_n\} S_n - r^{n-2} F_n \cot\theta \frac{dS_n}{d\theta}\right] \quad\ldots\ldots(60).$$

In any particular case the stress-difference can be evaluated by means of these formulae.

Harmonic Inequalities of Low Degrees.

34. We are going to proceed with an approximate solution applicable to small integral values of n. We have to begin by evaluating the four constants A, B, C, D. The constants C, D can be expressed in terms of A, B only by equations (47) and (48) of p. 27, and the constants A, B are determined in terms of the values at $r = a$ of the functions γ_n, Φ_n, and so on. The functions γ_n and so on have been expressed completely in terms of integrals, and we wish to obtain a first approximation to them on the supposition that $a - b$, or t, is small compared with a or b. In working out this approximation we shall at the same time introduce the simplification that arises if $\rho_0 = 2\rho_1$. This means to say that the mean density of the layer of compensation is assumed to be half of the mean density of the core, so that it is in accordance with the known fact that the mean density of surface rocks is about half the mean density of the earth.

35. In evaluating approximately the integrals by which γ_n, ... are expressed we put $r - b = x$, expand all powers of r in powers of x, and keep only the terms of lowest degrees. We note that, when $r = a$, $x = t$. The factor $r - a$, where it occurs outside a sign of integration, will be retained without substitution. For example, we have from (26), p. 19,

$$\gamma_n = \frac{\frac{4}{3}\pi\gamma\rho_1^2\epsilon_n}{a^{n+4}t^2}\cdot n\cdot\left[\frac{b^3}{b^{2n+3}} b^{2n+3}\frac{1}{4}x^4 + 6\frac{b^3}{b^{2n+3}} b^{2n+2}\frac{1}{4.5}x^5\right.$$
$$\left. - 6(n-1)\frac{b^3}{b^{2n+3}} b^{2n+2}\frac{1}{b^{2n+2}} b^{2n+1}\frac{1}{4.5.6}x^6 + \frac{1}{b^{2n+3}} b^{2n+6}\frac{1}{4}x^4\right]$$
$$- \frac{\frac{4}{3}\pi\gamma\rho_1^2\epsilon_n}{a^{n+4}t}\cdot n\cdot\left[\frac{b^3}{b^{2n+3}} b^{2n+3}\frac{1}{3}x^3 + 6\frac{b^3}{b^{2n+3}} b^{2n+2}\frac{1}{3.4}x^4\right.$$
$$\left. - 6(n-1)\frac{b^3}{b^{2n+3}} b^{2n+2}\frac{1}{b^{2n+2}} b^{2n+1}\frac{1}{3.4.5}x^5 + \frac{1}{b^{2n+3}} b^{2n+6}\frac{1}{3}x^3\right].$$

The terms of lowest order are those in x^4/t^2 and x^3/t, and, if these alone are retained, we may in the factors that multiply them ignore the distinction between a and b, and thus find as the approximate form for γ_n

$$\gamma_n = -\frac{\frac{4}{3}\pi\gamma\rho_1{}^2\epsilon_n}{a^{n+1}} . n . \left(\frac{2x^3}{3t} - \frac{x^4}{2t^2}\right) \quad \text{.....................(61).}$$

In particular $$\gamma_n(a) = -\frac{\frac{4}{3}\pi\gamma\rho_1{}^2\epsilon_n}{a^{n+1}} . \frac{nt^2}{6} \quad \text{.................................(62).}$$

In the same way we find

$$\frac{d}{dr}(r^{2n+3}\gamma_n) = -\tfrac{4}{3}\pi\gamma\rho_1{}^2\epsilon_n . \left[2n\,a^{n+2}\frac{(a-r)\,x^2}{t^2} + n\,a^{n+1}\left(\frac{2x^3}{t} - \frac{3x^4}{2t^2}\right)\right] \text{...(63).}$$

In particular $$\frac{d}{dr}(r^{2n+3}\gamma_n)_a = -\tfrac{4}{3}\pi\gamma\rho_1{}^2\epsilon_n . \tfrac{1}{2}a^{n+1}\,nt^2 \text{.................(64).}$$

Again $$\phi_n = -\frac{\frac{4}{3}\pi\gamma\rho_1{}^2\epsilon_n}{a^{n+1}}\left(\frac{4x^3}{t} - \frac{3x^4}{t^2}\right) \quad \text{.....................(65).}$$

In particular $$\phi_n(a) = -\frac{\frac{4}{3}\pi\gamma\rho_1{}^2\epsilon_n}{a^{n+1}}\,t^2 \quad \text{........................(66).}$$

Further $$\Phi_n = -\frac{\frac{4}{3}\pi\gamma\rho_1{}^2\epsilon_n}{a^{n-1}}\left(\frac{2x^3}{3t} - \frac{x^4}{2t^2}\right) \quad \text{.....................(67).}$$

In particular $$\Phi_n(a) = -\frac{\frac{4}{3}\pi\gamma\rho_1{}^2\epsilon_n}{a^{n-1}} . \frac{t^2}{6} \quad \text{........................(68).}$$

Hence we find

$$2n(n-1)\,\Phi_n(a) + \frac{1}{a^{2n}}\frac{d}{dr}(r^{2n+3}\gamma_n)_a - 2na^2\gamma_n(a) = -\frac{\frac{4}{3}\pi\gamma\rho_1{}^2\epsilon_n t^2}{a^{n-1}} . \frac{n}{6} \text{...(69),}$$

and

$$2n(n-1)\,\Phi_n(a) - a^2\phi_n(a) + 4a^2\gamma_n(a) = -\frac{\frac{4}{3}\pi\gamma\rho_1{}^2\epsilon_n t^2}{a^{n-1}} . \frac{n^2+n-3}{3} \text{....(70).}$$

36. Now in equations (52) and (53) of p. 28 the coefficients of A and B contain t as a factor, and, omitting powers of t above the first in these coefficients, we get

$$\frac{At}{(2n+1)^2 a^{2n}}\{2n^2+1+2n(n+2)\} + \frac{Bat}{2n+1}\{2n^2+4n+3+2(n^2-1)\}$$
$$= \frac{\frac{4}{3}\pi\gamma\rho_1{}^2\epsilon_n t^2}{a^{n-1}} . \frac{n}{6},$$

and

$$\frac{At}{(2n+1)^2 a^{2n}}\{2n^2+1-2(n+1)(n+2)\}$$
$$+\frac{Bat}{2n+1} . \frac{n+1}{n} . \{2n(n-1)-(2n^2+4n+3)\} = \frac{\frac{4}{3}\pi\gamma\rho_1{}^2\epsilon_n t^2}{a^{n-1}} . \frac{n^2+n-3}{3}.$$

On solving these equations we find

$$A = \tfrac{4}{3}\pi\gamma\rho_1^2\epsilon_n t a^{n+1}\frac{n(n-1)(4n^2+10n+3)}{18} \quad\text{..............(71)},$$

$$B = -\tfrac{4}{3}\pi\gamma\rho_1^2\epsilon_n t a^{-n}\frac{n(4n^3+6n^2-7n-6)}{18(2n+1)} \quad\text{..............(72)}.$$

Again to the same order of approximation the equation (47) is

$$C = \frac{Aa^2}{2(2n+1)} + Ba^{2n+3}\frac{2n^2+4n+3}{2n(n+2)(2n+3)},$$

and this gives

$$C = \tfrac{4}{3}\pi\gamma\rho_1^2\epsilon_n t a^{n+3}\frac{4n^4+6n^3-7n^2-9n+9}{36(2n+3)} \quad\text{..............(73)}.$$

Similarly equation (48) becomes

$$2(n-1)D = \frac{A}{a^{2n-1}}\frac{2n^2+1}{n(2n-1)(2n+1)^2} - Ba^2\frac{n^2-1}{n(2n+1)},$$

and this gives

$$D = \tfrac{4}{3}\pi\gamma\rho_1^2\epsilon_n t a^{-n+2}\frac{4n^4+10n^3-n^2-7n+9}{36(2n-1)(2n+1)} \quad\text{...........(74)}.$$

This completes the determination of the constants in the case where n is a small integer.

37. To calculate the stresses P, Q, R, S introduced on p. 29 we have to pick out the most important terms in the expressions $\mu r^{n-2}F_n$, $-\mu r^n G_n$, $-\frac{\mu}{r^{n+2}}\frac{d}{dr}(r^{2n+3}G_n)$, and now we may put $r=a$ except in the expressions $(r-a)$ and $(r-b)$, and we may also put a for b.

The most important terms of $\mu r^{n-2}F_n$ are

$$a^{n-2}\left[-\frac{(n-2)A}{2n(2n-1)(2n+1)a^{2n-1}} + \frac{(n+3)Ba^2}{2n(2n+3)} + \frac{C}{(2n+1)a^{2n+1}} + D\right],$$

which reduce to

$$\tfrac{4}{3}\pi\gamma\rho_1^2\epsilon_n t\left(\tfrac{1}{6}\right) \quad\text{..................................(75)}.$$

The most important terms of $-\mu r^n G_n$ are

$$a^n\left[-\frac{A}{2(2n+1)a^{2n+1}} + \frac{B}{2n+3} + \frac{C}{a^{2n+3}}\right],$$

which reduce to

$$-\tfrac{4}{3}\pi\gamma\rho_1^2\epsilon_n t\,\frac{4n^2-2n-3}{36} \quad\text{........................(76)}.$$

The most important terms of $-\frac{\mu}{r^{n+2}}\frac{d}{dr}(r^{2n+3}G_n)$ are

$$\frac{1}{a^{n+2}}\left[\tfrac{4}{3}\pi\gamma\rho_1^2\epsilon_n 2na^{n+2}\frac{(r-a)(r-b)^2}{t^2} - \frac{Aa}{2n+1} + Ba^{2n+2}\right],$$

which reduce to

$$\tfrac{4}{3}\pi\gamma\rho_1^2\epsilon_n 2n\frac{(r-a)(r-b)^2}{t^2} - \tfrac{4}{3}\pi\gamma\rho_1^2\epsilon_n t\,\frac{n(4n^2+4n-9)}{18} \quad\text{......(77)}.$$

Hence the most important terms in P, Q, R, S are

$$P = -\tfrac{4}{3}\pi\gamma\rho_1^2\epsilon_n t\left(\frac{2n^2+2n+3}{18}S_n + \tfrac{1}{3}\cot\theta\frac{dS_n}{d\theta}\right) \quad\text{........(78)},$$

$$Q = \tfrac{4}{3}\pi\gamma\rho_1^2\epsilon_n t\left(\frac{4n^2+4n-3}{18}S_n + \tfrac{1}{3}\cot\theta\frac{dS_n}{d\theta}\right) \quad\text{........(79)},$$

$$R = -\tfrac{4}{3}\pi\gamma\rho_1^2\epsilon_n t\,\frac{n^2+n-3}{9}S_n \quad\text{........(80)},$$

$$S = \tfrac{4}{3}\pi\gamma\rho_1^2\epsilon_n 2\,\frac{(r-a)(r-b)^2}{t^2}\frac{dS_n}{d\theta} \quad\text{........(81)}.$$

These expressions admit of certain verifications in that they make $P+Q+R=0$, and make S vanish at $r=a$ and at $r=b$.

38. With a view to the calculation of the stress-difference we note that, to the same order of approximation as was adopted above,

$$P - R = -\tfrac{4}{3}\pi\gamma\rho_1^2\epsilon_n t\left(\tfrac{1}{2}S_n + \tfrac{1}{3}\cot\theta\frac{dS_n}{d\theta}\right) \quad\text{........(82)}.$$

To this order all the quantities P, Q, R are the same at all depths in the layer of compensation, and the quantity S^2, which vanishes at both the bounding surfaces of the layer, has its maximum value somewhere on the surface $r-b=\tfrac{2}{3}t$, that is at a depth equal to $\tfrac{1}{3}$ the thickness of the layer, and at this depth we have

$$S^2 = \left(\tfrac{4}{3}\pi\gamma\rho_1^2\epsilon_n t\,\tfrac{8}{27}\frac{dS_n}{d\theta}\right)^2 \quad\text{........(83)}.$$

The expression $(P-R)^2+4S^2$ is therefore equal to

$$(\tfrac{4}{3}\pi\gamma\rho_1^2\epsilon_n t)^2\left\{\left(\tfrac{1}{2}S_n + \tfrac{1}{3}\cot\theta\frac{dS_n}{d\theta}\right)^2 + \left(\tfrac{16}{27}\frac{dS_n}{d\theta}\right)^2\right\} \quad\text{........(84)}.$$

39. We have seen in Chapter I that the earth's surface presents a large inequality which is expressed by an harmonic of the first degree. We put $n=1$ and $S_n=\cos\theta$. Then

$$Q = -\tfrac{4}{3}\pi\gamma\rho_1^2\epsilon_1 t\,\tfrac{1}{18}\cos\theta,$$

and $$\{(P-R)^2+4S^2\}^{\frac{1}{2}} = (\tfrac{4}{3}\pi\gamma\rho_1^2\epsilon_1 t)\,\{(\tfrac{1}{6}\cos\theta)^2 + (\tfrac{16}{27}\sin\theta)^2\}^{\frac{1}{2}},$$

the maximum of this occurs when $\theta=\tfrac{1}{2}\pi$ and is $\tfrac{4}{3}\pi\gamma\rho_1^2\epsilon_1 t\,\tfrac{16}{27}$, which is much greater than the greatest value of Q. Hence the maximum stress-difference occurs at a depth equal to one-third of the thickness of the layer of compensation, and at the equatorial circle of the inequality (the circle at which it changes from elevation to depression). This maximum value is approximately equal to $\tfrac{8}{27}\frac{t}{a}g\rho_1\epsilon_1$, since ρ_1 is taken to be $\tfrac{1}{2}\rho_0$, and ρ_0 is approximately equal to the mean density of the earth. If t/a is $\frac{1}{50}$ (see above p. 8), the maximum stress-difference is about ·006 of the weight of a column of rock of height equal to the maximum height (ϵ_1) of the inequality. For the purpose in hand this maximum height may be taken to be 2 km. (see Chapter I), and the weight of the column per unit of area is 0·55 metric tonnes, so that the maximum stress-difference amounts to 0·0033 metric tonnes per square cm. This amount is quite trivial compared with the tenacity, or the crushing strength, of any reasonably strong material, e.g. granite, marble or even sandstone.

It appears therefore that the materials of which the earth is composed could support a much larger inequality of the type here in question than actually exists.

It is perhaps worthy of note that, if the inequality were of a greater height than the material could support, collapse would occur at places where the gradient is steepest, that is to say at the great circle of zero elevation, and not at the places of maximum depression and elevation. This conclusion seems to be rather contrary to the expectation which one would naturally have.

40. When $n=2$ we have

$$S_n = \tfrac{3}{2}\cos^2\theta - \tfrac{1}{2},$$

$$\frac{dS_n}{d\theta} = -3\sin\theta\cos\theta, \quad \cot\theta\,\frac{dS_n}{d\theta} = -3\cos^2\theta.$$

Hence
$$Q = \tfrac{4}{3}\pi\gamma\rho_1{}^2\epsilon_2 t\,(\tfrac{3}{4}\cos^2\theta - \tfrac{7}{12}),$$

and
$$\{(P-R)^2 + 4S^2\}^{\frac{1}{2}} = \tfrac{4}{3}\pi\gamma\rho_1{}^2\epsilon_2 t\,\{\tfrac{1}{16} + \tfrac{2129}{648}\cos^2\theta - \tfrac{4015}{1296}\cos^4\theta\}^{\frac{1}{2}}.$$

The maximum of Q (absolute value) is $\frac{4}{3}\pi\gamma\rho_1{}^2\epsilon_2 t\,\frac{7}{12}$, and it occurs when $\theta = 90°$.

The maximum value of $\{(P-R)^2+4S^2\}^{\frac{1}{2}}$ is about $\frac{4}{3}\pi\gamma\rho_1{}^2\epsilon_2 t$ (1·3434), and it occurs when $\theta = 43° 16'$ nearly. The maximum stress-difference is found to be the maximum value of $\{(P-R)^2+4S^2\}^{\frac{1}{2}}$, and this is approximately $0·67 \times g\rho_1\epsilon_2 t/a$. If, as before, t/a is $\frac{1}{50}$, this is about 0·0134 times the weight of a column of rock of a height equal to the greatest elevation that answers to the harmonic inequality in question.

If we take the maximum elevation to be 2 km. ($\epsilon_2 = 2 \times 10^5$), the corresponding tenacity required amounts to about 0·0074 metric tonnes per square cm., which again is quite small compared with the tenacities of most hard rocks.

There is no reason to think that, apart from the ellipticity of the meridians due to rotation, the earth's surface presents any harmonic inequality of the second degree with an amplitude of anything like 2 km. (see Chapter I). On the other hand the ellipsoidal inequality which it does present is certainly not zonal. Since any harmonic of the second degree can be expressed as the sum of a small number (2 or 3) of zonal harmonics with different axes, and since the stress-difference arising from a sum of harmonic inequalities is certainly less than the sum of the stress-differences due to them severally, we may conclude that such ellipsoidal inequalities as the surface of the earth presents, apart from the ellipticity of the meridians, could easily be supported by any reasonably strong materials.

It should be noted that, just as in the case of the first harmonic, the maximum stress-difference occurs at a depth equal to one-third of the thickness of the layer of compensation. But it does not occur either at the places where the height of the inequality is greatest, or at those where the gradient is steepest, but at intermediate places.

The maintenance of the greatest ellipsoidal inequality, the ellipticity of the meridians, does not require any tenacity of the material. The stress involved is hydrostatic pressure. If we took account of the rotation we should have to modify the values of p_0 and p_1, so that these quantities would no longer be expressible as functions of r only. It is unlikely that the requisite modification would alter sensibly the order of magnitude of the tangential stresses required to support the continents.

41. When $n = 3$ we have

$$S_n = \tfrac{5}{2}\cos^3\theta - \tfrac{3}{2}\cos\theta, \quad \frac{dS_n}{d\theta} = -\tfrac{3}{2}\sin\theta\,(5\cos^2\theta - 1),$$

$$\cot\theta\,\frac{dS_n}{d\theta} = -\tfrac{3}{2}\cos\theta\,(5\cos^2\theta - 1).$$

Hence $$Q = \tfrac{4}{3}\pi\gamma\rho_1{}^2\epsilon_3 t\,\tfrac{1}{4}\cos\theta\,(15\cos^2\theta - 13).$$

The maximum of the absolute value of Q occurs when $\theta = 57°\,3'$ nearly, and is approximately $(1{\cdot}164)\,\tfrac{4}{3}\pi\gamma\rho_1{}^2\epsilon_3 t$.

Also

$$\{(P-R)^2 + 4S^2\}^{\frac{1}{2}} = \tfrac{4}{3}\pi\gamma\rho_1{}^2\epsilon_3 t\,\{\tfrac{64}{81} - \tfrac{11183}{1296}\cos^2\theta + \tfrac{18325}{648}\cos^4\theta - \tfrac{23575}{1296}\cos^6\theta\}^{\frac{1}{2}},$$

and the maximum of this occurs when $\theta = 22°\,45'$ nearly, and is about $(1{\cdot}65)\,\tfrac{4}{3}\pi\gamma\rho_1{}^2\epsilon_3 t$.

The maximum stress-difference is the maximum value of

$$\tfrac{1}{2}[-3Q + \sqrt{\{(P-R)^2 + 4S^2\}}],$$

it occurs when $\theta = 50°\,20'$ nearly, and is about $(2{\cdot}08)\,\tfrac{4}{3}\pi\gamma\rho_1{}^2\epsilon_3 t$. Hence the maximum stress-difference is about $1{\cdot}04 \times g\rho_1\epsilon_3 t/a$. If, as before, $t/a = \frac{1}{50}$, it is approximately the weight of a column of rock of height equal to 0·0208 of the greatest height of the harmonic inequality, and, if this greatest height is 2 km., the requisite tenacity is about 0·0114 of a metric tonne per square cm.

At a place given by $\theta = 50^\circ\, 20'$, and at a depth equal to one-third of the thickness of the layer of compensation the stress-difference has the value written above. Just as in the previous cases we may conclude that any reasonably strong material could support such inequalities of the third degree as the surface of the earth actually presents.

42. The results obtained in the foregoing discussion are extremely favourable to the hypothesis of isostasy. It appears that, if the superficial elevations and depressions expressed by the continental block and ocean basins are correlated with suitable inequalities of density, in accordance with the hypothesis, the requisite tangential stresses may everywhere be quite moderate, and the inequalities could be supported easily by any reasonably strong solid material.

The hypothesis has been supposed to be applicable not only to the main features of the shape of the lithosphere but also to the more local irregularities which are mountains and "deeps." For the expression of these irregularities spherical harmonic terms of high degrees would be needed. To get anything like a correct representation of the Alps, for instance, a very large number of terms would be needed, but the amplitudes of them individually would probably be rather small compared with the 2 km. which has been allowed as the maximum amplitude of the larger inequalities. The forces required to support such irregularities may be very different from those required to support an inequality which is well represented by a single spherical harmonic term, or a few such terms, and so the investigation on similar lines to those of this Chapter, but dealing with the case of n large, does not throw so much light on the actual support of mountains as the previous investigation does on the support of continents. As, however, there seems at present to be no other way of attacking the question, an investigation of this kind will be given in the next Chapter.

CHAPTER III

THE PROBLEM OF THE ISOSTATIC SUPPORT OF THE MOUNTAINS

43. To illustrate, so far as the methods of the last Chapter permit, the way in which the hypothesis of isostasy affects the problem of how the mountains are supported, we shall consider the outer surface of the layer of compensation to have a single inequality expressed by a zonal spherical harmonic of high degree. Near the pole of the harmonic the inequality would appear as a rounded isolated mountain, surrounded by a circular valley, which is again enclosed by a circular mountain ridge, and beyond this there would be a series of ridges and valleys. Towards the equatorial plane of the harmonic, the mountain ridges and intervening valleys assume a profile which approximates to a simple sine-curve. Of course this configuration is quite unlike that of any actual mountains, though something like it may be partially developed wherever there is a series of parallel mountain-chains with intervening valleys, e.g. in British Columbia where there are four mountain-ranges running nearly north and south. A little consideration of the actual heights of known mountains suggests that a height of 4 km.* for the altitude of the crests above the valley bottoms would be an outside estimate for any such inequality.

For the most part we shall confine our attention to the special example in which the degree of the harmonic is 50. This corresponds to a series of mountain-chains about 400 km. apart. But it will be desirable at first to proceed with a general theory.

44. In the notation of the last Chapter, when n, the degree of the harmonic, is large, the product nt/a cannot be neglected, and the approximate method previously employed fails. Instead of approximating to the values of the integrals which occur in §§ 21—23, we must obtain for them complete expressions which we can afterwards compute in special cases. By a process of successive integration by parts we can express each of the integrals in question as a sum of a few powers of $(r-b)$. We proceed to exemplify the process.

* This is the estimate adopted by Sir G. Darwin, *loc. cit.*, *ante* p. 6.

We have

$$\int_b^r r^{2n+3}(r-b)^3\,dr = \frac{r^{2n+4}}{2n+4}(r-b)^3 - \frac{3}{2n+4}\int_b^r r^{2n+4}(r-b)^2\,dr$$

$$= \frac{r^{2n+4}}{2n+4}(r-b)^3 - \frac{3r^{2n+5}(r-b)^2}{(2n+4)(2n+5)} + \frac{3.2}{(2n+4)(2n+5)}\int_b^r r^{2n+5}(r-b)\,dr$$

$$= \frac{r^{2n+4}}{2n+4}(r-b)^3 - \frac{3r^{2n+5}(r-b)^2}{(2n+4)(2n+5)} + \frac{3.2r^{2n+6}(r-b)}{(2n+4)(2n+5)(2n+6)} - \frac{3.2(r^{2n+7}-b^{2n+7})}{(2n+4)(2n+5)(2n+6)(2n+7)}.$$

Hence

$$\int_b^r r^{2n+3}(r-b)^3\,dr$$

$$= \frac{6}{(2n+4)(2n+5)(2n+6)(2n+7)}\Bigg[b^{2n+7} - r^{2n+7} + (2n+7)\,r^{2n+6}(r-b) - \frac{(2n+7)(2n+6)}{2}r^{2n+5}(r-b)^2 + \frac{(2n+7)(2n+6)(2n+5)}{3\,!}r^{2n+4}(r-b)^3\Bigg].$$

This can be written

$$\int_b^r r^{2n+3}(r-b)^3\,dr$$

$$= -\frac{3\,!}{2^4}\frac{r^{2n+7}}{n^4}\left[\frac{1-(b/r)^{2n+7}}{\left(1+\frac{4}{2n}\right)\left(1+\frac{5}{2n}\right)\left(1+\frac{6}{2n}\right)\left(1+\frac{7}{2n}\right)} - \frac{2nx/r}{\left(1+\frac{4}{2n}\right)\left(1+\frac{5}{2n}\right)\left(1+\frac{6}{2n}\right)} + \frac{2^2n^2x^2/r^2}{2\,!\left(1+\frac{4}{2n}\right)\left(1+\frac{5}{2n}\right)} - \frac{2^3n^3x^3/r^3}{3\,!\left(1+\frac{4}{2n}\right)}\right],$$

where x is written for $(r-b)$.

45. By the process exemplified above we may express all the integrals in which $2n$ occurs as an index. For this purpose we introduce the notation

$$F(\kappa, s) = \frac{1-(b/r)^{2n+\kappa}}{\left(1+\frac{\kappa-s}{2n}\right)\left(1+\frac{\kappa-s+1}{2n}\right)\dots\left(1+\frac{\kappa}{2n}\right)} - \frac{2nx/r}{\left(1+\frac{\kappa-s}{2n}\right)\left(1+\frac{\kappa-s+1}{2n}\right)\dots\left(1+\frac{\kappa-1}{2n}\right)}$$

$$+ \frac{2^2n^2x^2/r^2}{2\,!\left(1+\frac{\kappa-s}{2n}\right)\left(1+\frac{\kappa-s+1}{2n}\right)\dots\left(1+\frac{\kappa-2}{2n}\right)} - \dots + (-1)^s\frac{2^sn^sx^s/r^s}{s\,!\left(1+\frac{\kappa-s}{2n}\right)},$$

then we have the following results*:—

$$\int_b^r r^{2n+3}(r-b)^3\,dr = -\frac{3\,!}{2^4}\frac{r^{2n+7}}{n^4}F(7,3),$$

$$\int_b^r \frac{1}{r^{2n+2}}\int_b^r r^{2n+3}(r-b)^3\,dr\,.\,dr = \frac{1}{1+\frac{1}{2n}}\frac{3\,!}{2^5}\frac{r^6}{n^5}F(7,3)$$
$$+\frac{1}{1+\frac{1}{2n}}\frac{r^2}{2n}x^4\left(\frac{1}{4}-\frac{1}{10}\frac{x}{r}+\frac{1}{60}\frac{x^2}{r^2}\right),$$

$$\int_b^r r^{2n+1}(r-b)^3\,dr = -\frac{3\,!}{2^4}\frac{r^{2n+5}}{n^4}F(5,3),$$

$$\int_b^r \frac{1}{r^{2n+2}}\int_b^r r^{2n+1}(r-b)^3\,dr\,.\,dr = \frac{3\,!}{2^5}\frac{r^4}{n^5}F(5,4),$$

$$\int_b^r r^{2n+2}\int_b^r \frac{1}{r^{2n+2}}\int_b^r r^{2n+1}(r-b)^3\,dr\,.\,dr\,.\,dr = \frac{3\,!}{2^6}\frac{r^{2n+7}}{n^5}\{F(5,4)-F(7,4)\},$$

$$\int_b^r r\int_b^r \frac{1}{r^{2n+2}}\int_b^r r^{2n+1}(r-b)^3\,dr\,.\,dr\,.\,dr = -\frac{1}{1-\frac{1}{2n}}\frac{3\,!}{2^6}\frac{r^6}{n^6}F(5,4)$$
$$+\frac{1}{1-\frac{1}{2n}}\frac{3\,!}{5\,!}\frac{r}{2n}x^5\left(1-\frac{1}{6}\frac{x}{r}\right),$$

$$\int_b^r \frac{1}{r^{2n+2}}\int_b^r r^{2n+2}\int_b^r \frac{1}{r^{2n+2}}\int_b^r r^{2n+1}(r-b)^3\,dr\,.\,dr\,.\,dr\,.\,dr$$
$$= -\frac{1}{1-\frac{1}{2n}}\frac{3\,!}{2^7}\frac{r^6}{n^6}\left\{F(5,4)-\frac{2^5n^5x^5/r^5}{5\,!}+\frac{2^6n^6x^6/r^6}{6\,!}\right\}$$
$$+\frac{1}{1+\frac{1}{2n}}\frac{3\,!}{2^7}\frac{r^6}{n^6}\left\{F(7,4)-\frac{2^5n^5x^5/r^5}{5\,!}+\frac{2^6n^6x^6/r^6}{6\,!}\left(1+\frac{1}{n}\right)\right\},$$

$$\int_b^r r^{2n+2}\int_b^r (r-b)^3\,dr\,.\,dr = \frac{3\,!}{2^5}\frac{r^{2n+7}}{n^5}F(7,4),$$

$$\int_b^r \frac{1}{r^{2n+2}}\int_b^r r^{2n+2}\int_b^r (r-b)^3\,dr\,.\,dr\,.\,dr = -\frac{1}{1+\frac{1}{2n}}\frac{3\,!}{2^6}\frac{r^6}{n^6}F(7,4)$$
$$+\frac{1}{1+\frac{1}{2n}}\frac{3\,!}{5\,!}\frac{r}{2n}x^5\left(1-\frac{1}{6}\frac{x}{r}\right),$$

$$\int_b^r r^{2n+6}(r-b)^3\,dr = -\frac{3\,!}{2^4}\frac{r^{2n+10}}{n^4}F(10,3),$$

* All the results obtained in this section and in § 46 may, of course, be verified by differentiation.

$$\int_b^r \frac{1}{r^{2n+2}} \int_b^r r^{2n+6}(r-b)^3\,dr\,.\,dr = \frac{1}{1+\frac{1}{2n}} \frac{3\,!}{2^5} \frac{r^9}{n^5} F(10,\,3)$$

$$+ \frac{1}{1+\frac{1}{2n}} \frac{r^5}{2n} x^4 \left(\frac{1}{4} - \frac{1}{4}\frac{x}{r} + \frac{1}{6}\frac{x^2}{r^2} - \frac{1}{14}\frac{x^3}{r^3} + \frac{1}{56}\frac{x^4}{r^4} - \frac{1}{504}\frac{x^5}{r^5}\right).$$

In like manner we have also the following set of results:—

$$\int_b^r r^{2n+3}(r-b)^2\,dr = \frac{2\,!}{2^3} \frac{r^{2n+6}}{n^3} F(6,\,2),$$

$$\int_b^r \frac{1}{r^{2n+2}} \int_b^r r^{2n+3}(r-b)^2\,dr\,.\,dr = -\frac{1}{1+\frac{1}{2n}} \frac{2\,!}{2^4} \frac{r^5}{n^4} F(6,\,2)$$

$$+ \frac{1}{1+\frac{1}{2n}} \frac{r^2}{2n} x^3 \left(\frac{1}{3} - \frac{1}{6}\frac{x}{r} + \frac{1}{30}\frac{x^2}{r^2}\right),$$

$$\int_b^r r^{2n+1}(r-b)^2\,dr = \frac{2\,!}{2^3} \frac{r^{2n+4}}{n^3} F(4,\,2),$$

$$\int_b^r \frac{1}{r^{2n+2}} \int_b^r r^{2n+1}(r-b)^2\,dr\,.\,dr = -\frac{2\,!}{2^4} \frac{r^3}{n^4} F(4,\,3),$$

$$\int_b^r r^{2n+2} \int_b^r \frac{1}{r^{2n+2}} \int_b^r r^{2n+1}(r-b)^2\,dr\,.\,dr\,.\,dr = \frac{2\,!}{2^5} \frac{r^{2n+6}}{n^4} \{-F(4,\,3) + F(6,\,3)\},$$

$$\int_b^r r \int_b^r \frac{1}{r^{2n+2}} \int_b^r r^{2n+1}(r-b)^2\,dr\,.\,dr\,.\,dr = \frac{1}{1-\frac{1}{2n}} \frac{2\,!}{2^5} \frac{r^5}{n^5} F(4,\,3)$$

$$+ \frac{1}{1-\frac{1}{2n}} \frac{2\,!}{4\,!} \frac{r}{2n} x^4 \left(1 - \frac{1}{5}\frac{x}{r}\right),$$

$$\int_b^r \frac{1}{r^{2n+2}} \int_b^r r^{2n+2} \int_b^r \frac{1}{r^{2n+2}} \int_b^r r^{2n+1}(r-b)^2\,dr\,.\,dr\,.\,dr\,.\,dr$$

$$= \frac{1}{1-\frac{1}{2n}} \frac{2\,!}{2^6} \frac{r^5}{n^5} \left\{F(4,\,3) + \frac{2^4 n^4 x^4/r^4}{4\,!} - \frac{2^5 n^5 x^5/r^5}{5\,!}\right\}$$

$$- \frac{1}{1+\frac{1}{2n}} \frac{2\,!}{2^6} \frac{r^5}{n^5} \left\{F(6,\,3) + \frac{2^4 n^4 x^4/r^4}{4\,!} - \frac{2^5 n^5 x^5/r^5}{5\,!}\left(1+\frac{1}{n}\right)\right\},$$

$$\int_b^r r^{2n+2} \int_b^r (r-b)^2\,dr\,.\,dr = -\frac{2\,!}{2^4} \frac{r^{2n+6}}{n^4} F(6,\,3),$$

$$\int_b^r \frac{1}{r^{2n+2}} \int_b^r r^{2n+2} \int_b^r (r-b)^2 \, dr \, . \, dr \, . \, dr = \frac{1}{1+\frac{1}{2n}} \frac{2\,!}{2^5} \frac{r^5}{n^5} F(6, 3)$$

$$+ \frac{1}{1+\frac{1}{2n}} \frac{2\,!}{4\,!} \frac{r}{2n} x^4 \left(1 - \frac{1}{5}\frac{x}{r}\right),$$

$$\int_b^r r^{2n+6} (r-b)^2 \, dr = \frac{2\,!}{2^3} \frac{r^{2n+9}}{n^3} F(9, 2),$$

$$\int_b^r \frac{1}{r^{2n+2}} \int_b^r r^{2n+6} (r-b)^2 dr \, . \, dr = -\frac{1}{1+\frac{1}{2n}} \frac{2\,!}{2^4} \frac{r^8}{n^4} F(9, 2)$$

$$+ \frac{1}{1+\frac{1}{2n}} \frac{r^5}{2n} x^3 \left(\frac{1}{3} - \frac{5}{12}\frac{x}{r} + \frac{1}{3}\frac{x^2}{r^2} - \frac{1}{6}\frac{x^3}{r^3} + \frac{1}{21}\frac{x^4}{r^4} - \frac{1}{168}\frac{x^5}{r^5}\right).$$

46. In addition to these we require some simpler integrals which do not depend upon n. The following results can be obtained without difficulty.

$$\int_b^r r^2 (r-b)^3 \, dr = r^2 x^4 \left(\frac{1}{4} - \frac{1}{10}\frac{x}{r} + \frac{1}{60}\frac{x^2}{r^2}\right),$$

$$\int_b^r r \int_b^r (r-b)^3 \, dr \, . \, dr = \frac{1}{20} r x^5 \left(1 - \frac{1}{6}\frac{x}{r}\right),$$

$$\int_b^r r^5 (r-b)^3 \, dr = r^5 x^4 \left(\frac{1}{4} - \frac{1}{4}\frac{x}{r} + \frac{1}{6}\frac{x^2}{r^2} - \frac{1}{14}\frac{x^3}{r^3} + \frac{1}{56}\frac{x^4}{r^4} - \frac{1}{504}\frac{x^5}{r^5}\right),$$

$$\int_b^r r^2 (r-b)^2 \, dr = r^2 x^3 \left(\frac{1}{3} - \frac{1}{6}\frac{x}{r} + \frac{1}{30}\frac{x^2}{r^2}\right),$$

$$\int_b^r r \int_b^r (r-b)^2 \, dr \, . \, dr = \frac{1}{12} r x^4 \left(1 - \frac{1}{5}\frac{x}{r}\right),$$

$$\int_b^r r^5 (r-b)^2 \, dr = r^5 x^3 \left(\frac{1}{3} - \frac{5}{12}\frac{x}{r} + \frac{1}{3}\frac{x^2}{r^2} - \frac{1}{6}\frac{x^3}{r^3} + \frac{1}{21}\frac{x^4}{r^4} - \frac{1}{168}\frac{x^5}{r^5}\right).$$

These particular results have been used incidentally in evaluating the integrals which depend upon n.

47. I computed these integrals to four places of decimals for four values of r, viz.: a, $a - \frac{1}{10}t$, $a - \frac{2}{10}t$, $a - \frac{3}{10}t$, where t stands, as before, for $a - b$, the mean thickness of the layer of compensation. I took $n = 50$, and $t/a = \frac{1}{50}$. In the appended tabular statement the result of the computation is expressed by recording the numerical coefficients of certain simple expressions. The first column contains the integral, the second the simple expression, the third, fourth, fifth and sixth in order the values of the coefficients of this expression for $r = a$, $r = a - 0{\cdot}1t$, $r = a - 0{\cdot}2t$, $r = a - 0{\cdot}3t$. When the integral is expressed by two terms, one expression is put under the other. Certain integrals are omitted from the table because the values of their coefficients never amount to more than 0·0002. Two of the integrals have been computed for $r=a$ only, because their values are required in the determination of the constants, but not in the calculation of the stress-difference within the layer of compensation.

TABLE OF INTEGRALS.

Integral	expression	coefft. for $r=a$	coefft. for $r=a-0{\cdot}1t$	coefft. for $r=a-0{\cdot}2t$	coefft. for $r=a-0{\cdot}3t$
$\int_b^r r^2(r-b)^3\,dr$	r^2x^4	·2480	·2482	·2484	·2486
$\int_b^r r\int_b^r (r-b)^3\,dr\,.\,dr$	rx^5	·0498	·0498	·0499	·0499
$\int_b^r r^5(r-b)^3\,dr$	r^5x^4	·2452	·2456	·2460	·2465
$\int_b^r r^2(r-b)^2\,dr$	r^2x^3	·3300	·3303	·3307	·3310
$\int_b^r r\int_b^r (r-b)^2\,dr\,.\,dr$	rx^4	·0830	·0830	·0830	·0831
$\int_b^r r^5(r-b)^2\,dr$	r^5x^3	·3251	·3259	·3267	·3274
$\int_b^r r^{2n+3}(r-b)^3\,dr$	$\frac{r^{2n+7}}{n^4}$	·1740	·1184	·0772	·0472
$\int_b^r \frac{1}{r^{2n+2}}\int_b^r r^{2n+3}(r-b)^3\,dr\,.\,dr$	$\frac{r^2x^4}{n}$	·1228	·1229	·1230	·1231
	$-\frac{r^6}{n^5}$	·0861	·0586	·0382	·0234
$\int_b^r r^{2n+1}(r-b)^3\,dr$	$\frac{r^{2n+5}}{n^4}$	·1751			
$\int_b^r \frac{1}{r^{2n+2}}\int_b^r r^{2n+1}(r-b)^3\,dr\,.\,dr$	$\frac{r^4}{n^5}$	·0371	·0227	·0131	·0070
$\int_b^r r\int_b^r \frac{1}{r^{2n+2}}\int_b^r r^{2n+1}(r-b)^3 dr\,.\,dr\,.\,dr$	$\frac{rx^5}{n}$	·0251	·0252	·0252	·0252
	$-\frac{r^6}{n^6}$	·0187	·0124	·0066	·0035
$\int_b^r r^{2n+2}\int_b^r (r-b)^3\,dr\,.\,dr$	$\frac{r^{2n+7}}{n^5}$	·0369	·0226	·0130	·0069
$\int_b^r \frac{1}{r^{2n+2}}\int_b^r r^{2n+2}\int_b^r (r-b)^3\,dr.dr.dr$	$\frac{rx^5}{n}$	·0247	·0247	·0247	·0247
	$-\frac{r^6}{n^6}$	·0183	·0112	·0064	·0034

TABLE OF INTEGRALS (*continued*).

Integral	expression	coefft. for $r=a$	coefft. for $r=a-0{\cdot}1t$	coefft. for $r=a-0{\cdot}2t$	coefft. for $r=a-0{\cdot}3t$
$\int_b^r r^{2n+6}(r-b)^3\,dr$	$\frac{r^{2n+10}}{n^4}$	·1724	·1177	·0766	·0468
$\int_b^r \frac{1}{r^{2n+2}}\int_b^r r^{2n+6}(r-b)^3\,dr\,.\,dr$	$\frac{r^5x^4}{n}$	·1214	·1215	·1218	·1220
	$-\frac{r^9}{n^5}$	·0853	·0583	·0380	·0232
$\int_b^r r^{2n+3}(r-b)^2\,dr$	$\frac{r^{2n+6}}{n^3}$	·2135	·1627	·1195	·0839
$\int_b^r \frac{1}{r^{2n+2}}\int_b^r r^{2n+3}(r-b)^2\,dr\,.\,dr$	$\frac{r^2x^3}{n}$	·1634	·1635	·1637	·1639
	$-\frac{r^5}{n^4}$	·1057	·0805	·0591	·0414
$\int_b^r r^{2n+1}(r-b)^2\,dr$	$\frac{r^{2n+4}}{n^3}$	·2151			
$\int_b^r \frac{1}{r^{2n+2}}\int_b^r r^{2n+1}(r-b)^2\,dr\,.\,dr$	$\frac{r^3}{n^4}$	·0585	·0399	·0259	·0158
$\int_b^r r\int_b^r \frac{1}{r^{2n+2}}\int_b^r r^{2n+1}(r-b)^2\,dr\,.\,dr\,.\,dr$	$\frac{rx^4}{n}$	·0419	·0419	·0419	·0420
	$-\frac{r^5}{n^5}$	·0295	·0202	·0131	·0080
$\int_b^r r^{2n+2}\int_b^r (r-b)^2\,dr\,.\,dr$	$\frac{r^{2n+6}}{n^4}$	·0581	·0397	·0258	·0158
$\int_b^r \frac{1}{r^{2n+2}}\int_b^r r^{2n+2}\int_b^r (r-b)^2\,dr\,.\,dr\,.\,dr$	$\frac{rx^4}{n}$	·0411	·0411	·0411	·0411
	$-\frac{r^5}{n^5}$	·0288	·0196	·0128	·0078
$\int_b^r r^{2n+6}(r-b)^2\,dr$	$\frac{r^{2n+9}}{n^3}$	·2111	·1612	·1184	·0832
$\int_b^r \frac{1}{r^{2n+2}}\int_b^r r^{2n+6}(r-b)^2\,dr\,.\,dr$	$\frac{r^5x^3}{n}$	·1610	·1613	·1616	·1620
	$-\frac{r^8}{n^4}$	·1046	·0799	·0586	·0412

48. The next step is to compute the values of the functions denoted by $\gamma_n(r)$, ... for the same values of r. In the following tabular statement each of the functions is expressed as the product of a certain simple expression and a numerical coefficient. The function is placed in the first column and the simple expression in the second. In the third, fourth, fifth, and sixth columns are given the numerical coefficients for the values a, $a-0{\cdot}1t$, ...

		a	$a-0{\cdot}1t$	$a-0{\cdot}2t$	$a-0{\cdot}3t$
$\frac{d}{dr}(r^{2n+3}\gamma_n)$	$-\frac{4}{3}\pi\gamma\rho_1{}^2\epsilon_n ar^{n+2}$	·0070	·1479	·2067	·2118
γ_n	$-\frac{4}{3}\pi\gamma\rho_1{}^2\epsilon_n \frac{a}{nr^n}$	·0783	·0785	·0672	·0522
ϕ_n	$-\frac{4}{3}\pi\gamma\rho_1{}^2\epsilon_n \frac{1}{na^{n-1}}$	·1378			
Φ_n	$-\frac{4}{3}\pi\gamma\rho_1{}^2\epsilon_n \frac{a}{n^2r^{n-2}}$	·1194	·1089	·0873	·0645

49. From these results we find, on putting $n=50$ wherever necessary,

$$2n(n-1)\Phi_n(a)+\frac{1}{a^{2n}}\frac{d}{dr}(r^{2n+3}\gamma_n)_a-2na^2\gamma_n(a)=-\frac{\frac{4}{3}\pi\gamma\rho_1{}^2\epsilon_n}{a^{n-3}}(0{\cdot}0844)$$

and

$$2n(n-1)\Phi_n(a)-a^2\phi_n(a)+4a^2\gamma_n(a)=-\frac{\frac{4}{3}\pi\gamma\rho_1{}^2\epsilon_n}{a^{n-3}}(0{\cdot}2375).$$

The equations (52) and (53) of p. 28 now give for the constants A, B the values expressed by the equations

$$\frac{A}{2n+1}=\tfrac{4}{3}\pi\gamma\rho_1{}^2\epsilon_n a^{n+2}(0{\cdot}3610),$$

$$B=-\frac{\frac{4}{3}\pi\gamma\rho_1{}^2\epsilon_n}{a^{n-1}}(1{\cdot}0139).$$

From these values, by means of the equations (47) and (48) of p. 27, we find the values of the constants C, D, viz.:

$$C=\tfrac{4}{3}\pi\gamma\rho_1{}^2\epsilon_n a^{n+4}(0{\cdot}1721),$$

$$D=\frac{\frac{4}{3}\pi\gamma\rho_1{}^2\epsilon_n}{a^{n-3}}(0{\cdot}005519).$$

50. By the equations (43), (44), and (45) of p. 26 the functions G_n, $\frac{d}{dr}(r^{2n+3}G_n)$, F_n are expressed as the sums of terms containing the constants A, B, C, D and other terms. We may refer to the first sets of terms as the "contributions of the constants." In the following table we express the values* of these contributions for the four values of r (a, $a-0{\cdot}1t$,

* In obtaining these it is best not to substitute for C and D the values found in § 49, but to begin by eliminating them by means of (47) and (48) on p. 27.

$a - 0{\cdot}2\,t$, $a - 0{\cdot}3\,t$) as the products of certain simple expressions and certain numerical coefficients. The first column contains the function to which the constants make a contribution. The second column gives the simple expression. In the third, fourth, fifth and sixth columns are given the numerical coefficients.

		a	$a-0{\cdot}1t$	$a-0{\cdot}2t$	$a-0{\cdot}3t$
$-\mu G_n$	$-\frac{\frac{4}{3}\pi\gamma\rho_1^2\epsilon_n a}{nr^n}$	0·9111	0·8710	0·8317	0·7920
$-\mu\frac{d}{dr}(r^{2n+3}G_n)$	$-\frac{4}{3}\pi\gamma\rho_1^2\epsilon_n ar^{n+2}$	1·3749	1·3172	1·2727	1·2412
μF_n	$-\frac{\frac{4}{3}\pi\gamma\rho_1^2\epsilon_n a}{n^2r^{n-2}}$	0·1851	0·1248	0·0718	0·0220

We can now write down in a similar fashion a table of the functions.

		a	$a-0{\cdot}1t$	$a-0{\cdot}2t$	$a-0{\cdot}3t$
$-\mu G_n$	$-\frac{\frac{4}{3}\pi\gamma\rho_1^2\epsilon_n a}{nr^n}$	0·9894	0·9495	0·8989	0·8442
$-\mu\frac{d}{dr}(r^{2n+3}G_n)$	$-\frac{4}{3}\pi\gamma\rho_1^2\epsilon_n ar^{n+2}$	1·3819	1·4651	1·4794	1·4530
μF_n	$-\frac{\frac{4}{3}\pi\gamma\rho_1^2\epsilon_n a}{n^2r^{n-2}}$	0·3045	0·2337	0·1591	0·0865

51. By using the formulae (57), (59) and (60) of p. 31 we can form in a similar way a table of the quantities required in evaluating the stress-difference. A very little consideration shows that Q is much smaller than $P-R$. We therefore record the values of $P-R$ and S. In this record certain terms are omitted. The number n being rather large, we can see at once that a term like $n(2n-1)r^{n-2}F_nS_n$ is much more important than a term like $nr^{n-2}F_nS_n$. Also, if S_n is a zonal harmonic, so that $S_n = P_n(\cos\theta)$, we have the known formula*

$$\cot\theta\,\frac{dS_n}{d\theta} = -\cos\theta\,\frac{dP_n}{d(\cos\theta)} = -nP_n + \frac{1}{\sin\theta}\,\frac{dP_{n-1}}{d\theta},$$

from which it appears that $n^{-1}dS_n/d\theta$ is of the same order of magnitude as

* The formula is obtained by eliminating P_{n+1} between the two equations

$$(n+1)\,P_{n+1} + nP_{n-1} = (2n+1)\,\mu P_n, \qquad (\mu = \cos\theta),$$

$$\frac{dP_{n+1}}{d\mu} - \frac{dP_{n-1}}{d\mu} = (2n+1)\,P_n.$$

S_n. Further $n^2 r^{n-2} F_n$, $nr^n G_n$, and $\frac{1}{r^{n+2}} \frac{d}{dr} (r^{2n+3} G_n)$ are of the same order of magnitude. In the table the terms of highest order of magnitude are alone retained.

		a	$a-0{\cdot}1t$	$a-0{\cdot}2t$	$a-0{\cdot}3t$
$P-R$	$\frac{4}{3}\pi\gamma\rho_1^2\epsilon_n a S_n$	1·22	0·93	0·64	0·34
S	$\frac{4}{3}\pi\gamma\rho_1^2\epsilon_n a \frac{1}{n}\frac{dS_n}{d\theta}$	0	−0·02	0	0·06

52. To interpret these results we take first the case of an isolated mountain, and allow the maximum value of $\epsilon_n S_n$ (at the pole of the harmonic) to be 2 km. Then the greatest value of the stress-difference is found at the pole of the harmonic (beneath the base of the mountain) at the mean surface $r=a$. But, since the investigation cannot give the values of the stresses correctly at the surface, we shall take the value for $r=a-0{\cdot}1\,t$. Then the greatest stress-difference is slightly less than the weight of a column of the crust of height 1 km. The tenacity of the material requisite for the support of the mountain is about 0·26 metric tonnes per square cm., or it is a little greater than the tenacity of sheet lead (0·23 metric tonnes per square cm.).

We take next the case of a series of parallel mountain chains. We know that near its equatorial plane the zonal harmonic of degree n is approximately equal to*

$$\sqrt{\left(\frac{2}{n\pi\sin\theta}\right)}\sin\{(n+\tfrac{1}{2})\,\theta+\tfrac{1}{4}\pi\}.$$

We can therefore take $\epsilon_n S_n$ to be the ordinate of a curve of sines, and note that at the crests and valley-bottoms $dS_n/d\theta$ vanishes. The table shows as before that the greatest value of the stress-difference is found beneath the crests, and there it is equal to half the weight of a column of rock of height equal to half the height of the crests above the valley-bottoms. If the height of the crests above the valley-bottoms is 4 km. the maximum stress-difference is the same as before, that is to say the requisite tenacity is a little greater than that of sheet lead.

53. In the particular solution of the problem obtained by Sir G. Darwin† it was found that, with the constitution of the earth which he assumed, the requisite tenacity was that of cast tin (0·41 metric tonnes per square cm.); and if the tenacity were only that of sheet lead the mountains would collapse.

* Heine, *Kugelfunctionen*, 1878 edition, p. 175.

† *Loc. cit.*, ante p. 6.

By adopting the hypothesis of isostasy, in the special form that was given to it in the last Chapter, we have found that such mountains as actually exist on the earth may imply smaller stress-differences than those computed by Darwin, and can therefore be supported by materials of a smaller degree of tenacity. On the other hand it appears that much stronger materials are required to support existing mountains than to support existing continents.

Sir G. Darwin also found that in his solution the stress-difference was greatest at a depth of some 80 km. beneath the surface. In the above solution the stress-difference is greatest at the surface and continually diminishes as the depth increases.

It is worthy of note that, on the theory here worked out, the maximum stress-difference for a harmonic inequality of the first degree is found at the places where the gradient is steepest, not at the places of greatest elevation and depression, and it is found at a depth equal to one-third of the thickness of the layer of compensation. For harmonic inequalities of high degrees it is found at the places of greatest elevation and depression, and near the surface. For harmonics of low degrees, greater than unity, it is found at places intermediate between those of greatest elevation or depression and those where the gradient is steepest, and at depths which, according to the approximate methods of calculation adopted in the last Chapter, are equal to one-third of the thickness of the layer of compensation. It is probable that the depth at which the maximum stress-difference occurs diminishes regularly as the degree of the spherical harmonic inequality increases.

CHAPTER IV

GENERAL THEORY OF EARTH TIDES

54. The importance of corporeal (or bodily) tides in the earth arises from the influence which investigations concerning them have had upon our ideas about the internal constitution of the earth. Lord Kelvin appears to have been the first to point out that, whatever the constitution of the earth might be, it must as a whole yield to the tidal deforming attraction of the sun and moon; and he proposed to determine the rigidity of the earth by observing the amount by which the oceanic tides are diminished in consequence of the corporeal tides. In his classical investigation* the earth was regarded as a homogeneous incompressible elastic solid body, and the problem was treated as a statical one, or, in other words, the corporeal tide was calculated from an equilibrium theory; and it was shown that, if the rigidity were that of glass, the oceanic tides, calculated also by an equilibrium theory, would be reduced to two-fifths of their theoretical amount, and, if the rigidity were that of steel, they would be reduced to two-thirds. Lord Kelvin also pointed out that, for the purpose of observing the diminution of oceanic tides by corporeal tides, the most appropriate oceanic tide would be the fortnightly tide, because an argument due to Laplace went to show that it should obey the equilibrium theory, while its effects, if observed over a long interval of time, would not be liable to be disguised by meteorological causes.

Since the time when this investigation was published the problem has been much discussed, various points in the theory have been elucidated, and new methods of observing the corporeal tides have been devised. Two steps were taken at about the same time: one, a reduction by G. H. Darwin† of tidal observations with a view to determining the actual height of the fortnightly oceanic tides; the other, an attempt by G. H. Darwin and

* W. Thomson, "Dynamical problems regarding elastic spheroidal shells" and "On the rigidity of the earth," *Phil. Trans. R. Soc.*, London, vol. 153 (1863). Subsequent versions of the investigation will be found in Lord Kelvin's *Math. and Phys. Papers*, vol. III. and in Thomson and Tait's *Natural Philosophy*, Pt. II.

† The investigation was published as § 848 of the second edition of Thomson and Tait's *Natural Philosophy* (1883), and is reprinted in G. H. Darwin's *Scientific Papers*, vol. I. p. 340.

H. Darwin* to measure the lunar deflexion of gravity. It appeared from G. H. Darwin's reduction of tidal observations that the actual height of the fortnightly tide is about two-thirds of the theoretical equilibrium height. The experiments for determining the lunar deflexion of gravity were, however, inconclusive. Numerous observers, working with various instruments, also attempted to measure the lunar deflexion of gravity, among them von Rebeur Paschwitz, who advocated the use of a horizontal pendulum, and believed that with his pendulum he could detect the influence of earth tides. G. H. Darwin's conclusion in regard to the actual height of the fortnightly oceanic tides has been confirmed recently by W. Schweydar† by a reduction of much more numerous tidal observations, and Schweydar obtained at the same time a confirmatory result by a fresh reduction of the best series of Paschwitz' observations. But the most elaborate observations of the lunar deflexion of gravity are those which have been made in recent years by O. Hecker‡. He has proved decisively that corporeal tides exist, and has furnished very valuable numerical results by help of which the amounts of such tides may be determined.

55. The theory of the corporeal tides has been developed in various ways which may be described briefly by reference to Lord Kelvin's four simplifying assumptions:—(1) That the corporeal tides can be calculated by an equilibrium theory, (2) that the fortnightly oceanic tide may be calculated by an equilibrium theory, (3) that the earth may be treated as homogeneous, (4) that the earth may be treated as incompressible. In a general way we may be fairly confident that an equilibrium theory of the corporeal tides would be correct, whatever the rigidity of the earth might be, because the period of free oscillation (of tidal type) of a fluid sphere of the size and mass of the earth would be about 1 hr. 34 min.§. If the substance is as rigid as steel, instead of being fluid, and if it is homogeneous and incompressible, the period is about 1 hr. 6 min.|| These periods are very short compared with any tidal period, and it is unlikely that they would be lengthened very much by assuming any admissible constitution of the earth. Nevertheless, for the sake of completeness, and for another reason which will appear later, it seemed to be desirable to work out a dynamical theory of the corporeal tides. This will be given in Chapter V *infra*. A doubt may remain as to the applicability of an equilibrium theory to corporeal tides if, as has been suggested, the earth should consist of a solid nucleus covered with a solid crust from which it is separated by a layer of fluid matter. But, as we shall

* *Rep. Brit. Assoc.*, 1881, p. 93, or G. H. Darwin's *Scientific Papers*, vol. I. p. 389.

† W. Schweydar, "Ein Beitrag zur Bestimmung des Starrheitskoeffizienten der Erde," *Beiträge zur Geophysik*, Bd. 9 (1907).

‡ O. Hecker, "Beobachtungen an Horizontalpendeln...," *Veröff. d. königl. preusz. geodät. Inst.*, 1907.

§ See the first of the papers by Lord Kelvin (W. Thomson) cited on p. 49.

|| H. Lamb, "The vibrations of an elastic sphere," London, *Proc. Math. Soc.* vol. XIII. (1882).

see in the discussion of Hecker's observations, this constitution is very improbable.

56. The question of the applicability of an equilibrium theory to the fortnightly oceanic tides was raised by G. H. Darwin*. His investigation appeared to show that the fortnightly tide calculated on a dynamical theory would be decidedly less than (about two-thirds of) the theoretical equilibrium amount, unless the friction of the ocean bed is much greater than it had previously been supposed to be. The dynamical theory in question was based, as is usual in the dynamical theory of the tides, on the supposition that the displacement of the ocean is a function of latitude only, or, in other words, it was assumed that the tides might be calculated as if the sea were not interrupted by land barriers running north and south. Lord Rayleigh† afterwards showed that, if there were no such barriers, free steady motions, consisting of currents running along parallels of latitude, would be generated, and would cause the tides of long period, calculated on the dynamical theory, to fall decidedly short of their theoretical equilibrium values. It seems therefore that little doubt remains as to the correctness of calculating the fortnightly tide by an equilibrium theory.

57. The known fact that the earth is not homogeneous, but of a mean density about twice that of superficial rocks, suggests the question: Would the estimate of the rigidity be much affected, and in what sense would it be affected, if account could be taken of the heterogeneity? This question was first discussed by G. H. Darwin‡ by means of a probable hypothesis, from which it was concluded that, if the density increases from surface to centre, the planet as a whole yields rather less to tidal disturbances than it would do if its density were uniform. Hence he inferred that the estimate of rigidity should be diminished slightly on account of the heterogeneity. The question has since been discussed by G. Herglotz§ by a more elaborate analysis, with the result that Darwin's conclusion as to the sense of the correction was confirmed, but that the diminution might be much greater than he had made out.

A like enquiry may be made in regard to the effect of compressibility. There is no more reason for assuming the material of which the earth is composed to be absolutely incompressible than for assuming it to be absolutely homogeneous. Several attempts have been made to answer this question, but none of them is satisfactory. A new solution of the problem is offered in Chapter VIII *infra*.

* "Dynamical Theory of the tides of long period," *Proc. R. Soc. London*, vol. 41 (1886), or *Scientific Papers*, vol. I. p. 366.

† "Note on the theory of the fortnightly tide," *Phil. Mag.* (Ser. 6), vol. V. (1903).

‡ "Note on Thomson's theory of the tides of an elastic sphere," *Mess. of Math.* vol. VIII. (1879), or *Scientific Papers*, vol. II. p. 33.

§ G. Herglotz, *Zeitschr. f. Math. u. Phys.* Bd. 52 (1905).

58. The statical, or equilibrium, theory of earth tides was much improved when it was seen how to combine the results obtained by observations of fortnightly tides, or experiments with horizontal pendulums, with those that were found by observations of variations of latitude. No sooner had S. C. Chandler made known his discovery that the variation of latitude is roughly periodic in a period of about 427 days, instead of the period of about 306 days which the movement would have if the earth were absolutely rigid, than S. Newcomb* pointed out that the lengthening of the period was due to the yielding of the earth, and that it should be possible to deduce from the actual period an estimate of the rigidity of the earth. The heterogeneity of the earth's substance presented an unexpected difficulty in the way of deducing such an estimate, and in the first investigation of the matter, by S. S. Hough†, this difficulty was met by means of a "probable hypothesis." At a later date the question was taken up by Herglotz‡, who showed, on the basis of an assumed heterogeneous constitution, how Hough's hypothesis could be avoided, and an improved estimate could be deduced. He assumed that the earth could be treated as incompressible, and adopted Wiechert's law of density, according to which the earth consists of a metal nucleus of density 8·206 enclosed in a rocky shell of density 3·2, the ratio of the radius of the nucleus to the outer radius of the shell being 0·78 : 1§. It appeared that, on the basis of this constitution, the rigidity deduced from the observed height of the fortnightly tides was but little more than half that deduced from variations of latitude. A method of combining the results of the two kinds of observations was first proposed by W. Schweydar‖. He adopted Wiechert's law of density and Herglotz' assumption of incompressibility, but supposed the rigidity of the nucleus to be different from that of the shell, and he found the rigidities which must be attributed to both in order that the results which are deduced from the two kinds of observations may be reconciled.

59. A more general method has since been found¶. This may be described as follows:—The moon's tide-generating potential at any point within or near to the earth can be expressed with sufficient approximation by the formula

$$\gamma M D^{-3} r^2 \left(\tfrac{3}{2}\cos^2\theta' - \tfrac{1}{2}\right) \qquad\qquad (1),$$

where γ denotes the constant of gravitation, M the mass of the moon, D the distance between the earth's centre and the moon's centre, r, θ' the polar

* *Mon. Not. R. Astr. Soc.* 1892.

† S. S. Hough, "The rotation of an elastic spheroid," *Phil. Trans. R. Soc. London*, vol. 187 A (1896).

‡ *Loc. cit. ante*, p. 51.

§ E. Wiechert, *Göttingen Nachrichten*, 1897. In the paper cited on p. 51 Herglotz worked out the problem for a continuously varying density as well as for Wiechert's law.

‖ *Loc. cit. ante*, p. 50.

¶ A. E. H. Love, "The yielding of the earth to disturbing forces," *Proc. R. Soc. London*, Ser. A, vol. 82 (1909), p. 73.

coordinates of the point, referred to the centre of the earth as origin and the line of centres as polar axis. Let this expression, which is a spherical solid harmonic of the second degree, be denoted by W_2. Then W_2/g expresses the theoretical equilibrium height of the oceanic tide caused by the moon, g being the mean value of gravity at the earth's surface. In order to determine the height of the corporeal tide by an equilibrium theory, we may begin by assuming that the distribution of mass is spherically symmetrical, and that the rigidity and incompressibility (or modulus of compression) are constant over the same surfaces as the density. (If the rotation were taken into account the spherical surfaces of equal density would have to be replaced by ellipsoidal surfaces.) When this is the case, the radial displacement U and the cubical dilatation Δ, which are produced at any point by forces derived from the potential W_2, are expressed by the products of the solid harmonic W_2 and certain functions of r; thus we may write

$$U = H(r)\, W_2/g, \quad \Delta = f(r)\, W_2/g \qquad \text{(2)},$$

where the functions $H(r)$ and $f(r)$ depend upon the densities and elasticities answering to the various values of r. Now, whatever these functions may be, the potential due to the increment, or decrement, of density that accompanies the cubical dilatation, and to the superficial displacement of matter, is also expressed by the product of the same harmonic W_2 and some function of r, so that we may write for the potential V of the earth, deformed by the tidal forces, an expression of the form

$$V = V_0 + K(r)\, W_2 \qquad \text{(3)},$$

where V_0 denotes the potential of the undisturbed earth. Now write

$$h = H(a), \quad k = K(a) \qquad \text{(4)};$$

then h and k are two numbers which define the height of the earth tide at the surface and the inequality of potential that is produced by the earth tide. The potential of the earth at a point of the deformed surface is expressed with sufficient approximation by the formula

$$V_0(a) + h\frac{W_2}{g}\left(\frac{dV_0}{dr}\right)_{r=a} + kW_2 \qquad \text{(5)},$$

and, since $(dV_0/dr)_{r=a} = -g$, this is $V_0(a) + (k-h)\, W_2$; so that the tide-generating potential becomes $(1+k-h)\, W_2$ instead of W_2. On an equilibrium theory the oceanic tides are diminished, in consequence of the existence of corporeal tides, in the ratio

$$1 + k - h : 1.$$

According to the results (already cited) that have been obtained by observation of the fortnightly tide, this ratio is about $\frac{2}{3}$, or we have approximately

$$h - k = \tfrac{1}{3} \qquad \text{(6)}.$$

As we shall see presently, experiments with horizontal pendulums also lead to a numerical determination of the difference $h - k$, but they yield no new relation between h and k.

60. Variations of latitude arise in consequence of the non-coincidence of the earth's instantaneous axis and a principal axis of inertia. If no changes took place in the distribution of the earth's mass, and if there were no dissipative forces, the movement would be strictly periodic. If the earth were rigid, the period, as determined by precession, would be about 306 days. But a deformable body set in rotation about an axis which does not quite coincide with a principal axis must be strained in the same way as if it were subjected to certain body forces. These forces are derived from a potential which is expressed by a spherical solid harmonic of the second degree*.

The deformation of the earth by such forces can therefore be expressed by the same three functions $H(r)$, $f(r)$, $K(r)$ as occur in the solution of the tidal problem. Now it has been shown that the period τ of the movement depends on the number k, and is in other respects independent of the elastic quality of the earth, so that from a knowledge of τ we can deduce the value of k.

It has been shown† that approximately

$$k = \tfrac{4}{15} \quad \text{.................................(7).}$$

By combining the equations $h - k = \frac{1}{3}$, $k = \frac{4}{15}$, there results

$$h = \tfrac{3}{5} \quad \text{.................................(8),}$$

or, in words, the height of the earth tide is three-fifths of the theoretical equilibrium value of the oceanic tide. This result is independent of any hypothesis in regard to the compressibility of the material, and of any special law of density such as Wiechert's.

61. Although the combination of the two kinds of observations enables us to determine the actual height of the earth tides, provided, of course, that they obey an equilibrium theory, yet it does not lead to a more exact estimate of the earth's rigidity. There is not any one rigidity which is the "rigidity of the earth," but, the material of which the earth is composed being heterogeneous, there are different rigidities at different depths. The investigation

* Cf. S. S. Hough, *loc. cit.*, *ante* p. 52.

† The formula giving k in terms of τ is

$$k = \left(\frac{2g\epsilon}{a\omega^2} - 1\right)\left(1 - \frac{\tau_0}{\tau}\right),$$

where ϵ denotes the ellipticity of the meridians, ω the angular velocity of rotation, τ_0 the period calculated from the precessional constant on the assumption of absolute rigidity. See A. E. H. Love, *loc. cit.*, *ante* p. 52, and J. Larmor, "The relation of the earth's free precessional nutation to its resistance against tidal deformation," *Proc. R. Soc. London*, Ser. A, Vol. 82 (1909), p. 89.

of earth tides has proved decisively that the earth is not a fluid body coated over by a thin solid crust.

62. It remains to give some account of the results found in Hecker's experimental investigation of earth tides by means of horizontal pendulums. The theory of the experiment is simple. The force that is available for deflecting a horizontal pendulum is derived from a potential which consists effectively of three terms, viz.: the tide-generating potential of the moon, the tide-generating potential of the sun, and the potential of the earth (strained by the tidal forces) estimated at a point on the deformed surface. If the deformation of the earth can be calculated by an equilibrium theory, this potential is that which we before denoted by $(1 + k - h) W_2$, the sun being left out of account. If the earth were absolutely rigid, so that the forces produced no deformation in it, the potential of the forces that would act on the pendulum would be W_2. We should expect therefore that the

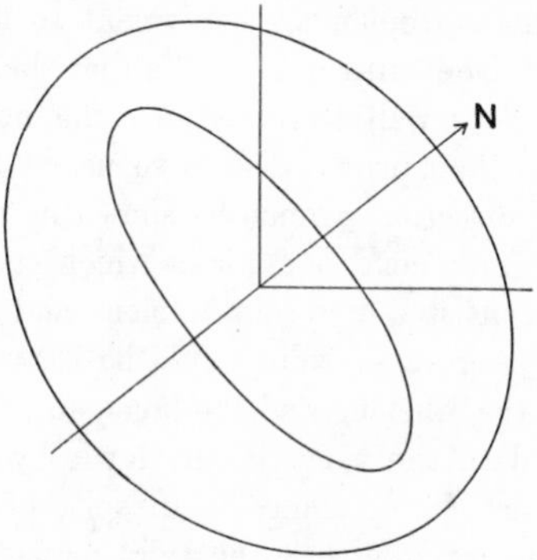

deflexion of the pendulum would be less than the theoretical amount that it would have if the earth were rigid in the ratio $1 + k - h : 1$. Now Hecker set up two horizontal pendulums in azimuths nearly north-west and north-east, recorded their deflexions by an automatic process for 882 days, and analysed the results so as to pick out the parts of the deflexions that were periodic in particular periods. The most important period is half a lunar day, the period of the principal lunar semi-diurnal tide, the tide denoted by M_2*. At Potsdam, where his observatory was, the forces corresponding to the tide M_2 would, if they acted alone, produce deflexions of a vertical pendulum in these two azimuths of amounts

$$0''\cdot00922 \cos(2t - 305^\circ\cdot5) \text{ and } 0''\cdot00900 \cos(2t - 48^\circ\cdot7),$$

where t denotes the lunar time that has elapsed since a certain epoch. The parts of the observed deflexions which had the same period were found to be equivalent to deflexions of a vertical pendulum of amounts

$$0''\cdot00622 \cos(2t - 285^\circ\cdot4) \text{ and } 0''\cdot00543 \cos(2t - 63^\circ\cdot2).$$

* G. H. Darwin, *Scientific Papers*, vol. I. p. 20.

These results can be exhibited graphically by tracing curves of which the first and second of these expressions in each case are the ordinate and abscissa. The result is shown in the diagram on p. 55, where the outer curve represents the principal lunar semi-diurnal term of the deflexion of gravity that would be due to the moon if the earth were absolutely rigid, and the inner curve represents on the same scale the corresponding term of the observed deflexion*.

63. The first inference from these results is that there is no doubt about the yielding of the earth to the tidal forces; the earth is not absolutely rigid. The second inference is that the average amount of the yielding shown by these observations is very nearly the same as that inferred from observations of the fortnightly oceanic tide; corresponding central radii vectores of the inner and outer curves are nearly in the ratio 2 : 3 on the average all round the curve. On the assumption that the earth tide may be calculated by an equilibrium theory, this statement is equivalent to the relation $h - k = \frac{1}{3}$, which was used above. The third inference is that the use of an equilibrium theory appears to be very well supported by the observations. The two curves are ellipses with their principal axes so nearly coincident in direction that the difference of direction cannot be shown in the diagram. We saw above (p. 50) that the only condition under which such a theory might fail would be if the earth consisted of a solid nucleus and a solid crust separated by a fluid layer. If this were so, tides would be set up by the attractions of the sun and moon in the nucleus and the layer and the crust, and it might be impossible to calculate the tides in the layer by a statical theory. It would be a very singular circumstance if, in spite of this constitution, the tides in the crust were in phase with the tidal forces, as they are shown by the observations to be.

64. Although the average value of the deflexions observed by Hecker, being about two-thirds of the theoretical deflexions, affords a striking confirmation of the result obtained from observations of the fortnightly tides, yet the fact that the inner curve in the diagram is much flatter than the outer requires explanation. The ratio of the minor to the major axis of the outer curve should be the sine of the latitude of the place of observation, for Potsdam about $\frac{4}{5}$. If, as was explained above, the potential of the forces acting on the pendulum were $(1 + k - h) W_2$, the inner curve should be similar and similarly situated to the outer, but, as a matter of fact, the ratio of the minor and major axes of the inner curve is less than $\frac{1}{2}$. This result indicates that the force acting on the pendulum is a larger fraction of the moon's force when it acts towards the east or the west than when it acts towards the north or the south, as if the earth at Potsdam were stiffer to

* The above diagram was drawn afresh from the formulae, but might have been taken from Hecker's *Tafel* vii by omitting the diurnal curve.

resist forces acting east or west than forces acting north or south. Various explanations of this anomaly have been proposed, among them one, suggested by Sir G. Darwin, is that it may be an effect of gyroscopic rigidity produced in the earth by its rotation. This suggestion, put into other words, would amount to proposing to take account of the rotation of the earth in calculating its deformation by tidal forces. To investigate the correctness of this explanation it is necessary to attempt a dynamical theory of earth tides.

Another explanation, proposed by Hecker, is that the observed effect may be due to the situation of his observatory in Western Europe, with the Atlantic Ocean to the west and the great mass of Asia to the east. The investigation of the corporeal tides in a rotating spheroidal planet will throw light on this suggestion also.

CHAPTER V

EFFECT OF INERTIA ON EARTH TIDES

65. In order to investigate the manner in which the rotation of the earth affects the theory of the corporeal tides, it will be sufficient to consider the problem under certain simplifying assumptions. The sense of the correction which should be made in the ordinary theory can hardly be different from that which may thus be found, and it is unlikely that the order of magnitude can be very different.

It will be assumed here that the earth may be treated as a homogeneous incompressible elastic solid body of a finite degree of rigidity. The body will be supposed to be in a state of initial stress by which its own gravity is balanced throughout its volume. Further it will be supposed to rotate uniformly, and the initial stress will be taken to be so adjusted that the equations of motion of the body rotating steadily are satisfied. The initial stress will be assumed to be hydrostatic pressure, and, when necessary, it will be assumed that the undisturbed surface is an ellipsoid of revolution of small ellipticity. Further the complete expression for the tide-generating potential will be replaced by the potential corresponding to the principal lunar semi-diurnal tide.

66. We shall use cartesian rectangular coordinates x, y, z, the origin being at the centre of the undisturbed body, the axis of z being the axis of rotation, and the axes of x and y rotating with the body. We shall denote the density of the body by ρ, the angular velocity by ω, the initial pressure by p_0, and the potential of the undisturbed body by V_0. Then we have the equations of motion of the undisturbed body, in the forms

$$\left.\begin{aligned} -\rho\omega^2 x &= \rho\frac{\partial V_0}{\partial x} - \frac{\partial p_0}{\partial x} \\ -\rho\omega^2 y &= \rho\frac{\partial V_0}{\partial y} - \frac{\partial p_0}{\partial y} \\ 0 &= \rho\frac{\partial V_0}{\partial z} - \frac{\partial p_0}{\partial z} \end{aligned}\right\} \quad \ldots\ldots\ldots\ldots\ldots\ldots(1).$$

We shall suppose the body to be strained by the application of forces derived from the potential W, and shall denote the displacement at a point by (u, v, w). The potential of the body at a point will be $V_0 + V'$, where V' is the additional potential due to the deformation of the body. We shall denote the rigidity of the body by μ. Then the stress at a point (x, y, z) is expressed by six components of stress, which may be taken to be

$$X_x = -p_0 - p' + 2\mu\frac{\partial u}{\partial x}, \quad Y_y = -p_0 - p' + 2\mu\frac{\partial v}{\partial y}, \quad Z_z = -p_0 - p' + 2\mu\frac{\partial w}{\partial z},$$

$$Y_z = \mu\left(\frac{\partial w}{\partial y} + \frac{\partial v}{\partial z}\right), \quad Z_x = \mu\left(\frac{\partial u}{\partial z} + \frac{\partial w}{\partial x}\right), \quad X_y = \mu\left(\frac{\partial v}{\partial x} + \frac{\partial u}{\partial y}\right),$$

where p' denotes an additional pressure at the point (x, y, z).

Then the equations of motion referred to the moving axes are

$$\rho\left\{\frac{\partial^2 u}{\partial t^2} - 2\omega\frac{\partial v}{\partial t} - \omega^2(x+u)\right\} = \rho\left(\frac{\partial V_0}{\partial x} + \frac{\partial V'}{\partial x} + \frac{\partial W}{\partial x}\right) - \frac{\partial p_0}{\partial x} - \frac{\partial p'}{\partial x} + \mu\nabla^2 u,$$

$$\rho\left\{\frac{\partial^2 v}{\partial t^2} + 2\omega\frac{\partial u}{\partial t} - \omega^2(y+v)\right\} = \rho\left(\frac{\partial V_0}{\partial y} + \frac{\partial V'}{\partial y} + \frac{\partial W}{\partial y}\right) - \frac{\partial p_0}{\partial y} - \frac{\partial p'}{\partial y} + \mu\nabla^2 v,$$

$$\rho\frac{\partial^2 w}{\partial t^2} = \rho\left(\frac{\partial V_0}{\partial z} + \frac{\partial V'}{\partial z} + \frac{\partial W}{\partial z}\right) - \frac{\partial p_0}{\partial z} - \frac{\partial p'}{\partial z} + \mu\nabla^2 w.$$

By means of equations (1) these may be simplified so as to become

$$\left.\begin{aligned}\rho\left(\frac{\partial^2 u}{\partial t^2} - 2\omega\frac{\partial v}{\partial t} - \omega^2 u\right) &= \rho\left(\frac{\partial V'}{\partial x} + \frac{\partial W}{\partial x}\right) - \frac{\partial p'}{\partial x} + \mu\nabla^2 u\\ \rho\left(\frac{\partial^2 v}{\partial t^2} + 2\omega\frac{\partial u}{\partial t} - \omega^2 v\right) &= \rho\left(\frac{\partial V'}{\partial y} + \frac{\partial W}{\partial y}\right) - \frac{\partial p'}{\partial y} + \mu\nabla^2 v\\ \rho\frac{\partial^2 w}{\partial t^2} &= \rho\left(\frac{\partial V'}{\partial z} + \frac{\partial W}{\partial z}\right) - \frac{\partial p'}{\partial z} + \mu\nabla^2 w\end{aligned}\right\}\ldots\ldots(2).$$

Further we have the equation expressing the assumption of incompressibility in the form

$$\frac{\partial u}{\partial x} + \frac{\partial v}{\partial y} + \frac{\partial w}{\partial z} = 0 \quad \ldots\ldots\ldots\ldots\ldots\ldots\ldots(3).$$

Let l, m, n denote the direction cosines of the outward-drawn normal to the undisturbed bounding surface. Then V' is the potential of a distribution of mass on this surface with a superficial density

$$\rho(lu + mv + nw),$$

so that V' satisfies the equation

$$\nabla^2 V' = 0 \quad \ldots\ldots\ldots\ldots\ldots\ldots\ldots(4).$$

The system of equations (2), (3), (4) are five differential equations connecting the five unknowns, u, v, w, V', p' with the known quantity W. The surface characteristic equation for V', that is to say the equation by which its normal derivative at the surface is connected with the superficial density, is one of the boundary conditions; and the remaining boundary conditions must express the fact that the deformed surface is free from traction.

67. In order to obtain solutions of this system of equations, in such forms that the boundary conditions may be satisfied, it is convenient to proceed by an approximate method. The first approximation is obtained by ignoring the rotation and the ellipticity, and omitting the left-hand members of equations (2). The problem so simplified is the purely statical problem of a homogeneous incompressible sphere held strained by the forces derived from the potential W. The solution is known from Lord Kelvin's investigation*. For a second approximation we substitute the values of u, v, w, obtained from the first approximation in the left-hand members of equations (2) and solve the equations again, retaining, however, the supposition that the undisturbed surface is spherical. By a third approximation we may take account of the ellipticity of the undisturbed surface. Thus we shall write

$$u = u_0 + u_1 + u_2, \quad v = v_0 + v_1 + v_2, \quad w = w_0 + w_1 + w_2,$$
$$p' = p_0' + p_1 + p_2, \quad V' = V_0' + V_1 + V_2.$$

Then $u_0, \ldots$ are the quantities found in Lord Kelvin's solution, $u_1, \ldots$ are the quantities found by the second approximation above described, and $u_2, \ldots$ are those found by the third approximation. The quantities $u_1, \ldots$ may be referred to as the "correction for inertia," and the quantities $u_2, \ldots$ as the "correction for ellipticity." In connexion with the suggestion (p. 57) that gyroscopic rigidity might account for the earth seeming to be stiffer to resist forces that act east and west than forces that act north and south, it is necessary to determine $u_1, \ldots$. In this Chapter we shall consider the correction for inertia only, and we shall defer an investigation of the correction for ellipticity to the following Chapter.

68. The equations satisfied by $u_0, \ldots$ are the vector equation

$$\left(\frac{\partial}{\partial x}, \frac{\partial}{\partial y}, \frac{\partial}{\partial z}\right)(\rho V_0' + \rho W - p_0') + \mu \nabla^2 (u_0, v_0, w_0) = 0 \quad \ldots\ldots(5),$$

with the two equations

$$\frac{\partial u_0}{\partial x} + \frac{\partial v_0}{\partial y} + \frac{\partial w_0}{\partial z} = 0, \quad \nabla^2 V_0' = 0 \quad \ldots\ldots\ldots\ldots\ldots\ldots\ldots(6).$$

The function W, as well as V_0', satisfies Laplace's equation, and it appears at once from the vector equation (5) that p_0' also satisfies Laplace's equation. To express the boundary conditions it is convenient to introduce a quantity ζ_0 by the equation

$$\zeta_0 = u_0 x + v_0 y + w_0 z \quad \ldots\ldots\ldots\ldots\ldots\ldots\ldots\ldots(7),$$

so that, if r denotes distance from the centre, ζ_0/r denotes the radial displacement. It is also convenient to introduce a quantity $(V_0')_0$, which is the

* *Loc. cit., ante* p. 49.

potential at external points of those masses of which V_0' is the potential at internal points. Then, if a denotes the radius of the unstrained sphere, the surface characteristic equation for the potential takes the form

$$\frac{\partial (V_0')_0}{\partial r} - \frac{\partial V_0'}{\partial r} = -4\pi\gamma\rho\frac{\zeta_0}{r} \quad\text{..........................(8)},$$

and this equation holds at $r=a$. Now V_0' may be expressed as a sum of spherical solid harmonics, say

$$V_0' = \Sigma a_n \frac{r^n}{a^n} S_n \quad\text{..................................(9)},$$

where S_n is a spherical surface harmonic of positive integral degree n; and $(V_0')_0$ is therefore given by the formula

$$(V_0')_0 = \Sigma a_n \frac{a^{n+1}}{r^{n+1}} S_n.$$

Further the initial state is that of a homogeneous gravitating sphere in which gravitation is balanced by hydrostatic pressure, so that we have

$$\left.\begin{aligned} V_0 &= \tfrac{2}{3}\pi\gamma\rho(3a^2 - r^2) = \tfrac{1}{2}g(3a^2 - r^2)/a \\ p_0 &= \tfrac{2}{3}\pi\gamma\rho(a^2 - r^2) = \tfrac{1}{2}g(a^2 - r^2)/a \end{aligned}\right\} \quad\text{..............(10)},$$

where g is written for $\frac{4}{3}\pi\gamma\rho a$. Let l', m', n' denote the direction cosines of the outward-drawn normal at a point on the deformed surface. The equation of this surface is of the form $r = a + U$, where U denotes the value of ζ_0/r at $r=a$. The conditions that the deformed surface may be free from traction are three equations of the type

$$l'\left(-p_0 - p_0' + 2\mu\frac{\partial u_0}{\partial x}\right) + m'\mu\left(\frac{\partial v_0}{\partial x} + \frac{\partial u_0}{\partial y}\right) + n'\mu\left(\frac{\partial u_0}{\partial z} + \frac{\partial w_0}{\partial x}\right) = 0 \quad\text{...(11)}.$$

These hold at the surface $r=a+U$. We have to express them in an approximate form, in which squares and products of quantities of the order of the displacement are neglected. First we observe that p_0 vanishes at $r=a$, and therefore, at $r=a+U$, we may write with sufficient approximation instead of p_0 the expression

$$U\left(\frac{\partial p_0}{\partial r}\right)_{r=a}.$$

Since all the quantities which are multiplied by l', m' or n' are now small of the order of the displacement we may replace l', ... by the direction cosines of the normal to the unstrained sphere, that is by x/r, y/r, z/r, and then the equation (11) takes the form

$$\frac{x}{r}\left(\frac{g\rho\zeta_0}{r} - p_0'\right) + \frac{\mu}{r}\left(\frac{\partial \zeta_0}{\partial x} + r\frac{\partial u_0}{\partial r} - u_0\right) = 0 \quad\text{..............(12)}.$$

The three equations of this type hold at the surface $r=a$.

69. The solution of this system of equations and conditions can now be written down*. The function W being a spherical solid harmonic of the second degree, we have

$$\left.\begin{aligned} u_0 &= N\frac{a}{g}\left\{\left(2-\frac{5r^2}{4a^2}\right)\frac{\partial W}{\partial x}+\frac{x}{a^2}W\right\} \\ v_0 &= N\frac{a}{g}\left\{\left(2-\frac{5r^2}{4a^2}\right)\frac{\partial W}{\partial y}+\frac{y}{a^2}W\right\} \\ w_0 &= N\frac{a}{g}\left\{\left(2-\frac{5r^2}{4a^2}\right)\frac{\partial W}{\partial z}+\frac{z}{a^2}W\right\} \\ \zeta_0 &= N\frac{a}{g}5\left(1-\frac{r^2}{2a^2}\right)W \\ p_0' &= N\rho W\left(\tfrac{5}{2}-\mu/g\rho a\right) \\ V_0' &= \tfrac{3}{2}NW \end{aligned}\right\} \quad \text{.............. (13)},$$

where N is written for $1\Big/\left(1+\dfrac{19\mu}{2g\rho a}\right)$.

70. The above solution is independent of the special form of W, provided only that W is a spherical solid harmonic of the second degree. In what follows we shall confine our attention to the principal lunar semi-diurnal tide. Let $2\pi/\sigma$ be the period of this tide. Then W is proportional to the surface harmonic

$$\sin^2\theta\cos(2\phi+\sigma t),$$

where θ and ϕ are the co-latitude (measured from the North Pole) and the longitude (measured eastwards from a chosen meridian) of a place on the earth's surface. We shall take this to be the real part of

$$\sin^2\theta\, e^{i(2\phi+\sigma t)},$$

and shall proceed with the theory as if W were proportional to this complex expression. In the end we keep only the real part of our solution. All the quantities such as u_1 will then be proportional to $e^{i\sigma t}$. When expressed in terms of x and y, W will be a linear combination of the two real harmonics x^2-y^2 and xy, but it is independent of z. This circumstance will be found to simplify the problem. It is worth noting that

$$x\frac{\partial W}{\partial y}-y\frac{\partial W}{\partial x}$$

is a spherical solid harmonic of the second degree which is similar in its properties to W. We shall write W' for this harmonic, so that

$$W' = x\frac{\partial W}{\partial y}-y\frac{\partial W}{\partial x} \quad \text{........................ (14)}.$$

* The solution is easily verified. It might have been extracted from Lord Kelvin's paper. With a view to the subsequent development of the theory it seemed to be worth while to indicate in some detail the method of formation of the boundary conditions.

71. To determine the quantities $u_1, \dots$ we put

$$u = u_0 + u_1, \quad v = v_0 + v_1, \quad w = w_0 + w_1, \quad p' = p_0' + p_1, \quad V' = V_0' + V_1.$$

Then in the left-hand members of equations (2) of p. 59 we omit the terms containing $u_1, \dots$ and we simplify the right-hand members by using equations (5) of p. 60. Then the left-hand members contain only known quantities, expressed in terms of $u_0, \dots$, that is in terms of W. The right-hand members do not contain W or any of the letters with suffix 0. Further, since all the quantities that occur are proportional to $e^{i\sigma t}$, the operator $\partial/\partial t$ may be replaced by the coefficient $i\sigma$. Accordingly the simplified equations can be written

$$\left.\begin{aligned}
\mu\nabla^2 u_1 &= -\rho(\sigma^2 u_0 + 2i\omega\sigma v_0 + \omega^2 u_0) + \frac{\partial p_1}{\partial x} - \rho\frac{\partial V_1}{\partial x}\\
\mu\nabla^2 v_1 &= -\rho(\sigma^2 v_0 - 2i\omega\sigma u_0 + \omega^2 v_0) + \frac{\partial p_1}{\partial y} - \rho\frac{\partial V_1}{\partial y}\\
\mu\nabla^2 w_1 &= -\rho\sigma^2 w_0 \qquad\qquad\qquad\qquad\quad + \frac{\partial p_1}{\partial z} - \rho\frac{\partial V_1}{\partial z}
\end{aligned}\right\} \quad \text{.........(15).}$$

We have also the equations

$$\frac{\partial u_1}{\partial x} + \frac{\partial v_1}{\partial y} + \frac{\partial w_1}{\partial z} = 0 \quad \text{..........................(16),}$$

and

$$\nabla^2 V_1 = 0 \quad \text{..............................(17).}$$

By differentiating the left-hand and right-hand members of the equations (15) with respect to x, y and z respectively, adding the results, and using equations (16) and (17) we find

$$\nabla^2 p_1 = \rho\omega^2\left(\frac{\partial u_0}{\partial x} + \frac{\partial v_0}{\partial y}\right) + 2i\rho\omega\sigma\left(\frac{\partial v_0}{\partial x} - \frac{\partial u_0}{\partial y}\right).$$

Now

$$\frac{\partial u_0}{\partial x} + \frac{\partial v_0}{\partial y} = -\frac{\partial w_0}{\partial z} = -N\frac{W}{ag},$$

W being independent of z. Also

$$\frac{\partial v_0}{\partial x} - \frac{\partial u_0}{\partial y} = -N\frac{7W'}{2ag}.$$

Thus $\nabla^2 p_1$ is expressed as the sum of two spherical solid harmonics of the second degree; and therefore the most general possible expression for p_1 is given by the formula

$$p_1 = -N\rho\frac{a\omega^2}{g}\frac{r^2}{2a^2}\left(\frac{W}{7} + i\frac{\sigma}{\omega}W'\right) + \Sigma\varpi_n \quad \text{..............(18),}$$

where $\Sigma\varpi_n$ is a sum of spherical solid harmonics of positive integral degrees indicated by the suffixes, and we have to include in the solution as many of these harmonics as may be needed.

72. Again the radial displacement at the surface $r = a$ may be expressed as a sum of spherical surface harmonics, so that we may write

$$\left(\frac{\zeta_1}{r}\right)_{r=a} = \Sigma\frac{a^n}{r^n}\xi_n \quad \text{..........................(19),}$$

where ζ_1 stands for $xu_1 + yv_1 + zw_1$, and ξ_n is a spherical solid harmonic of the nth degree. The additional potential V_1 is due to mass distributed on the surface $r=a$ with a superficial density $\rho\,(\zeta_1/r)_{r=a}$, and therefore we have

$$V_1 = 3g\Sigma\,\frac{\xi_n}{2n+1} \qquad \text{.............................(20).}$$

73. We are now in a position to write down complete expressions for the quantities which occur in the right-hand members of equations (15). First we have the formulae

$$\frac{\partial p_1}{\partial x} = -N\rho\,\frac{\omega^2}{ag}\left\{\frac{r^2}{2}\left(\frac{1}{7}\frac{\partial W}{\partial x} + i\frac{\sigma}{\omega}\frac{\partial W'}{\partial x}\right) + x\left(\frac{W}{7} + i\frac{\sigma}{\omega}W'\right)\right\} + \Sigma\frac{\partial \varpi_n}{\partial x},$$

$$\frac{\partial p_1}{\partial y} = -N\rho\,\frac{\omega^2}{ag}\left\{\frac{r^2}{2}\left(\frac{1}{7}\frac{\partial W}{\partial y} + i\frac{\sigma}{\omega}\frac{\partial W'}{\partial y}\right) + y\left(\frac{W}{7} + i\frac{\sigma}{\omega}W'\right)\right\} + \Sigma\frac{\partial \varpi_n}{\partial y},$$

$$\frac{\partial p_1}{\partial z} = -N\rho\,\frac{\omega^2}{ag}\,z\left(\frac{W}{7} + i\frac{\sigma}{\omega}W'\right) + \Sigma\,\frac{\partial \varpi_n}{\partial z}.$$

Next we have three such formulae as

$$\frac{\partial V_1}{\partial x} = 3g\,\Sigma\,\frac{1}{2n+1}\,\frac{\partial \xi_n}{\partial x}.$$

In the third place we have, from the results given in § 69,

$$(\sigma^2+\omega^2)\,u_0 + 2i\omega\sigma v_0 = N\frac{a\omega^2}{g}\left[\left(1+\frac{\sigma^2}{\omega^2}\right)\left\{\left(2-\frac{5r^2}{4a^2}\right)\frac{\partial W}{\partial x} + \frac{x}{a^2}W\right\}\right.$$
$$\left. + 2i\,\frac{\sigma}{\omega}\left\{\left(2-\frac{5r^2}{4a^2}\right)\frac{\partial W}{\partial y} + \frac{y}{a^2}W\right\}\right],$$

$$(\sigma^2+\omega^2)\,v_0 - 2i\omega\sigma u_0 = N\,\frac{a\omega^2}{g}\left[\left(1+\frac{\sigma^2}{\omega^2}\right)\left\{\left(2-\frac{5r^2}{4a^2}\right)\frac{\partial W}{\partial y} + \frac{y}{a^2}W\right\}\right.$$
$$\left. - 2i\,\frac{\sigma}{\omega}\left\{\left(2-\frac{5r^2}{4a^2}\right)\frac{\partial W}{\partial x} + \frac{x}{a^2}W\right\}\right],$$

$$\sigma^2 w_0 = N\,\frac{a\sigma^2}{g}\,\frac{z}{a^2}\,W.$$

By using these formulae in equations (15) we obtain the following equations

$$\mu\nabla^2 u_1 = \Sigma\,\frac{\partial}{\partial x}\left(\varpi_n - \frac{3g\rho}{2n+1}\,\xi_n\right)$$
$$-N\rho\,\frac{a\omega^2}{g}\left[\frac{r^2}{14a^2}\frac{\partial W}{\partial x} + \frac{xW}{7a^2} + i\,\frac{\sigma}{\omega}\left(\frac{r^2}{2a^2}\,\frac{\partial W'}{\partial x} + \frac{xW'}{a^2}\right)\right.$$
$$\left. + \left(1+\frac{\sigma^2}{\omega^2}\right)\left\{\left(2-\frac{5r^2}{4a^2}\right)\frac{\partial W}{\partial x} + \frac{xW}{a^2}\right\} + 2i\frac{\sigma}{\omega}\left\{\left(2-\frac{5r^2}{4a^2}\right)\frac{\partial W}{\partial y} + \frac{yW}{a^2}\right\}\right],$$

$$\mu\nabla^2 v_1 = \Sigma\,\frac{\partial}{\partial y}\left(\varpi_n - \frac{3g\rho}{2n+1}\,\xi_n\right)$$
$$-N\rho\,\frac{a\omega^2}{g}\left[\frac{r^2}{14a^2}\,\frac{\partial W}{\partial y} + \frac{yW}{7a^2} + i\,\frac{\sigma}{\omega}\left(\frac{r^2}{2a^2}\,\frac{\partial W'}{\partial y} + \frac{yW'}{a^2}\right)\right.$$
$$\left. + \left(1+\frac{\sigma^2}{\omega^2}\right)\left\{\left(2-\frac{5r^2}{4a^2}\right)\frac{\partial W}{\partial y} + \frac{yW}{a^2}\right\} - 2i\,\frac{\sigma}{\omega}\left\{\left(2-\frac{5r^2}{4a^2}\right)\frac{\partial W}{\partial x} + \frac{xW}{a^2}\right\}\right],$$

$$\mu\nabla^2 w_1 = \Sigma\,\frac{\partial}{\partial z}\left(\varpi_n - \frac{3g\rho}{2n+1}\,\xi_n\right) - N\rho\,\frac{\omega^2}{ag}\left\{\left(\frac{1}{7}+\frac{\sigma^2}{\omega^2}\right)zW + i\,\frac{\sigma}{\omega}\,zW'\right\}.$$

The solutions of these equations consist of (1) particular integrals, which are any functions by which the equations can be satisfied, and (2) complementary solutions of the equations to which the above would be reduced if their right-hand members were 0. The complementary solutions are sums of spherical solid harmonics of positive integral degrees, and we shall denote them by $\Sigma\alpha_n$, $\Sigma\beta_n$, $\Sigma\gamma_n$. To obtain particular integrals we note the formulae of the types

$$\nabla^2\left(r^2\frac{\partial\varpi_n}{\partial x}\right)=2(2n+1)\frac{\partial\varpi_n}{\partial x},$$

$$\nabla^2\left(r^4\frac{\partial W}{\partial x}\right)=28r^2\frac{\partial W}{\partial x},$$

$$\nabla^2\left(r^2xW-\frac{r^4}{14}\frac{\partial W}{\partial x}\right)=18xW.$$

The most general possible solution (subject, of course, to the condition of finiteness at the centre) is therefore given by the formulae

$$\left.\begin{aligned}
u_1&=\Sigma\left\{\alpha_n+\frac{r^2}{2(2n+1)\mu}\frac{\partial\varpi_n}{\partial x}-\frac{3g\rho r^2}{2(2n+1)^2\mu}\frac{\partial\xi_n}{\partial x}\right\}\\
&\quad-N\frac{\rho a\omega^2}{\mu g}\left[\frac{r^4}{14\times 28a^2}\frac{\partial W}{\partial x}+\frac{1}{7\times 18a^2}\left(r^2xW-\frac{r^4}{14}\frac{\partial W}{\partial x}\right)\right.\\
&\qquad+i\frac{\sigma}{\omega}\left\{\frac{r^4}{56a^2}\frac{\partial W'}{\partial x}+\frac{1}{18a^2}\left(r^2xW'-\frac{r^4}{14}\frac{\partial W'}{\partial x}\right)\right\}\\
&\quad+\left(1+\frac{\sigma^2}{\omega^2}\right)\left\{\frac{r^2}{5}\frac{\partial W}{\partial x}-\frac{5r^4}{4\times 28a^2}\frac{\partial W}{\partial x}+\frac{1}{18a^2}\left(r^2xW-\frac{r^4}{14}\frac{\partial W}{\partial x}\right)\right\}\\
&\qquad\left.+2i\frac{\sigma}{\omega}\left\{\frac{r^2}{5}\frac{\partial W}{\partial y}-\frac{5r^4}{4\times 28a^2}\frac{\partial W}{\partial y}+\frac{1}{18a^2}\left(r^2yW-\frac{r^4}{14}\frac{\partial W}{\partial y}\right)\right\}\right]\\
v_1&=\Sigma\left\{\beta_n+\frac{r^2}{2(2n+1)\mu}\frac{\partial\varpi_n}{\partial y}-\frac{3g\rho r^2}{2(2n+1)^2\mu}\frac{\partial\xi_n}{\partial y}\right\}\\
&\quad-N\frac{\rho a\omega^2}{\mu g}\left[\frac{r^4}{14\times 28a^2}\frac{\partial W}{\partial y}+\frac{1}{7\times 18a^2}\left(r^2yW-\frac{r^4}{14}\frac{\partial W}{\partial y}\right)\right.\\
&\qquad+i\frac{\sigma}{\omega}\left\{\frac{r^4}{56a^2}\frac{\partial W'}{\partial y}+\frac{1}{18a^2}\left(r^2yW'-\frac{r^4}{14}\frac{\partial W'}{\partial y}\right)\right\}\\
&\quad+\left(1+\frac{\sigma^2}{\omega^2}\right)\left\{\frac{r^2}{5}\frac{\partial W}{\partial y}-\frac{5r^4}{4\times 28a^2}\frac{\partial W}{\partial y}+\frac{1}{18a^2}\left(r^2yW-\frac{r^4}{14}\frac{\partial W}{\partial y}\right)\right\}\\
&\qquad\left.-2i\frac{\sigma}{\omega}\left\{\frac{r^2}{5}\frac{\partial W}{\partial x}-\frac{5r^4}{4\times 28a^2}\frac{\partial W}{\partial x}+\frac{1}{18a^2}\left(r^2xW-\frac{r^4}{14}\frac{\partial W}{\partial x}\right)\right\}\right]\\
w_1&=\Sigma\left\{\gamma_n+\frac{r^2}{2(2n+1)\mu}\frac{\partial\varpi_n}{\partial z}-\frac{3g\rho r^2}{2(2n+1)^2\mu}\frac{\partial\xi_n}{\partial z}\right\}\\
&\quad-N\frac{\rho a\omega^2}{\mu g}\left[\frac{1}{7\times 18a^2}r^2zW+i\frac{\sigma}{\omega}\frac{1}{18a^2}r^2zW'+\frac{\sigma^2}{\omega^2}\frac{1}{18a^2}r^2zW\right]
\end{aligned}\right\}\ldots(21).$$

74. At this point an apparent difficulty arises because the condition of incompressibility, viz. equation (16) of p. 63, is not satisfied identically, and the left-hand member of this equation does not present itself immediately as a sum of spherical solid harmonics. If, however, we form the expression for

$$\partial u_1/\partial x + \partial v_1/\partial y + \partial w_1/\partial z,$$

we find, after some reduction, the formula

$$\frac{\partial u_1}{\partial x} + \frac{\partial v_1}{\partial y} + \frac{\partial w_1}{\partial z} = \Sigma\left\{\left(\frac{\partial \alpha_n}{\partial x} + \frac{\partial \beta_n}{\partial y} + \frac{\partial \gamma_n}{\partial z}\right) + \frac{n}{(2n+1)\mu}\left(\varpi_n - \frac{3g\rho}{2n+1}\xi_n\right)\right\}$$
$$- N\frac{\rho a \omega^2}{\mu g}\left[\frac{4}{5}\left(1+\frac{\sigma^2}{\omega^2}\right)W + \frac{4}{5}i\frac{\sigma}{\omega}W' - \frac{1}{9a^2}\left(z^2 - \frac{r^2}{7}\right)W\right].$$

Now it is easy to verify that

$$\nabla^2\{(6z^2 - x^2 - y^2)(x^2 - y^2)\} = 0$$

and

$$\nabla^2\{(6z^2 - x^2 - y^2)\,xy\} = 0,$$

and it follows that $(z^2 - \frac{1}{7}r^2)W$ is a spherical solid harmonic, and its degree is 4. Hence the condition of incompressibility becomes a relation connecting a number of spherical solid harmonics of various degrees, viz.:

$$\Sigma\left\{\psi_n + \frac{n}{(2n+1)\mu}\left(\varpi_n - \frac{3g\rho}{2n+1}\xi_n\right)\right\} = N\frac{\rho a \omega^2}{\mu g}\left\{\frac{4}{5}\left(1+\frac{\sigma^2}{\omega^2}\right)W + \frac{4}{5}i\frac{\sigma}{\omega}W' - \frac{1}{9a^2}W''\right\} \quad \text{.. ...(22)},$$

where

$$W'' = (z^2 - \tfrac{1}{7}r^2)\,W \quad \text{.........................(23)}$$

and

$$\psi_{n-1} = \frac{\partial \alpha_n}{\partial x} + \frac{\partial \beta_n}{\partial y} + \frac{\partial \gamma_n}{\partial z} \quad \text{.........................(24)}$$

for all the values of n that occur. Of course the terms of the same degree in the two members of equation (22) can be equated separately. In the right-hand member there are terms of the second and fourth degrees only, and therefore the terms of the left-hand member which are of degrees other than 2 and 4 must vanish.

75. Before proceeding to form the equations which express the condition that the deformed surface is free from traction, we note that another equation connecting the spherical harmonics which have been introduced can be obtained by forming an expression for ζ_1, or $u_1x + v_1y + w_1z$, from the results expressed in equations (21), and equating its value at the surface $r = a$ to the value at the same surface of the expression $a\Sigma\xi_n$, in accordance with (19) of p. 63. The result can be simplified slightly if we first introduce a function ϕ_{-n-2} by the equation

$$\phi_{-n-2} = \frac{\partial}{\partial x}\left(\frac{\alpha_n}{r^{2n+1}}\right) + \frac{\partial}{\partial y}\left(\frac{\beta_n}{r^{2n+1}}\right) + \frac{\partial}{\partial z}\left(\frac{\gamma_n}{r^{2n+1}}\right) \quad \text{..............(25)}.$$

Then ϕ_{-n-2} is a spherical solid harmonic of negative degree $-(n+2)$, and $r^{2n+3}\phi_{-n-2}$ is a spherical solid harmonic of positive degree $(n+1)$, and we have the identity

$$x\alpha_n + y\beta_n + z\gamma_n = \frac{1}{2n+1}\left(r^2\psi_{n-1} - r^{2n+3}\phi_{-n-2}\right) \quad \text{.........(26).}$$

We now find, after slight reduction,

$$\zeta_1 = \Sigma\left\{\frac{r^2}{2n+3}\psi_n - \frac{r^{2n+3}}{2n+1}\phi_{-n-2} + \frac{nr^2}{2(2n+1)\mu}\left(\varpi_n - \frac{3g\rho}{2n+1}\xi_n\right)\right\}$$
$$- N\frac{\rho a\omega^2}{\mu g}\left[\frac{2}{5}\left(1+\frac{\sigma^2}{\omega^2}\right)r^2W + \frac{2}{5}i\frac{\sigma}{\omega}r^2W' - \left(\frac{19}{21}+\frac{\sigma^2}{\omega^2}\right)\frac{r^4W}{24a^2}\right.$$
$$\left. - i\frac{\sigma}{\omega}\frac{r^4W'}{72a^2} - \frac{r^2W''}{18a^2}\right],$$

and thus we obtain the relation

$$\Sigma\left\{\left(a + \frac{3g\rho a^2 n}{2(2n+1)^2\mu}\right)\xi_n - \frac{na^2}{2(2n+1)\mu}\varpi_n - \frac{a^2}{2n+3}\psi_n + \frac{1}{2n+1}r^{2n+3}\phi_{-n-2}\right\}$$
$$= -N\frac{\rho a\omega^2}{\mu g}\left[\left\{\frac{2}{5}\left(1+\frac{\sigma^2}{\omega^2}\right) - \frac{1}{24}\left(\frac{19}{21}+\frac{\sigma^2}{\omega^2}\right)\right\}a^2W\right.$$
$$\left. + \left(\frac{2}{5}-\frac{1}{72}\right)i\frac{\sigma}{\omega}a^2W' - \frac{1}{18}W''\right] \quad \text{.........(27).}$$

76. The condition that the deformed surface is free from traction gives, as in § 68 *supra*, three equations of the type

$$\frac{x}{\mu}\left(g\rho\frac{\zeta_1}{r} - p_1\right) + \frac{\partial\zeta_1}{\partial x} + r\frac{\partial u_1}{\partial r} - u_1 = 0 \quad \text{..................(28),}$$

which hold at the surface $r = a$. Now we have

$$\frac{\partial\zeta_1}{\partial x} = \Sigma\left[\frac{r^2}{2n+3}\frac{\partial\psi_n}{\partial x} + \frac{2r^2}{(2n+1)(2n+3)}\left\{\frac{\partial\psi_n}{\partial x} - r^{2n+1}\frac{\partial}{\partial x}\left(\frac{\psi_n}{r^{2n+1}}\right)\right\}\right.$$
$$- \frac{1}{2n+1}\frac{\partial}{\partial x}\left(r^{2n+3}\phi_{-n-2}\right)$$
$$+ \frac{nr^2}{2(2n+1)\mu}\frac{\partial\varpi_n}{\partial x} + \frac{nr^2}{(2n+1)^2\mu}\left\{\frac{\partial\varpi_n}{\partial x} - r^{2n+1}\frac{\partial}{\partial x}\left(\frac{\varpi_n}{r^{2n+1}}\right)\right\}$$
$$\left. - \frac{3g\rho nr^2}{2(2n+1)^2\mu}\frac{\partial\xi_n}{\partial x} - \frac{3g\rho nr^2}{(2n+1)^3\mu}\left\{\frac{\partial\xi_n}{\partial x} - r^{2n+1}\frac{\partial}{\partial x}\left(\frac{\xi_n}{r^{2n+1}}\right)\right\}\right]$$
$$- N\frac{\rho a\omega^2}{\mu g}\left[\frac{2}{5}\left(1+\frac{\sigma^2}{\omega^2}\right)\left\{r^2\frac{\partial W}{\partial x} + \frac{2r^2}{5}\left(\frac{\partial W}{\partial x} - r^5\frac{\partial}{\partial x}\frac{W}{r^5}\right)\right\}\right.$$
$$- \left(\frac{19}{21}+\frac{\sigma^2}{\omega^2}\right)\frac{1}{24a^2}\left\{r^4\frac{\partial W}{\partial x} + \frac{4r^4}{5}\left(\frac{\partial W}{\partial x} - r^5\frac{\partial}{\partial x}\frac{W}{r^5}\right)\right\}$$
$$+ \frac{2}{5}i\frac{\sigma}{\omega}\left\{r^2\frac{\partial W'}{\partial x} + \frac{2r^2}{5}\left(\frac{\partial W'}{\partial x} - r^5\frac{\partial}{\partial x}\frac{W'}{r^5}\right)\right\}$$

$$-i\frac{\sigma}{\omega}\frac{1}{72a^2}\left\{r^4\frac{\partial W'}{\partial x}+\frac{4r^4}{5}\left(\frac{\partial W'}{\partial x}-r^5\frac{\partial}{\partial x}\frac{W'}{r^5}\right)\right\}$$

$$-\frac{1}{18a^2}\left\{r^2\frac{\partial W''}{\partial x}+\frac{2r^2}{9}\left(\frac{\partial W''}{\partial x}-r^9\frac{\partial}{\partial x}\frac{W''}{r^9}\right)\right\}\Bigg]\quad\ldots\ldots\ldots\ldots(29),$$

in which $x\psi_n$ has been replaced by

$$\frac{r^2}{2n+1}\left\{\frac{\partial\psi_n}{\partial x}-r^{2n+1}\frac{\partial}{\partial x}\left(\frac{\psi_n}{r^{2n+1}}\right)\right\}\quad\ldots\ldots\ldots\ldots(30),$$

and the other expressions of the same kind have been treated in the same way. The corresponding formulae for $\partial\zeta_1/\partial y$ and $\partial\zeta_1/\partial z$ can be written down by cyclical interchange of the letters x, y, z, and $\partial W/\partial z$ and $\partial W'/\partial z$ can be omitted wherever they would naturally occur.

From the results obtained in § 73 we can write down an expression for $r\partial u_1/\partial r - u_1$ by simply multipying each term of u_1 by its degree (as a homogeneous function of x, y, z) diminished by unity, and we can form in the same way expressions for $r\partial v_1/\partial r - v_1$ and $r\partial w_1/\partial r - w_1$. We find, after slight reduction,

$$r\frac{\partial u_1}{\partial r}-u_1=\Sigma\left\{(n-1)\,\alpha_n+\frac{nr^2}{2(2n+1)\mu}\frac{\partial}{\partial x}\left(\varpi_n-\frac{3g\rho}{2n+1}\xi_n\right)\right\}$$
$$-N\frac{\rho a\omega^2}{\mu g}\Bigg[\frac{r^4}{14\times 9a^2}\frac{\partial W}{\partial x}+\left(1+\frac{\sigma^2}{\omega^2}\right)\left(\frac{2r^2}{5}-\frac{7r^4}{36a^2}\right)\frac{\partial W}{\partial x}$$
$$+\frac{2}{9}\left\{\frac{1}{7}+\left(1+\frac{\sigma^2}{\omega^2}\right)\right\}\frac{r^4}{5a^2}\left(\frac{\partial W}{\partial x}-r^5\frac{\partial}{\partial x}\frac{W}{r^5}\right)$$
$$+i\frac{\sigma}{\omega}\left\{\frac{r^4}{18a^2}\frac{\partial W'}{\partial x}+\frac{2r^4}{45a^2}\left(\frac{\partial W'}{\partial x}-r^5\frac{\partial}{\partial x}\frac{W'}{r^5}\right)\right\}$$
$$+2i\frac{\sigma}{\omega}\left\{\left(\frac{2r^2}{5}-\frac{7r^4}{36a^2}\right)\frac{\partial W}{\partial y}+\frac{2r^4}{45a^2}\left(\frac{\partial W}{\partial y}-r^5\frac{\partial}{\partial y}\frac{W}{r^5}\right)\right\}\Bigg]\quad\ldots\ldots(31),$$

$$r\frac{\partial v_1}{\partial r}-v_1=\Sigma\left\{(n-1)\,\beta_n+\frac{nr^2}{2(2n+1)\mu}\frac{\partial}{\partial y}\left(\varpi_n-\frac{3g\rho}{2n+1}\xi_n\right)\right\}$$
$$-N\frac{\rho a\omega^2}{\mu g}\Bigg[\frac{r^4}{14\times 9a^2}\frac{\partial W}{\partial y}+\left(1+\frac{\sigma^2}{\omega^2}\right)\left(\frac{2r^2}{5}-\frac{7r^4}{36a^2}\right)\frac{\partial W}{\partial y}$$
$$+\frac{2}{9}\left\{\frac{1}{7}+\left(1+\frac{\sigma^2}{\omega^2}\right)\right\}\frac{r^4}{5a^2}\left(\frac{\partial W}{\partial y}-r^5\frac{\partial}{\partial y}\frac{W}{r^5}\right)$$
$$+i\frac{\sigma}{\omega}\left\{\frac{r^4}{18a^2}\frac{\partial W'}{\partial y}+\frac{2r^4}{45a^2}\left(\frac{\partial W'}{\partial y}-r^5\frac{\partial}{\partial y}\frac{W'}{r^5}\right)\right\}$$
$$-2i\frac{\sigma}{\omega}\left\{\left(\frac{2r^2}{5}-\frac{7r^4}{36a^2}\right)\frac{\partial W}{\partial x}+\frac{2r^4}{45a^2}\left(\frac{\partial W}{\partial x}-r^5\frac{\partial}{\partial x}\frac{W}{r^5}\right)\right\}\Bigg]\quad\ldots\ldots(32),$$

$$r\frac{\partial w_1}{\partial r}-w_1=\Sigma\left\{(n-1)\,\gamma_n+\frac{nr^2}{2(2n+1)\mu}\frac{\partial}{\partial z}\left(\varpi_n-\frac{3g\rho}{2n+1}\xi_n\right)\right\}$$
$$+N\frac{\rho a\omega^2}{\mu g}\left[\left(\frac{2}{63}+\frac{2\sigma^2}{9\omega^2}\right)\frac{r^9}{5a^2}\frac{\partial}{\partial z}\frac{W}{r^5}+i\frac{\sigma}{\omega}\frac{2r^9}{45a^2}\frac{\partial}{\partial z}\frac{W'}{r^5}\right]\quad\ldots\ldots\ldots(33).$$

Further we can write down the formula

$$-\frac{xp_1}{\mu} = -\Sigma\left\{\frac{r^2}{(2n+1)\mu}\left(\frac{\partial \varpi_n}{\partial x} - r^{2n+1}\frac{\partial}{\partial x}\frac{\varpi_n}{r^{2n+1}}\right)\right\}$$
$$+ N\frac{\rho a\omega^2}{\mu g}\left[\frac{r^4}{70a^2}\left(\frac{\partial W}{\partial x} - r^5\frac{\partial}{\partial x}\frac{W}{r^5}\right) + i\frac{\sigma}{\omega}\frac{r^4}{10a^2}\left(\frac{\partial W'}{\partial x} - r^5\frac{\partial}{\partial x}\frac{W'}{r^5}\right)\right]\text{...(34)},$$

and there are similar formulae for $-yp_1/\mu$ and $-zp_1/\mu$. These can be written down by cyclical interchange of the letters x, y, z, terms containing $\partial W/\partial z$ and $\partial W'/\partial z$ being omitted, as before. Again at the surface $r = a$ we have

$$x\zeta_1 = ax\Sigma\,\xi_n,$$

and $x\xi_n$ can be transformed, for any value of r, in the manner indicated by formula (30). Hence at the surface $r = a$ we have

$$\frac{g\rho}{\mu a}x\zeta_1 = \Sigma\left\{\frac{g\rho a^2}{(2n+1)\mu}\frac{\partial \xi_n}{\partial x} - \frac{g\rho}{(2n+1)\mu}r^{2n+3}\frac{\partial}{\partial x}\frac{\xi_n}{r^{2n+1}}\right\}\text{.......(35).}$$

Expressions for $g\rho y\zeta_1/\mu a$ and $g\rho z\zeta_1/\mu a$ can be formed in the same way, or they can be deduced from the above by cyclical interchange of the letters x, y, z.

77. The first of the three equations of the type (28) of p. 67, or as we shall name it the x-equation, is now to be formed by adding the right-hand members of the equations (29), (31), (34), and (35) and equating the result to zero. In forming the other two equations (the y- and z-equations) we must make the interchanges already indicated and use equation (32) or (33) instead of (31). It is unnecessary to write down the equations. Each of them has the form of a sum of terms equated to zero, and each term of the sum is either a spherical solid harmonic or the product of such a function and a power of r. The equations hold at the surface $r = a$, and therefore the powers of r that occur may be replaced by the like powers of a, and so the equations take the form of sums of spherical solid harmonics equated to zero. If such sums vanish at $r = a$ they vanish for all values of r, and those terms of any such sum which are of the same degree vanish separately. We may therefore pick out from each equation the terms which contain harmonics of the first, second, or any higher degree, and equate them separately to zero. An inspection of the formulae which have been given, including those in equations (22) and (27), shows what degrees can be represented. The functions of the type α that can occur have degrees 1, 3, or 5. The functions of the types ϖ, ξ, ψ that can occur have degrees 2 or 4. The functions of the type ϕ that can occur have degrees -3 and -5. When we pick out the terms that contain harmonics of the first degree the terms of (31), (32), and (33) which contain α_1, β_1, γ_1 explicitly have zero coefficients, and thus these harmonics cannot be determined directly by any of our equations; they can, however, be determined indirectly, if desired, by the values found for the functions ξ_2, ϕ_{-3} and the (zero) value assumed for ψ_0.

We now proceed to pick out from the x-equation, formed by the method described above, those terms which contain spherical solid harmonics of the first degree. We thus obtain the equation

$$\frac{g\rho a^2}{5\mu}\frac{\partial \xi_2}{\partial x}-\frac{a^2}{5\mu}\frac{\partial \varpi_2}{\partial x}+N\frac{\rho a\omega^2}{\mu g}\left(\frac{a^2}{70}\frac{\partial W}{\partial x}+i\frac{\sigma}{\omega}\frac{a^2}{10}\frac{\partial W'}{\partial x}\right)$$

$$+\frac{a^2}{5}\frac{\partial \psi_2}{\partial x}-\frac{1}{3}\frac{\partial}{\partial x}(r^5\phi_{-3})+\frac{7a^2}{25\mu}\left(\frac{\partial \varpi_2}{\partial x}-\frac{3g\rho}{5}\frac{\partial \xi_2}{\partial x}\right)+\frac{a^2}{5\mu}\left(\frac{\partial \varpi_2}{\partial x}-\frac{3g\rho}{5}\frac{\partial \xi_2}{\partial x}\right)$$

$$-N\frac{\rho a\omega^2}{\mu g}\left[\left\{\frac{14}{25}\left(1+\frac{\sigma^2}{\omega^2}\right)-\frac{3}{40}\left(\frac{19}{21}+\frac{\sigma^2}{\omega^2}\right)\right\}a^2\frac{\partial W}{\partial x}\right.$$

$$+i\frac{\sigma}{\omega}\left\{\left(\frac{14}{25}-\frac{1}{40}\right)a^2\frac{\partial W'}{\partial x}\right\}$$

$$\left.+\left\{\frac{1}{70}+\frac{1}{4}\left(1+\frac{\sigma^2}{\omega^2}\right)\right\}a^2\frac{\partial W}{\partial x}+i\frac{\sigma}{\omega}\frac{a^2}{10}\frac{\partial W'}{\partial x}+2i\frac{\sigma}{\omega}\frac{a^2}{4}\frac{\partial W}{\partial y}\right]=0 \quad \text{.........(36).}$$

The equation like the above which comes from the y-equation is obtained by interchanging x and y and changing the sign of the last term in the last bracket; and the corresponding equation that comes from the z-equation is obtained from the above by omitting all the terms that contain W or W' and substituting z for x in the remaining terms. By multiplying the left-hand members of the three equations by x, y, z respectively, adding the results, and omitting a factor $\frac{2}{5}a^2$, we find the equation

$$\psi_2-\frac{5}{3}\frac{r^5}{a^2}\phi_{-3}+\frac{7}{5\mu}\varpi_2-\frac{11g\rho}{25\mu}\xi_2$$

$$=N\frac{\rho a\omega^2}{\mu g}\left[\left(\frac{1039}{280}+\frac{147}{40}\frac{\sigma^2}{\omega^2}\right)W+i\frac{\sigma}{\omega}\frac{157}{40}W'\right] \quad \text{......(37).}$$

Now we go back to the x-equation and pick out all the terms that contain spherical harmonics of the third degree. We get

$$2\alpha_3+\frac{g\rho a^2}{9\mu}\frac{\partial \xi_4}{\partial x}-\frac{g\rho r^7}{5\mu}\frac{\partial}{\partial x}\frac{\xi_2}{r^5}-\frac{a^2}{9\mu}\frac{\partial \varpi_4}{\partial x}+\frac{r^7}{5\mu}\frac{\partial}{\partial x}\frac{\varpi_2}{r^5}$$

$$-N\frac{\rho a\omega^2}{\mu g}\left(\frac{r^7}{70}\frac{\partial}{\partial x}\frac{W}{r^5}+i\frac{\sigma}{\omega}\frac{r^7}{10}\frac{\partial}{\partial x}\frac{W'}{r^5}\right)+\frac{a^2}{9}\frac{\partial \psi_4}{\partial x}-\frac{2r^7}{35}\frac{\partial}{\partial x}\frac{\psi_2}{r^5}-\frac{1}{7}\frac{\partial (r^9\phi_{-5})}{\partial x}$$

$$+\frac{22a^2}{81\mu}\frac{\partial \varpi_4}{\partial x}-\frac{22g\rho a^2}{243\mu}\frac{\partial \xi_4}{\partial x}-\frac{2r^7}{25\mu}\frac{\partial}{\partial x}\frac{\varpi_2}{r^5}+\frac{6g\rho r^7}{125\mu}\frac{\partial}{\partial x}\frac{\xi_2}{r^5}+\frac{2a^2}{9\mu}\frac{\partial \varpi_4}{\partial x}-\frac{2g\rho a^2}{27\mu}\frac{\partial \xi_4}{\partial x}$$

$$-N\frac{\rho a\omega^2}{\mu g}\left[\left\{-\frac{4}{25}\left(1+\frac{\sigma^2}{\omega^2}\right)+\frac{1}{30}\left(\frac{19}{21}+\frac{\sigma^2}{\omega^2}\right)\right\}r^7\frac{\partial}{\partial x}\frac{W}{r^5}-i\frac{\sigma}{\omega}\frac{67}{450}r^7\frac{\partial}{\partial x}\frac{W'}{r^5}\right.$$

$$-\frac{11}{162}\frac{\partial W''}{\partial x}$$

$$\left.-\frac{2}{45}\left(\frac{8}{7}+\frac{\sigma^2}{\omega^2}\right)r^7\frac{\partial}{\partial x}\frac{W}{r^5}-i\frac{\sigma}{\omega}\frac{2}{45}r^7\frac{\partial}{\partial x}\frac{W'}{r^5}-2i\frac{\sigma}{\omega}\frac{2}{45}r^7\frac{\partial}{\partial y}\frac{W}{r^5}\right]=0 \quad \text{...(38).}$$

The corresponding equation which comes from the y-equation is obtained by interchanging x and y and changing the sign of the last term in the last bracket; and the corresponding equation which comes from the z-equation is obtained by substituting z for x in all the terms except those of the last line, and writing for the terms of this line

$$-\frac{2}{45}\left(\frac{1}{7}+\frac{\sigma^2}{\omega^2}\right) r^7 \frac{\partial}{\partial z}\frac{W}{r^5} - i\frac{\sigma}{\omega}\frac{2}{45} r^7 \frac{\partial}{\partial z}\frac{W'}{r^5}.$$

We now operate upon these equations as follows:—First we differentiate the left-hand members with respect to x, y, z in order and add the results. Then we multiply the three equations by x, y, z in order and add the results. The first process yields a relation connecting spherical harmonics of the second degree, and the second process a relation connecting harmonics of the second degree and others of the fourth degree; but the terms of this relation which contain harmonics of the second degree vanish identically in virtue of the relation obtained by the first process. The equation obtained by the first process is

$$\begin{aligned}2\psi_2 - \frac{21}{5}\Big\{&-\frac{g\rho}{\mu}\xi_2 + \frac{\varpi_2}{\mu} - \frac{2}{7}\psi_2 - \frac{2}{5\mu}\varpi_2 + \frac{6g\rho}{25\mu}\xi_2 \\ &+ N\frac{\rho a\omega^2}{\mu g}\left[\frac{21}{5}\left\{\frac{1}{14}W + i\frac{\sigma}{\omega}\frac{1}{2}W' - \frac{4}{5}\left(1+\frac{\sigma^2}{\omega^2}\right)W + \frac{1}{6}\left(\frac{19}{21}+\frac{\sigma^2}{\omega^2}\right)W\right.\right. \\ &\left. - i\frac{\sigma}{\omega}\frac{67}{90}W' - \frac{2}{9}\left(\frac{1}{7}+\frac{\sigma^2}{\omega^2}\right)W - i\frac{\sigma}{\omega}\frac{2}{9}W'\right\} \\ &\left. + i\frac{\sigma}{\omega}\frac{28}{45}W' + \frac{2}{45}\left\{\frac{\partial}{\partial x}\left(r^7\frac{\partial}{\partial x}\frac{W}{r^5}\right) + \frac{\partial}{\partial y}\left(r^7\frac{\partial}{\partial y}\frac{W}{r^5}\right)\right\}\right] = 0 \quad \text{............(39).}\end{aligned}$$

Here $$\frac{\partial}{\partial x}\left(r^7\frac{\partial}{\partial x}\frac{W}{r^5}\right) + \frac{\partial}{\partial y}\left(r^7\frac{\partial}{\partial y}\frac{W}{r^5}\right) = -16W,$$

as is easily verified. After omission of a factor $\frac{1}{5}$, the equation (39) becomes

$$\begin{aligned}16\psi_2 - \frac{63}{5\mu}\varpi_2 + \frac{19\times 21}{25\mu}g\rho\xi_2 \\ = N\frac{\rho a\omega^2}{\mu g}\left[\left(\frac{736}{45}+\frac{539}{30}\frac{\sigma^2}{\omega^2}\right)W + i\frac{\sigma}{\omega}\frac{301}{45}W'\right] \quad \text{.....(40).}\end{aligned}$$

The next step, as was explained, is to multiply the three equations of the type (38) by x, y, z in order and add. We observe that

$$x\alpha_3 + y\beta_3 + z\gamma_3 = \frac{r^2}{7}\psi_2 - \frac{r^9}{7}\phi_{-5},$$

and that $$r^7\left(x\frac{\partial}{\partial x} + y\frac{\partial}{\partial y}\right)\frac{W}{r^5} = -\frac{16}{7}r^2 W + 5W''.$$

Hence all the terms containing spherical harmonics of the second degree are the same as the terms we had just now each multiplied by $\frac{1}{7}r^2$, and, after omitting these terms and omitting also a factor $\frac{4}{9}a^2$, we obtain the equation

$$\psi_4 - \frac{27}{14}\frac{r^9\phi_{-5}}{a^2} + \frac{31}{9\mu}\varpi_4 - \frac{13}{27}\frac{g\rho}{\mu}\xi_4 = -N\frac{\rho a\omega^2}{\mu g}\frac{10}{9}\frac{W''}{a^2} \quad \text{......(41).}$$

Now again we have recourse to the x-equation, and pick out from it all the terms that contain spherical harmonics of the fifth degree. We get

$$4\alpha_5 - \frac{g\rho}{9\mu}r^{11}\frac{\partial}{\partial x}\frac{\xi_4}{r^9} + \frac{r^{11}}{9\mu}\frac{\partial}{\partial x}\frac{\varpi_4}{r^9} - \frac{2r^{11}}{99}\frac{\partial}{\partial x}\frac{\psi_4}{r^9} - \frac{4r^{11}}{81\mu}\frac{\partial}{\partial x}\frac{\varpi_4}{r^9}$$
$$+ \frac{4g\rho r^{11}}{243\mu}\frac{\partial}{\partial x}\frac{\xi_4}{r^9} - N\frac{\rho a\omega^2}{\mu g}\frac{r^{11}}{81a^2}\frac{\partial}{\partial x}\frac{W''}{r^9} = 0 \quad \text{.....(42).}$$

The y- and z- equations yield terms which can be written down by cyclical interchange of the letters α, β, γ and of the letters x, y, z. We differentiate the left-hand members of the three equations in order with respect to x, y, z and add the results, divide by 55/9 and obtain the equation

$$\frac{46}{55}\psi_4 + \frac{23}{27}\frac{g\rho}{\mu}\xi_4 - \frac{5}{9\mu}\varpi_4 = -N\frac{\rho a\omega^2}{\mu g}\frac{W''}{9a^2} \quad \text{...........(43).}$$

If we multiplied the three equations of the type (42) in order by x, y, z and added the results we should not obtain any new equation.

78. From the equations which express the condition that the deformed surface is free from traction we have obtained the four equations (37), (40), (41), (43). Additional equations are to be found by picking out from the equations (22) of p. 66 and (27) of p. 67 the terms that contain spherical harmonics of any of the degrees that occur. We thus find

$$\psi_2 + \frac{2}{5\mu}\varpi_2 - \frac{6g\rho}{25\mu}\xi_2 = N\frac{\rho a\omega^2}{\mu g}\left[\frac{4}{5}\left(1+\frac{\sigma^2}{\omega^2}\right)W + i\frac{\sigma}{\omega}\frac{4}{5}W'\right] \quad \text{...(44),}$$

$$\psi_4 + \frac{4}{9\mu}\varpi_4 - \frac{12g\rho}{81\mu}\xi_4 = -N\frac{\rho a\omega^2}{\mu g}\frac{1}{9a^2}W'' \quad \text{.......................(45)}$$

and

$$\frac{\psi_2}{7} - \frac{r^5\phi_{-3}}{3a^2} + \frac{1}{5\mu}\varpi_2 - \left(1+\frac{3g\rho a}{25\mu}\right)\frac{\xi_2}{a}$$
$$= N\frac{\rho a\omega^2}{\mu g}\left[\left\{\frac{2}{5}\left(1+\frac{\sigma^2}{\omega^2}\right) - \frac{1}{24}\left(\frac{19}{21}+\frac{\sigma^2}{\omega^2}\right)\right\}W + i\frac{\sigma}{\omega}\frac{139}{360}W'\right] \quad \text{.....(46),}$$

$$\frac{\psi_4}{11} - \frac{r^9\phi_{-5}}{7a^2} + \frac{2}{9\mu}\varpi_4 - \left(1+\frac{6g\rho a}{81\mu}\right)\frac{\xi_4}{a} = -N\frac{\rho a\omega^2}{\mu g}\frac{1}{18a^2}W'' \quad \text{..............(47).}$$

79. The unknown harmonics of the second degree ψ_2, $r^5\phi_{-3}$, ϖ_2, ξ_2 are connected by the equations (37), (40), (44), and (46). To find the corresponding correction to the calculated height of earth tides and to the potential of the forces that can act on a horizontal pendulum we require the value of ξ_2. On solving the equations we find a result which can be written

$$\xi_2 = \frac{\dfrac{g\rho a}{\mu} \times \dfrac{a\omega^2}{g}}{1 + \dfrac{19\mu}{2g\rho a}} \times \frac{\left(\dfrac{8255}{36} + \dfrac{2765}{12}\dfrac{\sigma^2}{\omega^2}\right)\dfrac{W}{g} + i\dfrac{\sigma}{\omega}\dfrac{7915}{36}\dfrac{W'}{g}}{665 + 70\dfrac{g\rho a}{\mu}}.$$

The unknown harmonics of the fourth degree ψ_4, $r^9\phi_{-5}$, ϖ_4, ξ_4 are connected by the equations (41), (43), (45), and (47). On solving them we find a result which can be written

$$\xi_4 = -\frac{\dfrac{g\rho a}{\mu} \times \dfrac{a\omega^2}{g}}{1 + \dfrac{19\mu}{2g\rho a}} \times \frac{1}{34 + \dfrac{8g\rho a}{3\mu}} \times \frac{\left(z^2 - \dfrac{1}{7}r^2\right)W}{a^2 g} \quad \text{............(48).}$$

Since $W' = 2iW$, we have $iW' = -2W$, and so the real part of ξ_2, corresponding to the real part of W, can be written down in the form

$$\xi_2 = \frac{\dfrac{g\rho a}{\mu} \times \dfrac{a\omega^2}{g}}{1 + \dfrac{19\mu}{2g\rho a}} \times \frac{\dfrac{8255}{36} - \dfrac{7915}{18}\dfrac{\sigma}{\omega} + \dfrac{2765}{12}\dfrac{\sigma^2}{\omega^2}}{665 + 70\dfrac{g\rho a}{\mu}} \frac{W}{g} \quad \text{............(49).}$$

In equations (48) and (49) W can be regarded as real and given by equation (52) below.

80. The potential of the forces* that act on a horizontal pendulum would be W if the earth were absolutely rigid. If the earth were a homogeneous incompressible elastic solid sphere at rest it would be

$$W + V_0' - (g/a)(\zeta_0)_a, \text{ or } W(1 - N).$$

When the correction for inertia is taken into account it becomes

$$W(1 - N) + 3g\left(\tfrac{1}{5}\xi_2 + \tfrac{1}{9}\xi_4\right) - g\left(\xi_2 + \xi_4\right),$$

or

$$W(1 - N) - g\left(\tfrac{2}{5}\xi_2 + \tfrac{2}{3}\xi_4\right) \quad \text{........................(50).}$$

To see the order of magnitude of ξ_2 we observe that, if the rigidity denoted by μ is that of steel, the number $g\rho a/\mu$ is about 5, also $a\omega^2/g$ is $\frac{1}{289}$. Further σ/ω is nearly 2. It follows that ξ_2 is of the order $\frac{1}{600}W/g$. Hence the term of the above potential which depends upon ξ_2 yields a very small correction to the calculated force acting on the pendulum, and this correction is the same fraction of the force whatever the direction of the force may be. Thus the correction for the height of the earth tide denoted by ξ_2 does not tend to alter the shape of the diagram (p. 55 *ante*) by which the forces are expressed.

* The principal lunar semi-diurnal term alone is considered.

81. To investigate the effect of ξ_4 we write

$$\xi_4 = -Q\frac{(z^2 - \tfrac{1}{7}r^2)\,W}{a^2 g} \quad\text{..........................(51)},$$

$$W = \tau r^2 \sin^2\theta \cos(2\phi + \sigma t)\text{........................(52)}.$$

Hence the potential Ω of the additional forces acting on the pendulum is given by

$$\Omega = \tfrac{2}{3}Q\tau a^2(\cos^2\theta - \tfrac{1}{7})\sin^2\theta\cos(2\phi + \sigma t)\text{...........(53)}.$$

Denote the eastward and southward components of the additional force by X and Y; then

$$X = \frac{1}{a\sin\theta}\frac{\partial\Omega}{\partial\phi}, \qquad Y = \frac{1}{a}\frac{\partial\Omega}{\partial\theta} \quad\text{.................(54)}.$$

Hence
$$\left.\begin{aligned} X &= -\tfrac{4}{3}Q\tau a(\cos^2\theta - \tfrac{1}{7})\sin\theta\sin(2\phi + \sigma t) \\ Y &= \tfrac{4}{3}Q\tau a(\cos^2\theta - \tfrac{1}{7})\sin\theta\cos\theta\cos(2\phi + \sigma t) \\ &\quad - \tfrac{4}{3}Q\tau a\sin^3\theta\cos\theta\cos(2\phi + \sigma t) \end{aligned}\right\} \text{...........(55)}.$$

The forces expressed by X and the first line of Y are, in any latitude, constant multiples of the forces calculated without regard to inertia, and therefore they have no effect in altering the shape of the diagram; but the force expressed by the second line of Y is a force acting north or south and always opposing the direct force of the moon. The effect of it is to make the diagram narrower than it otherwise would be in the north-south direction, without affecting its dimensions in the east-west direction. The occurrence of this term in the expression for the force shows that gyroscopic rigidity has the effect of flattening the diagram in the observed sense. Since, however, Q is of the order $\frac{1}{8000}$, when the rigidity is that of steel, the effect so produced is quite outside the limits of error of the observations.

CHAPTER VI

EFFECT OF THE SPHEROIDAL FIGURE OF THE EARTH ON EARTH TIDES

82. We proceed to investigate the correction for ellipticity. With the notation introduced in § 67 the equations to be satisfied by u_2, ... are three equations of the type

$$\rho\frac{\partial V_2}{\partial x} - \frac{\partial p_2}{\partial x} + \mu\nabla^2 u_2 = 0 \quad \text{..................(1).}$$

We also have the two equations

$$\frac{\partial u_2}{\partial x} + \frac{\partial v_2}{\partial y} + \frac{\partial w_2}{\partial z} = 0 \quad \text{..................(2),}$$

$$\nabla^2 V_2 = 0 \quad \text{..................(3).}$$

From these we find at once $\nabla^2 p_2 = 0$, and therefore we may put

$$p_2 = \Sigma \varpi_n \quad \text{..................(4),}$$

where ϖ_n denotes a spherical solid harmonic of the nth degree.

We shall also write $$V_2 = \Sigma U_n \quad \text{..................(5),}$$

where U_n denotes a spherical solid harmonic of the nth degree.

83. We can now write down the general forms of u_2, v_2, w_2. We have

$$\left.\begin{aligned} u_2 &= \Sigma\left\{\alpha_n + \frac{r^2}{2(2n+1)\mu}\frac{\partial}{\partial x}(\varpi_n - \rho U_n)\right\} \\ v_2 &= \Sigma\left\{\beta_n + \frac{r^2}{2(2n+1)\mu}\frac{\partial}{\partial y}(\varpi_n - \rho U_n)\right\} \\ w_2 &= \Sigma\left\{\gamma_n + \frac{r^2}{2(2n+1)\mu}\frac{\partial}{\partial z}(\varpi_n - \rho U_n)\right\} \end{aligned}\right\} \quad \text{..........(6),}$$

where α_n, β_n, γ_n denote spherical solid harmonics of the nth degree.

We shall use the symbols ψ_n and ϕ_{-n-2} in the same senses as in equations (24) and (25) on p. 66. We have at once from (2)

$$\psi_n = -\frac{n}{(2n+1)\mu}(\varpi_n - \rho U_n) \quad \text{..................(7).}$$

Also we find

$$\zeta_2 = xu_2 + yv_2 + zw_2 = \Sigma \left\{ \frac{r^2}{2n+1} \psi_{n-1} - \frac{r^{2n+3}}{2n+1} \phi_{-n-2} + \frac{nr^2}{2(2n+1)\mu} (\varpi_n - \rho U_n) \right\} \quad \text{...(8)}.$$

It is convenient to write

$$\left(\frac{\zeta_2}{r}\right)_{r=a} = \Sigma \left(\frac{a^n}{r^n} \xi_n\right) \quad \text{.........................(9)},$$

where ξ_n is a spherical solid harmonic of the nth degree. We find, on eliminating $(\varpi_n - \rho U_n)$,

$$a\xi_n = -\frac{(2n+1)a^2}{2(2n+3)} \psi_n - \frac{r^{2n+1}}{2n-1} \phi_{-n-1} \quad \text{..............(10)}.$$

The equation (10) holds for all the values of n that occur.

84. The problem immediately before us is that of forming the boundary conditions by which the unknown harmonics such as ξ_n are to be determined. We shall take the equation of the undisturbed surface to be

$$r = a\left(1 - \frac{2}{3}\epsilon \frac{2z^2 - x^2 - y^2}{2a^2}\right),$$

or

$$r = a + \frac{\epsilon}{3} \frac{x^2 + y^2 - 2z^2}{a} \quad \text{.......................(11)}.$$

This form affords a sufficient approximation. The direction cosines l, m, n of the normal to this surface are given with sufficient approximation by the formulae

$$\left.\begin{aligned} l &= \frac{x}{a}\left\{1 + \frac{\epsilon(x^2 + y^2 - 2z^2)}{3a^2} - \frac{2\epsilon}{3}\right\} \\ m &= \frac{y}{a}\left\{1 + \frac{\epsilon(x^2 + y^2 - 2z^2)}{3a^2} - \frac{2\epsilon}{3}\right\} \\ n &= \frac{z}{a}\left\{1 + \frac{\epsilon(x^2 + y^2 - 2z^2)}{3a^2} + \frac{4\epsilon}{3}\right\} \end{aligned}\right\} \quad \text{................(12)}.$$

It is worth noting that these formulae give

$$lx + my + nz = a\left(1 + \epsilon \frac{x^2 + y^2 - 2z^2}{3a^2}\right) \quad \text{..............(13)}.$$

We note also that $$\frac{r^2}{a^2} = 1 + 2\epsilon \frac{x^2 + y^2 - 2z^2}{3a^2} \quad \text{.......................(14)}.$$

All these formulae are correct to the first power of the ellipticity ϵ.

85. The first boundary condition is the surface characteristic equation for the potential. The potential at any point within the undisturbed surface can be expressed as the sum of three terms

$$V_0 + V_0' + \Sigma U_n,$$

where V_0 denotes the potential of the undisturbed spheroid, V_0' the potential of the inequalities determined by the first approximation, and ΣU_n the expression already introduced for V_2. The value of V_0' was given in § 69. The corresponding expression for the external potential may be written

$$(V_0)_0 + (V_0')_0 + \Sigma U_n \frac{a^{2n+1}}{r^{2n+1}},$$

where $(V_0)_0$ is the potential of the undisturbed spheroid at external points, and $(V_0')_0$ is a function which (1) can be expressed as a sum of spherical solid harmonics of negative degrees, and (2) is equal to V_0' at the surface of the spheroid. Since V_0 and its normal derivative are continuous with $(V_0)_0$ and its normal derivative at the surface of the spheroid, it does not enter into the characteristic equation in question.

Also, since V_0' is a spherical solid harmonic of the second degree, and is independent of z, it may be shown without difficulty that

$$(V_0')_0 = \left(1 + \frac{20}{21}\epsilon\right)\frac{a^5}{r^5} V_0' - 5\epsilon \frac{a^9}{r^9}\frac{z^2 - \frac{1}{7}r^2}{a^2} V_0' \quad \text{..........(15)},$$

for this is a sum of spherical solid harmonics of negative degrees, and, if $\epsilon^2 V_0'$ is neglected, it is equal to V_0' when r/a is given by equation (11).

The surface characteristic equation for the potential can now be written

$$\left(l\frac{\partial}{\partial x} + m\frac{\partial}{\partial y} + n\frac{\partial}{\partial z}\right)\left[\left\{\left(1 + \frac{20}{21}\epsilon\right)\frac{a^5}{r^5} V_0' - 5\epsilon\frac{a^9}{r^9}\frac{z^2 - \frac{1}{7}r^2}{a^2} V_0' + \Sigma U_n \frac{a^{2n+1}}{r^{2n+1}}\right\} - (V_0' + \Sigma U_n)\right] = -4\pi\gamma\rho\,(lu + mv + nw) \text{...(16)},$$

where u, ... are written for $u_0 + u_2$, ... We have to express this equation as an approximate equation in which terms of order ϵu_0 are retained, but terms of the orders $\epsilon^2 u_0$ and ϵu_2 are neglected. The equation holds at the surface of the undisturbed spheroid. We may re-write it in the form

$$\left(l\frac{\partial}{\partial x} + m\frac{\partial}{\partial y} + n\frac{\partial}{\partial z}\right)\left(V_0'\frac{a^5}{r^5} - V_0'\right) + \frac{\partial}{\partial r}\left(\frac{20}{21}\epsilon V_0' \frac{a^5}{r^5} - 5\epsilon\frac{a^9}{r^9}\frac{z^2 - \frac{1}{7}r^2}{a^2} V_0'\right) - \Sigma(2n+1)\frac{a^{n-1}}{r^n} U_n = -4\pi\gamma\rho\left\{(lu_0 + mv_0 + nw_0) + \Sigma\frac{a^n}{r^n}\xi_n\right\} \text{...(17)}.$$

Now we find, after slight reduction,

$$\left(l\frac{\partial}{\partial x} + m\frac{\partial}{\partial y} + n\frac{\partial}{\partial z}\right)\left(V_0'\frac{a^5}{r^5} - V_0'\right) = -5\left(1 - 4\epsilon\frac{x^2 + y^2 - 2z^2}{3a^2}\right)\frac{V_0'}{a} \text{...(18)}.$$

Also we have $$V_0' = \tfrac{3}{2} N W,$$

and we find, from the values given for u_0, ... in § 69,

$$lu_0 + mv_0 + nw_0 = N\left(\frac{5}{2} - \epsilon - \frac{5}{6}\epsilon\frac{x^2 + y^2 - 2z^2}{a^2}\right)\frac{W}{g} \text{.........(19)},$$

where g is written for $\frac{4}{3}\pi\gamma\rho a$, as before. In obtaining this expression some reductions have been made, and terms of the order $\epsilon^2 W/g$ have been neglected.

On substituting these results in equation (17) we find that the terms containing W, and not containing ϵ, cancel, as they should, and we obtain an equation which can be written

$$\Sigma\left(g\xi_n - \frac{2n+1}{3}U_n\right) = N\epsilon\left(W - 5\frac{W''}{a^2}\right) \quad\text{..............(20)},$$

where W'' stands, as before, for the spherical harmonic of the fourth degree

$$(z^2 - \tfrac{1}{7}r^2)\,W.$$

86. We have next to form, correctly to the same order of approximation, the equations which express the condition that the deformed surface is free from traction. In the previous problem we could take p_0 and V_0 to be the pressure and potential in a homogeneous fluid *sphere* at rest under its own gravitation. It will now be necessary to take p_0 and V_0 to be the pressure and potential in a homogeneous fluid *spheroid* rotating steadily under its own gravitation; but it will be sufficient to use values for them which are correct to the first order in ϵ. These values can be written down, as follows:

$$V_0 = \frac{g}{2a}(3a^2 - r^2) + \frac{g\epsilon}{5a}(x^2 + y^2 - 2z^2) \quad\text{..............................(21)},$$

$$p_0 = \frac{g\rho}{a}\left\{\frac{1}{2}(a^2 - r^2) - \frac{4}{15}\epsilon(a^2 - r^2) + \frac{\epsilon}{3}(x^2 + y^2 - 2z^2)\right\} \quad\text{......(22)}.$$

In obtaining these formulae we utilize the relation

$$\omega^2 = \frac{16}{15}\pi\gamma\rho\epsilon = \frac{4g\epsilon}{5a}.$$

It is easily verified that, if ϵ^2 is neglected, these formulae satisfy equations (1) of p. 58, and that p_0 vanishes at the surface of the undisturbed spheroid.

87. Now let l', m', n' denote the direction cosines of the normal to the deformed surface. The equations which express the condition that this surface is free from traction are three equations of the type

$$-l'(p_0 + p_0' + p_2) + \mu\left\{\left(l'\frac{\partial u}{\partial x} + m'\frac{\partial u}{\partial y} + n'\frac{\partial u}{\partial z}\right) + \left(l'\frac{\partial u}{\partial x} + m'\frac{\partial v}{\partial x} + n'\frac{\partial w}{\partial x}\right)\right\} = 0 \quad\text{.........(23)}.$$

Here $u, \ldots$ stand for $u_0 + u_2, \ldots$. This will be called the x-equation. Just as on p. 61, p_0 vanishes at the undisturbed surface, and its value at the disturbed surface is expressed with sufficient approximation by the formula

$$(lu + mv + nw)\left(l\frac{\partial p_0}{\partial x} + m\frac{\partial p_0}{\partial y} + n\frac{\partial p_0}{\partial z}\right) \quad\text{..............(24)},$$

and we may therefore ignore the distinction between $l, \ldots$ and $l', \ldots$ in all the terms of equation (23). In evaluating lp_0' we must use the value of l given in equations (12); in evaluating lp_2 we may replace l by x/a. Similar simplifications may be made in the remaining terms of equation (23). We have to proceed by retaining terms of order ϵu_0, but neglecting terms of orders ϵu_2, $u_0 u_2$, and u_0^2. From the value of p_0 given in (22) we can obtain the equation

$$l\frac{\partial p_0}{\partial x} + m\frac{\partial p_0}{\partial y} + n\frac{\partial p_0}{\partial z} = -g\rho\left(1 - \frac{8}{15}\epsilon - \epsilon\frac{x^2+y^2-2z^2}{3a^2}\right) \text{......(25)},$$

and then the formula (24) can be replaced by

$$N\rho W\left(-\frac{5}{2} + \frac{7}{3}\epsilon + \frac{5}{3}\epsilon\frac{x^2+y^2-2z^2}{a^2}\right) - g\rho\frac{\zeta_2}{a} \text{ ....(26).}$$

In obtaining this we have used the result found in equation (19). Hence the first term $-l'p_0$ in the x-equation (23) is given by the equation

$$-l'p_0 = N\rho W\frac{x}{a}\left(\frac{5}{2} - 4\epsilon - \frac{5}{6}\epsilon\frac{x^2+y^2-2z^2}{a^2}\right) + g\rho\frac{x}{a}\Sigma\xi_n \text{......(27).}$$

The corresponding term of the y-equation is found by interchanging x and y in (27); but the corresponding term of the z-equation will be found by the same process to be given by the equation

$$-n'p_0 = N\rho W\frac{z}{a}\left(\frac{5}{2} + \epsilon - \frac{5}{6}\epsilon\frac{x^2+y^2-2z^2}{a^2}\right) + g\rho\frac{z}{a}\Sigma\xi_n \text{ ...(28).}$$

Again, the second term $-l'p_0'$ of the x-equation (23) is given by

$$-l'p_0' = -N\rho W\frac{x}{a}\left(\frac{5}{2} - \frac{\mu}{g\rho a}\right)\left(1 - \frac{2}{3}\epsilon + \epsilon\frac{x^2+y^2-2z^2}{3a^2}\right) \text{......(29).}$$

The second term of the y-equation is found from this by interchanging x and y. The corresponding term of the z-equation is given by

$$-n'p_0' = -N\rho W\frac{z}{a}\left(\frac{5}{2} - \frac{\mu}{g\rho a}\right)\left(1 + \frac{4}{3}\epsilon + \epsilon\frac{x^2+y^2-2z^2}{3a^2}\right) \text{ ...(30).}$$

The terms of the type $-l'p_2$ can all be written in such forms as

$$-l'p_2 = -\frac{x}{a}\Sigma\varpi_n \text{ ....(31)}$$

by cyclical interchange of the letters x, y, z.

88. The terms of the x-equation (23) which contain μ as a factor can be written

$$\mu\left(l\frac{\partial u}{\partial x} + m\frac{\partial u}{\partial y} + n\frac{\partial u}{\partial z} + l\frac{\partial u}{\partial x} + m\frac{\partial v}{\partial x} + n\frac{\partial w}{\partial x}\right),$$

and this is the same as

$$\mu\left[\left(1 - \frac{2}{3}\epsilon + \epsilon\frac{x^2+y^2-2z^2}{3a^2}\right)\left(\frac{x}{a}\frac{\partial u_0}{\partial x} + \frac{y}{a}\frac{\partial u_0}{\partial y} + \frac{z}{a}\frac{\partial u_0}{\partial z} + \frac{x}{a}\frac{\partial u_0}{\partial x} + \frac{y}{a}\frac{\partial v_0}{\partial x} + \frac{z}{a}\frac{\partial w_0}{\partial x}\right)\right.$$
$$\left. + 2\epsilon\frac{z}{a}\left(\frac{\partial u_0}{\partial z} + \frac{\partial w_0}{\partial x}\right) + \frac{1}{a}\left(\frac{\partial \zeta_2}{\partial x} + r\frac{\partial u_2}{\partial r} - u_2\right)\right] \text{...(32).}$$

But we find from the expressions for u_0, ... given in § 69

$$\left(\frac{x}{a}\frac{\partial u_0}{\partial x}+\dots\right)=\frac{N}{g}\left\{-\frac{x}{a^2}W+4\left(1-\frac{r^2}{a^2}\right)\frac{\partial W}{\partial x}\right\}$$

$$=-\frac{N}{g}\left(\frac{x}{a^2}W+8\epsilon\frac{x^2+y^2-2z^2}{3a^2}\frac{\partial W}{\partial x}\right) \quad \text{.........(33)},$$

and we also find

$$\frac{\partial u_0}{\partial z}+\frac{\partial w_0}{\partial x}=-\frac{3}{2}\frac{N}{g}\frac{z}{a}\frac{\partial W}{\partial x} \quad \text{.........(34)},$$

W being independent of z. Further we have

$$\frac{\partial \zeta_2}{\partial x}=\Sigma\left[\frac{r^2}{2n+3}\frac{\partial \psi_n}{\partial x}+\frac{2r^2}{(2n+1)(2n+3)}\left\{\frac{\partial \psi_n}{\partial x}-r^{2n+1}\frac{\partial}{\partial x}\frac{\psi_n}{r^{2n+1}}\right\}\right.$$

$$-\frac{1}{2n+1}\frac{\partial}{\partial x}(r^{2n+3}\phi_{-n-2})+\frac{nr^2}{2(2n+1)\mu}\frac{\partial}{\partial x}(\varpi_n-\rho U_n)$$

$$\left.+\frac{nr^2}{(2n+1)^2\mu}\left\{\left(\frac{\partial \varpi_n}{\partial x}-\rho\frac{\partial U_n}{\partial x}\right)-r^{2n+1}\frac{\partial}{\partial x}\frac{\varpi_n-\rho U_n}{r^{2n+1}}\right\}\right]$$

and

$$r\frac{\partial u_2}{\partial r}-u_2=\Sigma\left[(n-1)\alpha_n+\frac{nr^2}{2(2n+1)\mu}\frac{\partial(\varpi_n-\rho U_n)}{\partial x}\right],$$

so that we have

$$\frac{\partial \zeta_2}{\partial x}+r\frac{\partial u_2}{\partial r}-u_2$$

$$=\Sigma\left[(n-1)\alpha_n+\frac{r^2}{2n+1}\frac{\partial \psi_n}{\partial x}-\frac{2r^{2n+3}}{(2n+1)(2n+3)}\frac{\partial}{\partial x}\frac{\psi_n}{r^{2n+1}}-\frac{1}{2n+1}\frac{\partial}{\partial x}(r^{2n+3}\phi_{-n-2})\right.$$

$$\left.+\frac{2n(n+1)r^2}{(2n+1)^2\mu}\frac{\partial(\varpi_n-\rho U_n)}{\partial x}-\frac{nr^{2n+3}}{(2n+1)^2\mu}\frac{\partial}{\partial x}\frac{\varpi_n-\rho U_n}{r^{2n+1}}\right] \quad \text{...(35)}.$$

The other expressions of this type can be written down by cyclical interchange of the letters α, β, γ and x, y, z. In particular, the corresponding terms of the z-equation can be written down in this way. We have still to express the terms

$$\mu\left(l\frac{\partial w_0}{\partial x}+m\frac{\partial w_0}{\partial y}+n\frac{\partial w_0}{\partial z}+l\frac{\partial u_0}{\partial z}+m\frac{\partial v_0}{\partial z}+n\frac{\partial w_0}{\partial z}\right),$$

which occur in the z-equation. The coefficient of μ in this expression is

$$\left(1-\frac{2}{3}\epsilon+\epsilon\frac{x^2+y^2-2z^2}{3a^2}\right)\left(\frac{x}{a}\frac{\partial w_0}{\partial x}+\frac{y}{a}\frac{\partial w_0}{\partial y}+\frac{z}{a}\frac{\partial w_0}{\partial z}+\frac{x}{a}\frac{\partial u_0}{\partial z}+\frac{y}{a}\frac{\partial v_0}{\partial z}+\frac{z}{a}\frac{\partial w_0}{\partial z}\right)$$

$$+4\epsilon\frac{z}{a}\frac{\partial w_0}{\partial z} \quad \text{...(36)},$$

and we find

$$\left(\frac{x}{a}\frac{\partial w_0}{\partial x}+\dots\right)=-\frac{N}{g}\frac{z}{a^2}W \quad \text{.........(37)},$$

and

$$\frac{\partial w_0}{\partial z}=\frac{N}{g}\frac{W}{a} \quad \text{.........(38)},$$

W being independent of z.

89. To form the boundary conditions of the type now under discussion we have only to collect the terms. We shall write down the x-equation and the z-equation. The x-equation is

$$N\rho W \frac{x}{a}\left(\frac{5}{2} - 4\epsilon - \frac{5}{6}\epsilon\frac{x^2+y^2-2z^2}{a^2}\right) + g\rho\frac{x}{a}\Sigma\xi_n$$

$$-N\rho W\frac{x}{a}\left(\frac{5}{2}-\frac{\mu}{g\rho a}\right)\left(1-\frac{2}{3}\epsilon+\frac{\epsilon}{3}\frac{x^2+y^2-2z^2}{a^2}\right) - \frac{x}{a}\Sigma\varpi_n$$

$$-N\frac{\mu}{g}\left\{\frac{x}{a^2}W\left(1-\frac{2}{3}\epsilon+\frac{\epsilon}{3}\frac{x^2+y^2-2z^2}{a^2}\right)+\frac{8}{3}\epsilon\frac{x^2+y^2-2z^2}{a^2}\frac{\partial W}{\partial x}+3\epsilon\frac{z^2}{a^2}\frac{\partial W}{\partial x}\right\}$$

$$+\Sigma\left[(n-1)\alpha_n + \frac{r^2}{2n+1}\frac{\partial\psi_n}{\partial x} - \frac{2r^{2n+3}}{(2n+1)(2n+3)}\frac{\partial}{\partial x}\frac{\psi_n}{r^{2n+1}}\right.$$

$$-\frac{1}{2n+1}\frac{\partial}{\partial x}(r^{2n+3}\phi_{-n-2})$$

$$\left.+\frac{2n(n+1)r^2}{(2n+1)^2\mu}\frac{\partial(\varpi_n-\rho U_n)}{\partial x} - \frac{nr^{2n+3}}{(2n+1)^2\mu}\frac{\partial}{\partial x}\frac{\varpi_n-\rho U_n}{r^{2n+1}}\right]=0 \quad\text{............(39)},$$

and the z-equation is

$$N\rho W\frac{z}{a}\left(\frac{5}{2}+\epsilon-\frac{5}{6}\epsilon\frac{x^2+y^2-2z^2}{a^2}\right)+g\rho\frac{z}{a}\Sigma\xi_n$$

$$-N\rho W\frac{z}{a}\left(\frac{5}{2}-\frac{\mu}{g\rho a}\right)\left(1+\frac{4}{3}\epsilon+\frac{\epsilon}{3}\frac{x^2+y^2-2z^2}{a^2}\right)-\frac{z}{a}\Sigma\varpi_n$$

$$-N\frac{\mu}{g}W\frac{z}{a^2}\left(1-\frac{14}{3}\epsilon+\frac{\epsilon}{3}\frac{x^2+y^2-2z^2}{a^2}\right)$$

$$+\Sigma\left[(n-1)\gamma_n+\frac{r^2}{2n+1}\frac{\partial\psi_n}{\partial z}-\frac{2r^{2n+3}}{(2n+1)(2n+3)}\frac{\partial}{\partial z}\frac{\psi_n}{r^{2n+1}}\right.$$

$$-\frac{1}{2n+1}\frac{\partial}{\partial z}(r^{2n+3}\phi_{-n-2})$$

$$\left.+\frac{2n(n+1)r^2}{(2n+1)^2\mu}\frac{\partial(\varpi_n-\rho U_n)}{\partial z}-\frac{nr^{2n+3}}{(2n+1)^2\mu}\frac{\partial}{\partial z}\frac{\varpi_n-\rho U_n}{r^{2n+1}}\right]=0\quad\text{...............(40)}.$$

The terms of these equations which contain W and are independent of ϵ cancel, as they should; the remaining terms are either of the order ξ_n or of the order $\epsilon W/g$, and therefore the equations may be taken to hold at the spherical surface $r=a$, instead of the undisturbed spheroidal surface.

90. The terms of the x-equation which contain W are

$$-N\rho\frac{x}{a}W\left(\frac{7}{3}\epsilon+\frac{5}{3}\epsilon\frac{x^2+y^2-2z^2}{a^2}\right)-N\frac{\mu}{g}\left(\frac{3z^2}{a^2}+\frac{8}{3}\frac{x^2+y^2-2z^2}{a^2}\right)\epsilon\frac{\partial W}{\partial x},$$

and those of the z-equation are

$$-N\rho\frac{z}{a}W\left(\frac{7}{3}\epsilon+\frac{5}{3}\epsilon\frac{x^2+y^2-2z^2}{a^2}\right)+N\frac{\mu}{g}6\epsilon\frac{z}{a^2}W.$$

Now W, $(z^2-\frac{1}{7}r^2)\,W$, zW and $(z^2-\frac{1}{5}r^2)(\partial W/\partial x)$ are spherical harmonics of degrees 2, 4, 3, 3 respectively, W being independent of z. Also we have

$$\tfrac{8}{3}(x^2+y^2-2z^2)+3z^2=\tfrac{5}{3}r^2+(r^2-5z^2) \quad \text{..............(41)},$$

and

$$x^2+y^2-2z^2=\tfrac{4}{7}r^2-3\,(z^2-\tfrac{1}{7}r^2) \quad \text{....................(42)}.$$

Hence, by putting $r=a$ where necessary, we reduce the terms of the x-equation which contain W to

$$-N\rho\epsilon\frac{x}{a}\left(\frac{23}{7}W-5\frac{W''}{a^2}\right)-N\frac{\mu}{g}\epsilon\left\{\frac{5}{3}\frac{\partial W}{\partial x}+\frac{r^2-5z^2}{a^2}\frac{\partial W}{\partial x}\right\},$$

where W'' stands, as before, for $(z^2-\frac{1}{7}r^2)\,W$; and we also reduce the terms of the z-equation which contain W to

$$-N\rho\epsilon\frac{z}{a}\left(\frac{23}{7}W-5\frac{W''}{a^2}\right)+N\frac{\mu}{g}6\epsilon\frac{z}{a^2}W.$$

91. On transforming all the terms such as $x\varpi_n$, in the usual way, and substituting from equation (7) of p. 75 for $\varpi_n-\rho U_n$, we find that the x-equation takes the form

$$\frac{1}{a}\Sigma\left[\frac{a^2}{2n+1}\frac{\partial}{\partial x}(g\rho\xi_n-\varpi_n)-\frac{r^{2n+3}}{2n+1}\frac{\partial}{\partial x}\frac{g\rho\xi_n-\varpi_n}{r^{2n+1}}\right]$$
$$+\frac{\mu}{a}\Sigma\left[(n-1)\,\alpha_n-a^2\frac{\partial\psi_n}{\partial x}+\frac{r^{2n+3}}{2n+3}\frac{\partial}{\partial x}\frac{\psi_n}{r^{2n+1}}-\frac{1}{2n+1}\frac{\partial}{\partial x}(r^{2n+3}\phi_{-n-2})\right]$$
$$-N\frac{\rho}{a}\epsilon\left[\frac{23}{7}\left(\frac{a^2}{5}\frac{\partial W}{\partial x}-\frac{r^7}{5}\frac{\partial}{\partial x}\frac{W}{r^5}\right)-\frac{5}{9}\left(\frac{\partial W''}{\partial x}-\frac{r^{11}}{a^2}\frac{\partial}{\partial x}\frac{W''}{r^9}\right)\right]$$
$$-N\frac{\mu}{g}\epsilon\left(\frac{5}{3}\frac{\partial W}{\partial x}+\frac{r^2-5z^2}{a^2}\frac{\partial W}{\partial x}\right)=0 \quad \text{..(43)}.$$

The y-equation can be written down by putting β for α and y for x; and the first three lines of the z-equation can be written down in the same way by putting γ for α and z for x, but the last line of the left-hand member of the z-equation is

$$+N\frac{\mu}{g}\epsilon\,.\,6\frac{z}{a^2}W \quad \text{........................(44)}.$$

This statement implies the occurrence of certain terms containing $\partial W/\partial z$. These terms vanish identically, and it makes no difference whether we suppose them to occur or not.

The left-hand members of these equations are sums of terms each of which is a spherical solid harmonic of some positive integral degree, and the sum vanishes at $r=a$, and therefore vanishes for all values of r. It follows that the sum of all the terms of any one degree vanishes. Just as in the problem of Chapter V we see that the harmonics of the type α_n are of the first, third, and fifth degrees, those of the types ξ_n, ϖ_n, ψ_n are of the second and fourth degrees, and those of the type ϕ are of degrees -3 and -5.

92. On picking out from the x-equation all the terms which contain spherical harmonics of the first degree, we find

$$\frac{1}{a}\left[\frac{a^2}{5}\frac{\partial}{\partial x}(g\rho\xi_2-\varpi_2)-\mu a^2\frac{\partial\psi_2}{\partial x}-\frac{\mu}{3}\frac{\partial}{\partial x}(r^5\phi_{-3})\right]=N\left(\frac{23}{35}\rho a+\frac{5\mu}{3g}\right)\epsilon\frac{\partial W}{\partial x}.$$

The y- and z-equations yield precisely similar results, W being independent of z. Hence we find the equation

$$g\rho\xi_2-\varpi_2-5\mu\psi_2-\frac{5}{3}\mu\frac{r^5\phi_{-3}}{a^2}=N\left(\frac{23}{7}\rho+\frac{25}{3}\frac{\mu}{ga}\right)\epsilon W \quad\text{......(45).}$$

93. Now we go back to the x-equation, and pick out all the terms which contain spherical harmonics of the third degree. We find

$$\frac{1}{a}\left[\frac{a^2}{7}\frac{\partial}{\partial x}(g\rho\xi_4-\varpi_4)-\frac{r^7}{5}\frac{\partial}{\partial x}\frac{g\rho\xi_2-\varpi_2}{r^5}\right]$$
$$+\frac{\mu}{a}\left[2\alpha_3-a^2\frac{\partial\psi_4}{\partial x}+\frac{r^7}{7}\frac{\partial}{\partial x}\frac{\psi_2}{r^5}-\frac{1}{7}\frac{\partial}{\partial x}(r^9\phi_{-5})\right]$$
$$+N\frac{\rho}{a}\epsilon\left(\frac{23}{35}r^7\frac{\partial}{\partial x}\frac{W}{r^5}+\frac{5}{9}\frac{\partial W''}{\partial x}\right)-N\frac{\mu}{g}\epsilon\frac{r^2-5z^2}{a^2}\frac{\partial W}{\partial x}=0 \quad\text{............(46).}$$

The y-equation yields a similar result, but the last term of the z-equation is

$$+N\frac{\mu}{g}.6\epsilon\frac{z}{a^2}W.$$

We differentiate the left-hand members of the three equations of the type (46) with respect to x, y, z in order, and add the results, and thus find the equation

$$g\rho\xi_2-\varpi_2-\frac{5}{21}\mu\psi_2=N\left(\frac{23}{7}\rho-\frac{10}{21}\frac{\mu}{ga}\right)\epsilon W \quad\text{..............(47).}$$

Again, we multiply the left-hand members of the three equations of type (46) by x, y, z in order, and add the results, and thus find the equation

$$g\rho\xi_4-\varpi_4-7\mu\psi_4-\frac{3}{2}\mu\frac{r^9\phi_{-5}}{a^2}=-N\left(\frac{35}{9}\rho+28\frac{\mu}{ga}\right)\epsilon\frac{W''}{a^2} \quad\text{...(48).}$$

In obtaining this equation we have taken account of the relation

$$x\alpha_3+y\beta_3+z\gamma_3=\frac{1}{7}(r^2\psi_2-r^9\phi_{-5}).$$

We have also noted that the last terms of the three equations give

$$-N\frac{\mu}{g}\epsilon W\left(\frac{2r^2-10z^2}{a^2}-\frac{6z^2}{a^2}\right),$$

which is the same as $\quad N\dfrac{\mu}{g}\epsilon\left(\dfrac{2}{7}\dfrac{r^2}{a^2}W+16\dfrac{W''}{a^2}\right),$

so that, on putting $r=a$ where necessary, we find that the terms of the resulting equation which contain spherical harmonics of the second degree are the same, except for a common factor, as those which occurred in the equation found by differentiating.

94. We now go back to the x-equation and pick out from it all the terms which contain spherical harmonics of the fifth degree. We find

$$\frac{\mu}{a}\left[4\alpha_5+\frac{r^{11}}{11}\frac{\partial}{\partial x}\frac{\psi_4}{r^9}\right]-\frac{1}{a}\frac{r^{11}}{9}\frac{\partial}{\partial x}\frac{g\rho\xi_4-\varpi_4}{r^9}-N\frac{\rho}{a}\frac{5}{9}\epsilon\frac{r^{11}}{a^2}\frac{\partial}{\partial x}\frac{W''}{r^9}=0 \quad \text{...(49)}.$$

The y- and z-equations yield precisely similar results. We differentiate the left-hand members of the three equations with respect to x, y, z in order, add the results, and multiply by $9a/55$, and thus find the equation

$$g\rho\xi_4-\varpi_4-\frac{9}{55}\mu\psi_4=-N\rho 5\epsilon\frac{W''}{a^2} \quad \text{.................(50)}.$$

Just as in the corresponding problem of Chapter V, no new equation is obtained by multiplying the left-hand members of the equations of type (49) by x, y, z and adding the results.

95. The set of equations connecting the unknown harmonics of the second degree with the known harmonics are now equations (45) and (47) and three equations derived from (7), (10), and (20). We write down the set of five equations:

$$\rho U_2-\varpi_2-\frac{5}{2}\mu\psi_2=0,$$

$$\frac{\xi_2}{a}+\frac{5}{14}\psi_2+\frac{1}{3}\frac{r^5\phi_{-3}}{a^2}=0,$$

$$g\rho\xi_2-\frac{5}{3}\rho U_2=N\rho\epsilon W,$$

$$g\rho\xi_2-\varpi_2-5\mu\psi_2-\frac{5}{3}\mu\frac{r^5\phi_{-3}}{a^2}=N\left(\frac{23}{7}\rho+\frac{25}{3}\frac{\mu}{ga}\right)\epsilon W,$$

$$g\rho\xi_2-\varpi_2-\frac{5}{21}\mu\psi_2=N\left(\frac{23}{7}\rho-\frac{10}{21}\frac{\mu}{ga}\right)\epsilon W.$$

On solving these we find

$$\left.\begin{aligned}\xi_2&=N\frac{282+653\mu/g\rho a}{42+399\mu/g\rho a}\epsilon\frac{W}{g}\\ U_2-g\xi_2&=-N\frac{690+2503\mu/g\rho a}{210+1995\mu/g\rho a}\epsilon W\end{aligned}\right\} \quad \text{..............(51)}.$$

In like manner we may write down the set of five equations connecting spherical harmonics of the fourth degree:

$$\rho U_4 - \varpi_4 - \frac{9}{4}\mu\psi_4 = 0,$$

$$\frac{\xi_4}{a} + \frac{9}{22}\psi_4 + \frac{1}{7}\frac{r^9\phi_{-5}}{a^2} = 0,$$

$$g\rho\xi_4 - 3\rho U_4 = -N\rho 5\epsilon\frac{W''}{a^2},$$

$$g\rho\xi_4 - \varpi_4 - 7\mu\psi_4 - \frac{3}{2}\mu\frac{r^9\phi_{-5}}{a^2} = -N\left(\frac{35}{9}\rho + 28\frac{\mu}{ga}\right)\epsilon\frac{W''}{a^2},$$

$$g\rho\xi_4 - \varpi_4 - \frac{9}{55}\mu\psi_4 = -N5\rho\epsilon\frac{W''}{a^2}.$$

On solving these we find

$$\left.\begin{aligned} \xi_4 &= -N\frac{4060 + 38556\mu/g\rho a}{1118 + 28917\mu/2g\rho a}\epsilon\frac{W''}{a^2} \\ U_4 - g\xi_4 &= N\frac{9140 + 99603\mu/g\rho a}{2236 + 28917\mu/g\rho a}\epsilon\frac{W''}{a^2} \end{aligned}\right\} \quad \text{...............(52).}$$

The quantities ξ_2 and ξ_4 give the correction to the calculated height of the corporeal tides, and the quantities $U_2 - g\xi_2$ and $U_4 - g\xi_4$ are useful for determining corrections to the calculated potential of the forces that act upon a horizontal pendulum.

96. To obtain expressions for the forces that act on a horizontal pendulum we have to evaluate the potential

$$V_0 + \tfrac{1}{2}\omega^2(x^2 + y^2) + V_0' + V_2 + W$$

at a point on the deformed surface, and form derivatives of it in the directions of the meridians and parallels of the spheroid. Now the value of

$$V_0 + \tfrac{1}{2}\omega^2(x^2 + y^2)$$

at a point on the deformed surface is expressed with sufficient approximation by the formula

$$\text{const.} + (lu + mv + nw)\left(l\frac{\partial}{\partial x} + m\frac{\partial}{\partial y} + n\frac{\partial}{\partial z}\right)\{V_0 + \tfrac{1}{2}\omega^2(x^2 + y^2)\}.$$

This is the same as the value of

$$\text{const.} + \frac{1}{\rho}(lu + mv + nw)\left(l\frac{\partial p_0}{\partial x} + m\frac{\partial p_0}{\partial y} + n\frac{\partial p_0}{\partial z}\right)$$

at a point on the undisturbed surface, and the variable part of this is

$$NW\left(-\frac{5}{2} + \frac{7}{3}\epsilon + \frac{5}{3}\epsilon\frac{x^2 + y^2 - 2z^2}{a^2}\right) - g(\xi_2 + \xi_4).$$

The potential to be differentiated is therefore

$$W + V_0' + NW\left(-\frac{5}{2} + \frac{7}{3}\epsilon + \frac{5}{3}\epsilon\,\frac{x^2+y^2-2z^2}{a^2}\right) + U_2 + U_4 - g(\xi_2+\xi_4).$$

From the value of V_0' given in § 69 this is seen to be

$$W(1-N) + N\epsilon W\left(\frac{7}{3} + \frac{5}{3}\frac{x^2+y^2-2z^2}{a^2}\right) + U_2 + U_4 - g(\xi_2+\xi_4)\ \ldots(53).$$

We shall denote this expression by Ω.

97. The equation to the surface can be written $r = a + a\epsilon(\frac{1}{3} - \cos^2\theta)$.

Let ds_1, ds_2 denote elements of arc of the meridian and parallel; then, if a point moves on the surface from (r, θ, ϕ) to $(r+dr, \theta+d\theta, \phi+d\phi)$, we have, correctly to the first order of ϵ,

$$\left.\begin{aligned} dr &= 2a\epsilon\sin\theta\cos\theta\,d\theta \\ ds_1 &= a(1+\tfrac{1}{3}\epsilon - \epsilon\cos^2\theta)\,d\theta \end{aligned}\right\}\ \ldots\ldots\ldots\ldots\ldots\ldots(54),$$

and therefore, correctly to the same order,

$$\frac{\partial W}{\partial s_1} = 2\epsilon\sin\theta\cos\theta\frac{\partial W}{\partial r} + \frac{1}{a}\left(1 - \frac{\epsilon}{3} + \epsilon\cos^2\theta\right)\frac{\partial W}{\partial\theta}\ \ldots\ldots\ldots(55).$$

Again, W is of the form $\tau r^2\sin^2\theta\cos(2\phi+\sigma t)$, and therefore

$$\frac{\partial W}{\partial r} = \frac{\tan\theta}{r}\frac{\partial W}{\partial\theta}.$$

Hence, correctly to the same order as before, we have

$$\frac{\partial W}{\partial s_1} = \frac{1}{a}\left(1 + \frac{5}{3}\epsilon - \epsilon\cos^2\theta\right)\frac{\partial W}{\partial\theta}\ \ldots\ldots\ldots\ldots\ldots\ldots(56).$$

We also have $$\frac{\partial W}{\partial s_2} = \frac{1}{a}\left(1 - \frac{\epsilon}{3} + \epsilon\cos^2\theta\right)\frac{1}{\sin\theta}\frac{\partial W}{\partial\phi}\ \ldots\ldots\ldots\ldots\ldots(57).$$

These formulae must be used in differentiating the first term $W(1-N)$ of Ω.

In differentiating the remaining terms we may identify ds_1 with $a\,d\theta$ and ds_2 with $a\sin\theta\,d\phi$. We note the formulae

$$\begin{aligned}\frac{1}{a}\frac{\partial}{\partial\theta}\left(\epsilon W\frac{x^2+y^2-2z^2}{a^2}\right) &= \frac{\epsilon}{a}(1-3\cos^2\theta)\frac{\partial W}{\partial\theta} + \frac{6\epsilon}{a}\sin\theta\cos\theta\,W \\ &= \frac{\epsilon}{a}(4-6\cos^2\theta)\frac{\partial W}{\partial\theta}\ \ldots\ldots\ldots\ldots\ldots\ldots(58),\end{aligned}$$

and $$\frac{1}{a}\frac{\partial}{\partial\theta}\left(\epsilon\frac{W''}{a^2}\right) = \frac{\epsilon}{a}\left(2\cos^2\theta - \frac{8}{7}\right)\frac{\partial W}{\partial\theta}\ \ldots\ldots\ldots\ldots(59).$$

98. For brevity we shall now write

$$U_2 - g\xi_2 = Q_2\epsilon W,\quad U_4 - g\xi_4 = Q_4\epsilon\frac{W''}{a^2}\ \ldots\ldots\ldots\ldots(60).$$

Then we have

$$\frac{\partial\Omega}{\partial s_1}=\frac{1}{a}\frac{\partial W}{\partial\theta}\left[(1-N)\left(1+\frac{5}{3}\epsilon-\epsilon\cos^2\theta\right)+N\left\{\frac{7}{3}\epsilon+\frac{5}{3}\epsilon(4-6\cos^2\theta)\right\}\right.$$
$$\left.+Q_2\epsilon+Q_4\epsilon\left(2\cos^2\theta-\frac{8}{7}\right)\right]$$
$$=\frac{1}{a}\frac{\partial W}{\partial\theta}\left[1-N+\epsilon\left(\frac{5}{3}-\cos^2\theta\right)+N\epsilon\left(\frac{22}{3}-9\cos^2\theta\right)\right.$$
$$\left.+Q_2\epsilon+Q_4\epsilon\left(2\cos^2\theta-\frac{8}{7}\right)\right]\quad\ldots(61),$$

and

$$\frac{\partial\Omega}{\partial s_2}=\frac{1}{a\sin\theta}\frac{\partial W}{\partial\phi}\left[(1-N)\left(1-\frac{1}{3}\epsilon+\epsilon\cos^2\theta\right)+N\epsilon\left\{\frac{7}{3}+5\left(\frac{1}{3}-\cos^2\theta\right)\right\}\right.$$
$$\left.+Q_2\epsilon+Q_4\epsilon\left(\cos^2\theta-\frac{1}{7}\right)\right]$$
$$=\frac{1}{a\sin\theta}\frac{\partial W}{\partial\phi}\left[1-N+\epsilon\left(\cos^2\theta-\frac{1}{3}\right)+N\epsilon\left(\frac{13}{3}-6\cos^2\theta\right)\right.$$
$$\left.+Q_2\epsilon+Q_4\epsilon\left(\cos^2\theta-\frac{1}{7}\right)\right]\quad\ldots(62).$$

The left-hand member of (61) denotes the force acting southwards, and the left-hand member of (62) denotes the force acting eastwards, both calculated with a correction for the ellipticity. The factors of these expressions which stand outside the square brackets would, if multiplied by $(1-N)$, be the corresponding forces calculated without a correction. We see that both components of force are altered, but not in the same proportion.

99. A definite numerical example will make clear how the forces are affected by the corrections. We shall suppose that $N=\frac{1}{3}$, which makes $\mu/g\rho a$ equal to $\frac{4}{19}$. This gives $Q_2=-0{\cdot}6439$, $Q_4=1{\cdot}1974$ approximately. We shall also put $\cos\theta=\frac{4}{5}$. With these values we find for the expressions in square brackets in the right-hand members of (61) and (62) the approximate values $\frac{2}{3}+\epsilon(1{\cdot}0714)$ and $\frac{2}{3}+\epsilon(0{\cdot}4225)$. Thus both the forces are slightly increased, the southward component more than the eastward component. According to this result the diagram (p. 55) should have the inner curve slightly flattened relatively to the outer, but in the east-west direction instead of the north-south. The ratio of the two coefficients above-determined is about $1+\frac{1}{240}$, the value of ϵ being taken to be $\frac{1}{232}$ in accordance with the assumption of uniform density. Thus the correction is small of the order one part in 240.

It appears therefore that the ellipticity of the meridians does not account for the fact that the earth in the neighbourhood of Potsdam appears to be stiffer to resist forces that act east and west than forces that act north and south. If it made any difference the difference would seem to be the other way, but to be too small to be observed.

100. Although the results which have been obtained in this and the preceding Chapter are deduced from a theory based on simplifying assumptions, we seem to be justified in concluding that the reason for the observed fact is not to be sought in the rotation of the earth, or in the deviation from the spherical figure which is produced by the rotation. Without calculation we should expect the correction for inertia to be small of the order $a\omega^2/g$ which is $\frac{1}{289}$, and the correction for ellipticity to be small of the order ϵ, which is $\frac{1}{297}$; but these numbers might, from an *a priori* standpoint, be multiplied by rather large coefficients. We have found that $a\omega^2/g$ is actually multiplied by a rather small coefficient, while the coefficient by which ϵ is multiplied differs but little from unity. The same general argument, and a general survey of the analysis in the present Chapter, suggest that any inequality of figure, such as is involved in the distribution of land and water, would give rise to a correction, but that it would be very small. For none of the spherical harmonic inequalities of low degree that are concerned in the distribution have maxima so great as the spheroidal inequality of the geoid.

101. If this argument is sound we must not look for the cause of the observed discrepancy in either of the directions suggested by Dr Hecker and Sir G. Darwin. A possible cause may perhaps be found in the attraction of the tide-wave in the North Atlantic, and the accompanying excess pressure on the sea-bottom. A rough calculation shows that the first of these may be of about the right order of magnitude. The North Atlantic Ocean may be likened to a circular segment of a sphere having a radius of about 2000 km., and having its centre at a distance nearly equal to the radius in a direct line drawn through the earth from the place of observation. If the level of the water in this area were raised one metre, the attraction of the extra water at Potsdam would be a force acting nearly east and west of amount approximately equal to $\frac{1}{44 \times 10^6}$ of gravity. The maximum of the horizontal component of the moon's tide-generating force is about $\frac{1}{11 \times 10^6}$ of gravity. A periodic filling and emptying of the Atlantic basin, with a range of two metres, would produce just such an extra east-west force as appears to exist. Now the co-tidal lines of the North Atlantic* show that no such large area as that described above is even approximately in the same phase. On the other hand the co-tidal lines drawn for differences of one hour are very wide apart in the region lying to the west of the Spanish Peninsula. Also the range of the tide in the open ocean is almost certainly much larger than two metres. These considerations go to show that there is a strong probability that a horizontal pendulum at Potsdam would be influenced appreciably by the attraction of the tide-wave. The deformation of the earth produced by the pressure of the tide-wave on the sea-bottom† would also have an influence, which would probably be of the same order of magnitude.

* See the chart drawn by R. A. Harris, "Manual of tides," Part IV B, *Appendices to Rep. of U.S. Coast and Geod. Survey*, Washington, 1904.

† G. H. Darwin, *Rep. Brit. Assoc.* 1882, p. 95, or *Scientific Papers*, vol. I. p. 430.

CHAPTER VII

GENERAL THEORY OF A GRAVITATING COMPRESSIBLE PLANET

102. In many investigations of such problems of geodynamics as the problem of corporeal tides and the question of the free vibrations of the earth as a whole the simplifying assumption of absolute incompressibility is introduced. If this assumption is discarded, the analysis of such problems becomes much more complicated, because, as was first pointed out by J. H. Jeans*, the material of the earth, when it is deformed by external forces, or when it is vibrating, is compressed in some parts and expanded in others, and the attraction due to the inequalities of density may give rise to strains of the same order of magnitude as those that would be calculated by the ordinary theory. A method for dealing with this complication was devised by Lord Rayleigh†. This method may be described as follows:—The earth ought to be regarded as a body in a state of *initial stress*; this initial stress may be regarded as a hydrostatic pressure balancing the self-gravitation of the body in the initial state; the stress in the body, when disturbed, may be taken to consist of the initial stress compounded with an *additional stress*; the additional stress may be taken to be connected with the strain, measured from the initial state as unstrained state, by the same formulae as hold in an isotropic elastic solid body slightly strained from a state of zero stress. The theory, as here described, is ambiguous in the following sense:—The initial stress at a point of the body which is at (x, y, z) in the strained state may be (1) the pressure at (x, y, z) in the initial state, or it may be (2) the pressure in the initial state at that point which is displaced to (x, y, z) when the body is strained. There can be little doubt that the second alternative is the correct one‡. A small element of the body is moved from one place to another, and during the displacement it suffers compression and distortion. It ought to be regarded as carrying its initial pressure with it, and acquiring an additional state of stress depending upon the compression and distortion.

* J. H. Jeans, "On the vibrations and stability of a gravitating planet," *Phil. Trans. R. Soc. London*, A, Vol. 201 (1903), p. 157. See especially p. 160, ftn.

† *Loc. cit.*, *ante* p. 12.

‡ The first alternative was adopted in the paper by A. E. H. Love, "The gravitational stability of the earth," *Phil. Trans. R. Soc. London*, A, vol. 207 (1907), p. 171.

103. In the ordinary theory of elasticity the unstrained state of the body is taken to be an unstressed state. The body passes from the unstrained state to the strained state by a displacement, which is assumed to be small. It is usual to take the coordinates of the point occupied by a particle of the body in the unstrained state to be x, y, z, and the coordinates of the point occupied by the same particle in the strained state to be $x+u$, $y+v$, $z+w$; and then the strain is expressed by the six components

$$\frac{\partial u}{\partial x}, \quad \frac{\partial v}{\partial y}, \quad \frac{\partial w}{\partial z}, \quad \frac{\partial w}{\partial y}+\frac{\partial v}{\partial z}, \quad \frac{\partial u}{\partial z}+\frac{\partial w}{\partial x}, \quad \frac{\partial v}{\partial x}+\frac{\partial u}{\partial y}.$$

But these expressions would be unaltered, the strain being small, if x, y, z were the coordinates of the point occupied by a particle in the strained state and $x-u$, $y-v$, $z-w$ those of the point occupied by the same particle in the unstrained state. The equations of equilibrium, and those of vibratory motion, are formed, independently of any relation between stress and strain, by considering the equilibrium, or the kinetic reaction, of a small portion of the body in the position that it has when the body is strained*. In the process of forming these equations x, y, z are certainly regarded as the coordinates of a point occupied by a particle of the body in a strained state. It is, therefore, most convenient, whenever it becomes important, to regard $(-u, -v, -w)$ as the displacement by which the body would pass from the actual to the initial state. If this is done the ordinary stress-equations of equilibrium, or vibratory motion, and the ordinary relations between strains and displacements hold in problems involving initial stress.

EQUATIONS OF VIBRATORY MOTION.

104. We now proceed to an analytical formulation of the theory. The body is supposed to be disturbed by external forces which are derived from a potential. Under the action of the forces the shape of the body will be changed, and the density about a particle in the disturbed state will be different from the density about the same particle in the initial state. The potential due to the self-gravitation of the body must be formed at any instant in accordance with the instantaneous distribution of the mass throughout the volume bounded by the deformed surface. Let ρ denote the density of the matter which is at the point (x, y, z) at time t, and V the potential at the same point, and at the same time, of all the gravitational forces acting on the body, whether due to the attraction of external bodies or to the attraction of the body itself. The state of stress existing at the same point, and at the same time, may be specified by six components of stress, X_x,... and the

* See for example A. E. H. Love, *Elasticity* (2nd edition, 1906), Arts. 44, 54.

coordinates of the point occupied, in the unstrained state, by the particle which, in the strained state, is at the point (x, y, z), may be taken to be $x-u, y-v, z-w$. Then the equations of vibratory motion are three equations of the type

$$\rho\frac{\partial^2 u}{\partial t^2}=\rho\frac{\partial V}{\partial x}+\frac{\partial X_x}{\partial x}+\frac{\partial X_y}{\partial y}+\frac{\partial Z_x}{\partial z} \quad \text{.................(1).}$$

The equations of equilibrium are obtained by replacing the left-hand members by zero. In the tidal problem the potential of the tide-generating forces must be included in V. In the problem of free vibration V is the potential due to the instantaneous distribution of mass throughout the volume instantaneously occupied by the body.

105. The undisturbed surface will be taken to be spherical and of radius a, and the origin of coordinates will be taken to be at the centre The density, denoted by ρ_0, will be taken to be a constant, or a function of r the distance of a point from the centre. The potential V_0 will also be a function of r. The initial pressure p_0, which will also be expressible as a function of r, satisfies the three equations of the type

$$\rho_0\frac{\partial V_0}{\partial x}-\frac{\partial p_0}{\partial x}=0 \quad \text{..............................(2).}$$

106. Let U denote the radial component of the displacement (u, v, w), and let Δ denote the cubical dilatation, so that

$$\Delta=\frac{\partial u}{\partial x}+\frac{\partial v}{\partial y}+\frac{\partial w}{\partial z} \quad \text{..............................(3).}$$

Then the equation of the deformed surface is of the form

$$r=a+U_a \quad \text{................................(4),}$$

where U_a denotes the value of U at the surface $r=a$. The density at the point (x, y, z) in the strained state is expressed with sufficient approximation by the equation

$$\rho=\rho_0-U\frac{\partial \rho_0}{\partial r}-\rho_0\Delta.$$

The potential V is the sum of V_0 and the potential due to the inequalities of density. We shall write

$$V=V_0+W \quad \text{...............................(5).}$$

Then W is the potential due to external disturbing bodies, together with that due to a volume distribution of density $-\left(U\frac{\partial \rho_0}{\partial r}+\Delta\right)$, and that due to a distribution of mass on the surface $r=a$ with a superficial density $\rho_0(a)\,.\,U_a$, where $\rho_0(a)$ denotes the value of ρ_0 at $r=a$. The stress at the point (x, y, z) consists of the initial stress (pressure) at the point $(x-u,\ y-v,\ z-w)$, together with the additional stress connected with the strain by the ordinary formulae, so that we have three equations of the type*

$$X_x = -\left(p_0 - U\frac{\partial p_0}{\partial r}\right) + \lambda\Delta + 2\mu\frac{\partial u}{\partial x} \qquad \text{..................(6)},$$

and three of the type

$$Y_z = \mu\left(\frac{\partial w}{\partial y} + \frac{\partial v}{\partial z}\right) \qquad \text{..............................(7)}.$$

The quantity μ is the rigidity, and the quantity $\lambda + \frac{2}{3}\mu$ is the modulus of compression of the material. In a general theory we ought to take them to be functions of r, but, as we cannot make any progress with a theory in which λ, μ, and ρ_0 are functions of r, we shall treat them henceforward as constants. The density ρ at the point (x, y, z) is then given by the equation

$$\rho = \rho_0(1 - \Delta) \qquad \text{..................................(8)},$$

and W is the potential of a volume distribution of density $-\rho_0\Delta$, together with the surface distribution previously specified, and the potential of external disturbing bodies.

107. We shall now assume that u, v, w, as functions of t, are proportional to e^{ipt}. Then the equations of motion of the type (1) become three equations of the type

$$-\rho_0 p^2 u = (\lambda + \mu)\frac{\partial \Delta}{\partial x} + \mu\nabla^2 u - \frac{\partial}{\partial x}\left(p_0 - U\frac{\partial p_0}{\partial r}\right) + \rho_0(1 - \Delta)\frac{\partial V_0}{\partial x} + \rho_0\frac{\partial W}{\partial x},$$

or, by (2), they are of the type

$$(\lambda + \mu)\frac{\partial \Delta}{\partial x} + \mu\nabla^2 u + \rho_0 p^2 u + \rho_0\frac{\partial}{\partial x}\left(U\frac{\partial V_0}{\partial r}\right) - \rho_0\Delta\frac{\partial V_0}{\partial x} + \rho_0\frac{\partial W}{\partial x} = 0.$$

On substituting for V_0 its value given by the equation

$$V_0 = \tfrac{2}{3}\pi\gamma\rho_0(3a^2 - r^2),$$

these equations become three equations of the type

$$(\lambda + \mu)\frac{\partial \Delta}{\partial x} + \mu\nabla^2 u + \rho_0 p^2 u - \tfrac{4}{3}\pi\gamma\rho_0^2\frac{\partial}{\partial x}(rU) + \tfrac{4}{3}\pi\gamma\rho_0^2 x\Delta + \rho_0\frac{\partial W}{\partial x} = 0 \quad \text{...(9)}.$$

We have also the equations

$$\Delta = \frac{\partial u}{\partial x} + \frac{\partial v}{\partial y} + \frac{\partial w}{\partial z} \qquad \text{......................(3 \textit{bis})},$$

$$rU = xu + yv + zw \qquad \text{.......................(10)},$$

$$\nabla^2 W = 4\pi\gamma\rho_0\Delta \qquad \text{..............................(11)}.$$

* It is specifically in these equations that the effect of the ambiguity noted on p. 89, *ante*, makes its appearance. If the first of the two alternatives there explained were adopted, the term $-U\partial p_0/\partial r$ would be omitted. The method here adopted should in strictness be adopted also when absolute incompressibility is assumed. When this assumption is made an additional pressure is introduced, and this additional pressure is often taken to be equivalent to the limit of the product $-\lambda\Delta$, as Δ tends to zero and λ tends to become infinite. In strictness it should be taken to be equivalent to $-\lambda\Delta + U\partial p_0/\partial r$. The point here brought out does not affect any of the ordinary solutions for a planet treated as composed of incompressible material.

108. We have to obtain solutions of these equations in a form adapted to satisfy certain boundary conditions. These are the surface characteristic equation of the potential and the condition that the deformed surface is free from traction. The first of these takes different forms according as the problem is or is not concerned with the gravitation of external bodies. To express the condition that the deformed surface, $r = a + U_a$, is free from traction, we observe that, according to what has been said, the initial stress, specified by $p_0 - U\partial p_0/\partial r$, at a point on the deformed surface vanishes; therefore the traction, if any, across the deformed surface arises entirely from the additional stress. But the additional stress at a point on the deformed surface, $r = a + U_a$, differs from that at the corresponding point of the undisturbed surface, $r = a$, by a quantity of the order of the square of the displacement. The condition in question can therefore be expressed with sufficient approximation by equating to zero those parts of the component tractions across the surface $r = a$, which are contributed by the additional stress. The equations which are thus found are three of the type

$$\lambda x \Delta + \mu \left\{ \frac{\partial (rU)}{\partial x} + r \frac{\partial u}{\partial r} - u \right\} = 0 \quad\text{......(12)},$$

and they hold at the surface $r = a$. From the general formulae (6) and (7) for the stress-components it is easy to verify that the traction across the surface $r = a$ is a pressure equal to the weight of the inequality, that is to say, it is a pressure per unit of area equal to that due to a column of the material whose height is U_a. This is what we should expect.

Solution of the equations.

109. We can obtain a typical solution of the system of equations (3), (9), (10), and (11) by assuming that W is proportional to a spherical surface harmonic; and we can afterwards, if we wish, obtain a more general solution by a synthesis of typical solutions containing different surface harmonics. We assume therefore that W is of the form

$$W = K_n(r)\, W_n \quad\text{......(13)},$$

where W_n is a spherical solid harmonic of degree n, and $K_n(r)$ is some function of r, and we assume also that u, v, w are given by equations of the type

$$u = F_n(r) \frac{\partial W_n}{\partial x} + G_n(r)\, x W_n \quad\text{......(14)},$$

where $F_n(r)$ and $G_n(r)$ are some functions of r. The expressions for v and w are to be obtained by cyclical interchange of the letters x, y, z. We shall find that the functions K_n, F_n, G_n can be determined, and that the assumed form of solution is of sufficient generality to enable us to satisfy the boundary conditions.

110. The equations

$$W = K_n(r)\, W_n, \quad \nabla^2 W = 4\pi\gamma\rho_0 \Delta$$

give

$$4\pi\gamma\rho_0 \Delta = \left(\frac{d^2 K_n}{dr^2} + \frac{2}{r}\frac{dK_n}{dr}\right) W_n + 2\frac{1}{r}\frac{dK_n}{dr}\, n W_n$$

$$= \left(\frac{d^2 K_n}{dr^2} + \frac{2(n+1)}{r}\frac{dK_n}{dr}\right) W_n.$$

We shall write this equation

$$\Delta = f_n(r)\, W_n \quad \text{.............................(15)},$$

so that $f_n(r)$ is the function of r that is determined by the equation

$$f_n(r) = \frac{1}{4\pi\gamma\rho_0}\left(\frac{d^2 K_n}{dr^2} + \frac{2(n+1)}{r}\frac{dK_n}{dr}\right) \quad \text{..............(16)},$$

when the function $K_n(r)$ is known. We shall write also

$$\vartheta = \frac{d^2}{dr^2} + \frac{2(n+1)}{r}\frac{d}{dr} \quad \text{........................(17)},$$

so that the above equation (16) is

$$f_n = \frac{1}{4\pi\gamma\rho_0}\vartheta K_n,$$

the argument r of the functions not being expressed.

The assumed form of solution gives

$$rU = (nF_n + r^2 G_n)\, W_n \quad \text{.......................(18)},$$

and therefore U and Δ are the products of functions of r and the spherical harmonic W_n.

Again the assumed form of solution gives

$$\Delta = \left\{\frac{n}{r}\frac{dF_n}{dr} + r\frac{dG_n}{dr} + (n+3)\, G_n\right\} W_n,$$

and therefore the functions f_n, F_n, G_n, K_n are connected by the two equations

$$f_n = \frac{n}{r}\frac{dF_n}{dr} + r\frac{dG_n}{dr} + (n+3)\, G_n = \frac{1}{4\pi\gamma\rho_0}\vartheta K_n \quad \text{........(19)}.$$

Now we have the formulae

$$\frac{\partial \Delta}{\partial x} = f_n \frac{\partial W_n}{\partial x} + \frac{1}{r}\frac{df_n}{dr}\, x W_n,$$

$$\nabla^2 u = \left(\frac{d^2 F_n}{dr^2} + \frac{2n}{r}\frac{dF_n}{dr}\right)\frac{\partial W_n}{\partial x} + \left\{\frac{d^2 G_n}{dr^2} + \frac{2(n+2)}{r}\frac{dG_n}{dr}\right\} x W_n + 2G_n \frac{\partial W_n}{\partial x},$$

$$\frac{\partial (rU)}{\partial x} = (nF_n + r^2 G_n)\frac{\partial W_n}{\partial x} + \left\{\frac{n}{r}\frac{dF_n}{dr} + \frac{1}{r}\frac{d(r^2 G_n)}{dr}\right\} x W_n,$$

$$x\Delta = f_n x W_n,$$

$$\frac{\partial W}{\partial x} = K_n \frac{\partial W_n}{\partial x} + \frac{1}{r}\frac{dK_n}{dr}\, x W_n.$$

Then the equations of motion are satisfied identically if the two equations

$$(\lambda+\mu) f_n + \mu\left(\frac{d^2F_n}{dr^2} + \frac{2n}{r}\frac{dF_n}{dr} + 2G_n\right) - \tfrac{4}{3}\pi\gamma\rho_0^2\,(nF_n + r^2G_n)$$
$$+ \rho_0 K_n + \rho_0 p^2 F_n = 0 \ldots(20),$$

$$(\lambda+\mu)\frac{1}{r}\frac{df_n}{dr} + \mu\left(\frac{d^2G_n}{dr^2} + \frac{2(n+2)}{r}\frac{dG_n}{dr}\right) - \tfrac{4}{3}\pi\gamma\rho_0^2\frac{1}{r}\frac{d}{dr}(nF_n + r^2G_n)$$
$$+ \tfrac{4}{3}\pi\gamma\rho_0^2 f_n + \rho_0\frac{1}{r}\frac{dK_n}{dr} + \rho_0 p^2 G_n = 0 \ \ldots(21)$$

are satisfied. The four functions f_n, F_n, G_n, K_n are therefore connected by the four equations (19), (20) and (21). We may eliminate three of the functions and form a differential equation for the remaining one, and when this equation is solved we may seek the corresponding forms for the other functions. The following procedure is effective for this purpose:—

Operate with $\frac{1}{r}\frac{d}{dr}$ upon the left-hand member of (20) and subtract from the left-hand member of (21). This process gives an equation in which F_n does not occur explicitly, but only through the occurrence of $\frac{dF_n}{dr}$. Now an equation obtained from (19), viz.:

$$\frac{n}{r}\frac{dF_n}{dr} = \frac{\vartheta K_n}{4\pi\gamma\rho_0} - r\frac{dG_n}{dr} - (n+3)\,G_n,$$

can be used to eliminate F_n from the equation so formed and also from (21). The function f_n can always be eliminated by means of the equation

$$f_n = \frac{\vartheta K_n}{4\pi\gamma\rho_0},$$

and thus we can form two equations containing the functions K_n, G_n only. From these we can eliminate G_n and obtain an equation for K_n.

111. In accordance with these remarks we form from the two equations (20) and (21) the equation

$$\mu\left[\frac{d^2G_n}{dr^2} + \frac{2(n+1)}{r}\frac{dG_n}{dr} - \frac{1}{r}\frac{d}{dr}\left(\frac{d^2F_n}{dr^2} + \frac{2n}{r}\frac{dF_n}{dr}\right)\right]$$
$$+ \tfrac{1}{3}\rho_0\vartheta K_n + \rho_0 p^2\left(G_n - \frac{1}{r}\frac{dF_n}{dr}\right) = 0,$$

which, being simplified by means of the identity

$$\frac{1}{r}\frac{d}{dr}\left(\frac{d^2F_n}{dr^2} + \frac{2n}{r}\frac{dF_n}{dr}\right) = \vartheta\left(\frac{1}{r}\frac{dF_n}{dr}\right),$$

becomes

$$\mu\vartheta\left(G_n - \frac{1}{r}\frac{dF_n}{dr}\right) + \tfrac{1}{3}\rho_0\vartheta K_n + \rho_0 p^2\left(G_n - \frac{1}{r}\frac{dF_n}{dr}\right) = 0 \ \ldots\ldots(22).$$

Next we proceed to write down the formulae

$$\frac{1}{r}\frac{dF_n}{dr}=\frac{1}{n}\left\{\frac{\vartheta K_n}{4\pi\gamma\rho_0}-r\frac{dG_n}{dr}-(n+3)\,G_n\right\},$$

$$G_n-\frac{1}{r}\frac{dF_n}{dr}=\frac{1}{n}\left\{r\frac{dG_n}{dr}+(2n+3)\,G_n-\frac{\vartheta K_n}{4\pi\gamma\rho_0}\right\},$$

$$\frac{1}{r}\frac{d}{dr}(nF_n+r^2G_n)=\frac{\vartheta K_n}{4\pi\gamma\rho_0}-(n+1)\,G_n,$$

by the use of which the equation (22) becomes

$$\mu\vartheta\left\{r\frac{dG_n}{dr}+(2n+3)\,G_n-\frac{\vartheta K_n}{4\pi\gamma\rho_0}\right\}+\tfrac{1}{3}n\rho_0\vartheta K_n$$
$$+\rho_0 p^2\left\{r\frac{dG_n}{dr}+(2n+3)\,G_n-\frac{\vartheta K_n}{4\pi\gamma\rho_0}\right\}=0,$$

and the equation (21) becomes

$$\frac{(\lambda+\mu)}{4\pi\gamma\rho_0}\frac{1}{r}\frac{d}{dr}(\vartheta K_n)+\mu\left\{\frac{d^2G_n}{dr^2}+\frac{2(n+2)}{r}\frac{dG_n}{dr}\right\}-\tfrac{1}{3}\rho_0\vartheta K_n$$
$$+\tfrac{4}{3}\pi\gamma\rho_0^2(n+1)\,G_n+\tfrac{1}{3}\rho_0\vartheta K_n+\rho_0\frac{1}{r}\frac{dK_n}{dr}+\rho_0p^2G_n=0,$$

and these are

$$\left(\vartheta+\frac{p^2\rho_0}{\mu}-\tfrac{4}{3}n\frac{\pi\gamma\rho_0^2}{\mu}\right)\vartheta K_n-4\pi\gamma\rho_0\left(\vartheta+\frac{p^2\rho_0}{\mu}\right)\left\{r\frac{dG_n}{dr}+(2n+3)\,G_n\right\}=0 \qquad \text{......(23)},$$

and

$$(\lambda+\mu)\frac{1}{r}\frac{d}{dr}(\vartheta K_n)+4\pi\gamma\rho_0^2\frac{1}{r}\frac{dK_n}{dr}+4\pi\gamma\rho_0\left\{\mu\left(\frac{d^2G_n}{dr^2}+\frac{2(n+2)}{r}\frac{dG_n}{dr}\right)\right.$$
$$\left.+\tfrac{4}{3}(n+1)\,\pi\gamma\rho_0^2\,G_n+p^2\rho_0\,G_n\right\}=0 \qquad \text{......(24)}.$$

These are the two equations connecting G_n and K_n. To simplify the second of them (24) we form from it the equation

$$(\lambda+\mu)\frac{d^2(\vartheta K_n)}{dr^2}+4\pi\gamma\rho_0^2\frac{d^2K_n}{dr^2}+4\pi\gamma\rho_0\frac{d}{dr}\left[\mu\left\{r\frac{d^2G_n}{dr^2}+2(n+2)\frac{dG_n}{dr}\right\}\right.$$
$$\left.+\tfrac{4}{3}(n+1)\,\pi\gamma\rho_0^2rG_n+p^2\rho_0rG_n\right]=0,$$

we multiply the left-hand member of (24) by $2(n+1)$ and add, getting

$$(\lambda+\mu)\,\vartheta^2K_n+4\pi\gamma\rho_0^2\vartheta K_n$$
$$+4\pi\gamma\rho_0\left[\mu\left\{r\frac{d^3G_n}{dr^3}+(4n+7)\frac{d^2G_n}{dr^2}+\frac{4(n+1)(n+2)}{r}\frac{dG_n}{dr}\right\}\right.$$
$$\left.+\left\{\tfrac{4}{3}\pi\gamma\rho_0^2(n+1)+p^2\rho_0\right\}\left\{r\frac{dG_n}{dr}+(2n+3)\,G_n\right\}\right]=0,$$

we observe that

$$\vartheta\left\{r\frac{dG_n}{dr}+(2n+3)\,G_n\right\}=r\frac{d^3G_n}{dr^3}+(4n+7)\frac{d^2G_n}{dr^2}+\frac{4(n+1)(n+2)}{r}\frac{dG_n}{dr},$$

and we deduce the equation

$$(\lambda+\mu)\,\vartheta^2K_n+4\pi\gamma\rho_0{}^2\vartheta K_n$$
$$+\,4\pi\gamma\rho_0\left\{\mu\vartheta+\tfrac{4}{3}\pi\gamma\rho_0{}^2(n+1)+p^2\rho_0\right\}\left\{r\frac{dG_n}{dr}+(2n+3)\,G_n\right\}=0\quad\text{...(25).}$$

Then this equation and (23), which is

$$(\mu\vartheta+p^2\rho_0-\tfrac{4}{3}\pi\gamma\rho_0{}^2n)\,\vartheta K_n-4\pi\gamma\rho_0\,(\mu\vartheta+p^2\rho_0)\left\{r\frac{dG_n}{dr}+(2n+3)\,G_n\right\}=0,$$

give

$$\{(\lambda+2\mu)\,\vartheta+p^2\rho_0-\tfrac{4}{3}\pi\gamma\rho_0{}^2(n-3)\}\,\vartheta K_n$$
$$+\,4\pi\gamma\rho_0\,\tfrac{4}{3}\pi\gamma\rho_0{}^2(n+1)\left\{r\frac{dG_n}{dr}+(2n+3)\,G_n\right\}=0\quad\text{...(26).}$$

It is now easy to eliminate G_n and obtain the equation

$$[(\mu\vartheta+p^2\rho_0)\,\{(\lambda+2\mu)\,\vartheta+p^2\rho_0-\tfrac{4}{3}\pi\gamma\rho_0{}^2(n-3)\}$$
$$+\,\tfrac{4}{3}\pi\gamma\rho_0{}^2(n+1)\,\{\mu\vartheta+p^2\rho_0-\tfrac{4}{3}\pi\gamma\rho_0{}^2n\}]\,\vartheta K_n=0,$$

which is

$$[\mu(\lambda+2\mu)\,\vartheta^2+\{\tfrac{16}{3}\pi\gamma\rho_0{}^2\mu+(\lambda+3\mu)\,p^2\rho_0\}\,\vartheta$$
$$+\,\{p^4\rho_0{}^2+\tfrac{16}{3}\pi\gamma\rho_0{}^2p^2\rho_0-n(n+1)\,(\tfrac{4}{3}\pi\gamma\rho_0{}^2)^2\}]\,\vartheta K_n=0\quad\text{...(27),}$$

a linear differential equation of the sixth order to determine K_n as a function of r.

112. Let $-\alpha^2$ and β^2 denote the roots of the equation

$$\mu(\lambda+2\mu)\,\xi^2+\{\tfrac{16}{3}\pi\gamma\rho_0{}^2\mu+(\lambda+3\mu)\,p^2\rho_0\}\,\xi$$
$$-\,\{n(n+1)\,(\tfrac{4}{3}\pi\gamma\rho_0{}^2)^2-\tfrac{16}{3}\pi\gamma\rho_0{}^2p^2\rho_0-p^4\rho_0{}^2\}=0\quad\text{...(28),}$$

supposed to have one negative and one positive root, as it obviously has if p is small or zero. The equation (27) for K_n is then

$$(\vartheta+\alpha^2)(\vartheta-\beta^2)\,\vartheta K_n=0,$$

and it is solved by solving separately the three equations

$$(\vartheta+\alpha^2)\,K=0,\quad(\vartheta-\beta^2)\,K=0,\quad\vartheta K=0.$$

Complete primitives of these three linear equations, each containing two arbitrary constants, are not required, because the relevant solutions must satisfy certain conditions at the centre $r=0$ of the sphere. The function $K_n(r)\,W_n$ is the potential due to external bodies together with that due to a distribution of matter with a certain volume density throughout the sphere $r=a$ and that due to a distribution with a certain surface density on the surface $r=a$, and therefore $K_n(r)\,r^n$ is finite when $r=0$. This condition will exclude in each case one of two forms of solution of the equation for K.

The equation

$$(\vartheta + \alpha^2) K = 0$$

is

$$\frac{d^2K}{dr^2} + \frac{2(n+1)}{r}\frac{dK}{dr} + \alpha^2 K = 0,$$

and the relevant solution is

$$K = \psi_n(\alpha r) \qquad \text{.......(29)},$$

where

$$\psi_n(x) = \left(\frac{1}{x}\frac{d}{dx}\right)^n \frac{\sin x}{x} \qquad \text{.......(30)}.$$

In like manner the relevant solution of the equation

$$(\vartheta - \beta^2) K = 0$$

is

$$K = \chi_n(\beta r) \qquad \text{.......(31)},$$

where

$$\chi_n(x') = \left(\frac{1}{x'}\frac{d}{dx'}\right)^n \frac{\sinh x'}{x'} \qquad \text{.......(32)}.$$

The relevant solution of the equation

$$\vartheta K = 0$$

is

$$K = \text{const.}$$

We take therefore as a sufficient solution of (28) the form

$$K_n = A_n \psi_n(\alpha r) + B_n \chi_n(\beta r) + C_n \qquad \text{.......(33)},$$

where A_n, B_n, C_n are three undetermined constants.

113. A few properties of the functions ψ_n and χ_n are collected here. The function $\psi_n(x)$ can be expressed as a power series in the form

$$\psi_n(x) = \frac{(-1)^n}{1.3.5\ldots(2n+1)}\left\{1 - \frac{x^2}{2(2n+3)} + \frac{x^4}{2.4.(2n+3)(2n+5)} - \ldots + \frac{(-x^2)^k}{2.4\ldots 2k(2n+3)(2n+5)\ldots(2n+2k+1)} + \ldots\right\} \qquad \text{...(34)}.$$

It satisfies the differential equation

$$\frac{d^2\psi_n}{dx^2} + \frac{2(n+1)}{x}\frac{d\psi_n}{dx} + \psi_n = 0 \qquad \text{.......(35)},$$

and ψ-functions with different suffixes are connected by the equations

$$\frac{1}{x}\frac{d\psi_n}{dx} = \psi_{n+1} = -\frac{(2n+1)\psi_n + \psi_{n-1}}{x^2} \qquad \text{.......(36)}.$$

The function $\chi_n(x')$ can be expressed as a power series in the form

$$\chi_n(x') = \frac{1}{1.3.5\ldots(2n+1)}\left\{1 + \frac{x'^2}{2(2n+3)} + \frac{x'^4}{2.4.(2n+3)(2n+5)} + \ldots\right\} \qquad \text{......(37)}.$$

It satisfies the differential equation

$$\frac{d^2\chi_n}{dx'^2} + \frac{2(n+1)}{x'}\frac{d\chi_n}{dx'} - \chi_n = 0 \quad\text{.....................(38)},$$

and χ-functions with different suffixes are connected by the equations

$$\frac{1}{x'}\frac{d\chi_n}{dx'} = \chi_{n+1} = -\frac{(2n+1)\chi_n - \chi_{n-1}}{x'^2} \quad\text{...............(39)}.$$

The χ-functions can, of course, be expressed as ψ-functions of imaginary argument with appropriate numerical coefficients, and the ψ-functions can be expressed in terms of Bessel's functions of order *integer* + $\frac{1}{2}$, but it is more convenient to use the functions in the forms above set down.

114. To the three forms of solution of the equation for K_n there answer three types of deformation of the sphere. To obtain these we have to find the forms of F_n, G_n, f_n which answer to the three terms in the expression for K_n in the right-hand member of (33). In finding any one of these sets of functions we proceed as if K_n consisted of a single term.

Let us first suppose that $K_n = A_n\psi_n(\alpha r)$. Since $\vartheta K_n = -\alpha^2 K_n$, equation (26) gives

$$r\frac{dG_n}{dr} + (2n+3)G_n = -\frac{A_n\alpha^2}{4\pi\gamma\rho_0}\frac{\{(\lambda+2\mu)\alpha^2 + \frac{4}{3}\pi\gamma\rho_0^2(n-3) - p^2\rho_0\}}{\frac{4}{3}\pi\gamma\rho_0^2(n+1)}\psi_n(\alpha r).$$

Now the formula (36) shows that, if we put

$$G_n = A_n'\psi_{n+1}(\alpha r) \quad\text{...........................(40)},$$

the equation for G_n is satisfied provided that

$$A_n' = \frac{A_n\alpha^2}{4\pi\gamma\rho_0}\frac{(\lambda+2\mu)\alpha^2 + \frac{4}{3}\pi\gamma\rho_0^2(n-3) - p^2\rho_0}{\frac{4}{3}\pi\gamma\rho_0^2(n+1)}.$$

Now equation (28) gives

$$\{(\lambda+2\mu)\alpha^2 + \tfrac{4}{3}\pi\gamma\rho_0^2(n-3) - p^2\rho_0\}(\mu\alpha^2 - p^2\rho_0)$$
$$= (\mu\alpha^2 + \tfrac{4}{3}\pi\gamma\rho_0^2 n - p^2\rho_0)\tfrac{4}{3}\pi\gamma\rho_0^2(n+1),$$

and therefore we may write

$$A_n' = \frac{A_n\alpha^2}{4\pi\gamma\rho_0}\left(1 + \frac{\frac{4}{3}\pi\gamma\rho_0^2 n}{\mu\alpha^2 - p^2\rho_0}\right) \quad\text{.....................(41)}.$$

The form $A_n'\psi_{n+1}(\alpha r)$ is the relevant solution of the equation for G_n.

Now one of the equations in (19) is the same as

$$\frac{1}{r}\frac{dF_n}{dr} = G_n - \frac{1}{n}\left\{\frac{\alpha^2 K_n}{4\pi\gamma\rho_0} + r\frac{dG_n}{dr} + (2n+3)G_n\right\},$$

or we have
$$\frac{1}{r}\frac{dF_n}{dr} = A_n'\psi_{n+1}(\alpha r) - \frac{1}{n}\left(\frac{A_n\alpha^2}{4\pi\gamma\rho_0} - A_n'\right)\psi_n(\alpha r),$$

and from this by using (36) we obtain the relevant form of F_n, viz.

$$F_n = \frac{A_n'}{\alpha^2}\psi_n(\alpha r) + \left(\frac{A_n'}{n\alpha^2} - \frac{A_n}{4\pi\gamma\rho_0 n}\right)\psi_{n-1}(\alpha r) \qquad \text{(42)}.$$

Since F_n is determined by an equation giving dF_n/dr in terms of r, it seems as if an arbitrary constant might be added to the right-hand member of (42); but by substituting in (20) on p. 95 we could show that the constant must vanish.

The relevant form of f_n is at once found to be

$$f_n = -\frac{A_n\alpha^2}{4\pi\gamma\rho_0}\psi_n(\alpha r) \qquad \text{(43)}.$$

Again suppose that $K_n = B_n\chi_n(\beta r)$. We can then write down the following forms

$$\left.\begin{aligned} G_n &= B_n'\chi_{n+1}(\beta r) \\ F_n &= \frac{B_n'}{\beta^2}\chi_n(\beta r) - \left(\frac{B_n'}{n\beta^2} - \frac{B_n}{4\pi\gamma\rho_0 n}\right)\chi_{n-1}(\beta_r) \\ f_n &= \frac{B_n\beta^2}{4\pi\gamma\rho_0}\chi_n(\beta r) \end{aligned}\right\} \qquad \text{(44)},$$

where

$$B_n' = \frac{B_n\beta^2}{4\pi\gamma\rho_0}\left(1 - \frac{\frac{4}{3}\pi\gamma\rho_0^2 n}{\mu\beta^2 + p^2\rho_0}\right) \qquad \text{(45)}.$$

Finally suppose that $K_n = C_n$. We have now

$$\left.\begin{aligned} G_n &= 0 \\ F_n &= \frac{C_n}{\frac{4}{3}\pi\gamma\rho_0 n - p^2} \\ f_n &= 0 \end{aligned}\right\} \qquad \text{(46)}.$$

In using this form of solution it is generally convenient to write C_n' for the constant value of F_n, and express the constant C_n in terms of C_n' by means of the equation

$$C_n = \tfrac{4}{3}\pi\gamma\rho_0\left(n - \frac{p^2}{\frac{4}{3}\pi\gamma\rho_0}\right)C_n' \qquad \text{(47)}.$$

Boundary conditions.

115. With a view to the formation of the boundary conditions, which express the vanishing of the traction across the deformed surface, we require the values of the three expressions of the type

$$\lambda x\Delta + \mu\left\{\frac{\partial(rU)}{\partial x} + r\frac{\partial u}{\partial r} - u\right\}$$

answering to the three forms of K_n.

Let us first suppose that $K_n = A_n\psi_n(\alpha r)$. Then we have

$$\lambda x\Delta = -\frac{\lambda A_n \alpha^2}{4\pi\gamma\rho_0}\psi_n(\alpha r)\, x W_n.$$

Also we have

$$\begin{aligned} rU &= (nF_n + r^2G_n)W_n \\ &= \left[\frac{A_n'}{\alpha^2}\{n\psi_n(\alpha r) + \psi_{n-1}(\alpha r) + \alpha^2 r^2\psi_{n+1}(\alpha r)\} - \frac{A_n}{4\pi\gamma\rho_0}\psi_{n-1}(\alpha r)\right]W_n \\ &= -\left\{\frac{(n+1)A_n'}{\alpha^2}\psi_n(\alpha r) + \frac{A_n}{4\pi\gamma\rho_0}\psi_{n-1}(\alpha r)\right\}W_n. \end{aligned}$$

Hence

$$\begin{aligned} \frac{\partial(rU)}{\partial x} = &-\left\{\frac{(n+1)A_n'}{\alpha^2}\psi_n(\alpha r) + \frac{A_n}{4\pi\gamma\rho_0}\psi_{n-1}(\alpha r)\right\}\frac{\partial W_n}{\partial x} \\ &-\left\{(n+1)A_n'\psi_{n+1}(\alpha r) + \frac{\alpha^2 A_n}{4\pi\gamma\rho_0}\psi_n(\alpha r)\right\}x W_n. \end{aligned}$$

Again, we have

$$\begin{aligned} r\frac{du}{dr} - u &= \left\{r\frac{dF_n}{dr} + (n-2)F_n\right\}\frac{dW_n}{dx} + \left(r\frac{dG_n}{dr} + nG_n\right)x W_n \\ &= \left[\frac{A_n'}{\alpha^2}\left\{\alpha^2r^2\psi_{n+1}(\alpha r) + \frac{\alpha^2 r^2}{n}\psi_n(\alpha r) + (n-2)\psi_n(\alpha r) + \frac{n-2}{n}\psi_{n-1}(\alpha r)\right\}\right. \\ &\qquad \left. - \frac{A_n}{4\pi\gamma\rho_0 n}\{\alpha^2r^2\psi_n(\alpha r) + (n-2)\psi_{n-1}(\alpha r)\}\right]\frac{\partial W_n}{\partial x} \\ &\qquad + A_n'\{n\psi_{n+1}(\alpha r) - (2n+3)\psi_{n+1}(\alpha r) - \psi_n(\alpha r)\}x W_n \\ &= \left[\frac{A_n'}{\alpha^2}\left\{\frac{\alpha^2r^2}{n}\psi_n(\alpha r) - (n+3)\psi_n(\alpha r) - \frac{2}{n}\psi_{n-1}(\alpha r)\right\}\right. \\ &\qquad \left. - \frac{A_n}{4\pi\gamma\rho_0}\left\{\frac{\alpha^2r^2}{n}\psi_n(\alpha r) + \frac{n-2}{n}\psi_{n-1}(\alpha r)\right\}\right]\frac{\partial W_n}{\partial x} \\ &\qquad - A_n'\{(n+3)\psi_{n+1}(\alpha r) + \psi_n(\alpha r)\}x W_n. \end{aligned}$$

Accordingly the terms contributed to $\lambda x\Delta + \ldots$ by the term $A_n\psi_n(\alpha r)$ of K_n are

$$\begin{aligned} &\mu\left[\frac{A_n'}{\alpha^2}\left\{\frac{\alpha^2r^2}{n}\psi_n(\alpha r) - 2(n+2)\psi_n(\alpha r) - \frac{2}{n}\psi_{n-1}(\alpha r)\right\}\right. \\ &\qquad\qquad \left. - \frac{A_n}{4\pi\gamma\rho_0}\left\{\frac{\alpha^2r^2}{n}\psi_n(\alpha r) + \frac{2(n-1)}{n}\psi_{n-1}(\alpha r)\right\}\right]\frac{\partial W_n}{\partial x} \\ &\quad - \left[\mu A_n'\{2(n+2)\psi_{n+1}(\alpha r) + \psi_n(\alpha r)\} + (\lambda+\mu)\frac{\alpha^2 A_n}{4\pi\gamma\rho_0}\psi_n(\alpha r)\right]x W_n \end{aligned}$$

......(48).

In like manner the terms contributed to $\lambda x\Delta + \dots$ by the term $B_n \chi_n(\beta r)$ of K_n are

$$\mu\left[-\frac{B_n'}{\beta^2}\left\{\frac{\beta^2 r^2}{n}\chi_n(\beta r) + 2(n+2)\chi_n(\beta r) - \frac{2}{n}\chi_{n-1}(\beta r)\right\}\right.$$
$$\left.+\frac{B_n}{4\pi\gamma\rho_0}\left\{\frac{\beta^2 r^2}{n}\chi_n(\beta r) + \frac{2(n-1)}{n}\chi_{n-1}(\beta r)\right\}\right]\frac{\partial W_n}{\partial x}$$
$$-\left[\mu B_n'\{2(n+2)\chi_{n+1}(\beta r) - \chi_n(\beta r)\} - (\lambda+\mu)\frac{\beta^2 B_n}{4\pi\gamma\rho_0}\chi_n(\beta r)\right] x W_n \quad \dots\dots(49).$$

Finally the terms contributed to $\lambda x\Delta + \dots$ by the term C_n of K_n reduce to

$$2\mu(n-1)C_n'\frac{\partial W_n}{\partial x} \quad \dots\dots\dots\dots\dots\dots\dots(50).$$

116. The equation which expresses the condition that the x-component of the traction across the deformed surface vanishes is obtained by equating to zero the sum of the three formulae (48), (49) and (50), in which r is replaced by a. The corresponding conditions for the vanishing of the y- and z-components are obtained by writing $\partial W_n/\partial y$ and $\partial W_n/\partial z$ in order instead of $\partial W_n/\partial x$, and $y W_n$ and $z W_n$ in order instead of $x W_n$. To satisfy all three equations it is necessary that the coefficients of $\partial W_n/\partial x$ and $x W_n$ in the sum of (48), (49) and (50) should vanish when $r = a$. We thus obtain the two equations

$$\frac{A_n'}{\alpha^2}\left\{\frac{\alpha^2 a^2}{n}\psi_n(\alpha a) - 2(n+2)\psi_n(\alpha a) - \frac{2}{n}\psi_{n-1}(\alpha a)\right\}$$
$$-\frac{A_n}{4\pi\gamma\rho_0}\left\{\frac{\alpha^2 a^2}{n}\psi_n(\alpha a) + \frac{2(n-1)}{n}\psi_{n-1}(\alpha a)\right\}$$
$$-\frac{B_n'}{\beta^2}\left\{\frac{\beta^2 a^2}{n}\chi_n(\beta a) + 2(n+2)\chi_n(\beta a) - \frac{2}{n}\chi_{n-1}(\beta a)\right\}$$
$$+\frac{B_n}{4\pi\gamma\rho_0}\left\{\frac{\beta^2 a^2}{n}\chi_n(\beta a) + \frac{2(n-1)}{n}\chi_{n-1}(\beta a)\right\} + 2(n-1)C_n' = 0 \quad \dots\dots(51),$$

and

$$A_n'\{2(n+2)\psi_{n+1}(\alpha a) + \psi_n(\alpha a)\} + \left(1+\frac{\lambda}{\mu}\right)\frac{\alpha^2 A_n}{4\pi\gamma\rho_0}\psi_n(\alpha a)$$
$$+ B_n'\{2(n+2)\chi_{n+1}(\beta a) - \chi_n(\beta a)\} - \left(1+\frac{\lambda}{\mu}\right)\frac{\beta^2 B_n}{4\pi\gamma\rho_0}\chi_n(\beta a) = 0 \dots(52).$$

117. It will be convenient to form the surface characteristic equation for the potential in each special problem at the time when we require it;

but, as we always need a formula for U in order to form this equation, we record this formula here. We have

$$rU = (nF_n + r^2 G_n) W_n,$$

or

$$rU = \left[-\frac{A_n}{4\pi\gamma\rho_0}\psi_{n-1}(\alpha r) - \frac{n+1}{\alpha^2}A_n'\psi_n(\alpha r) + \frac{B_n}{4\pi\gamma\rho_0}\chi_{n-1}(\beta r) - \frac{n+1}{\beta^2}B_n'\chi_n(\beta r) + nC_n'\right]W_n \quad \ldots(53).$$

In the next two Chapters we shall be occupied with special problems which can be solved by means of the analysis developed in this Chapter.

Radial Displacement.

118. The typical solution found above could be adapted to the problem of purely radial displacements, but it is simpler to proceed by a special method. In equations (9) of p. 92 we put

$$u = U\frac{x}{r}, \qquad v = U\frac{y}{r}, \qquad w = U\frac{z}{r},$$

where U is a function of r, and observe that we have

$$\Delta = \frac{dU}{dr} + \frac{2U}{r},$$

$$\nabla^2 u = \frac{x}{r}\left(\frac{d^2U}{dr^2} + \frac{2}{r}\frac{dU}{dr} - \frac{2U}{r^2}\right) = \frac{\partial\Delta}{\partial x},$$

$$x\Delta - \frac{\partial(rU)}{\partial x} = \frac{x}{r}U.$$

Then these equations reduce to the single equation

$$(\lambda + 2\mu)\frac{d\Delta}{dr} + (p^2\rho_0 + \tfrac{4}{3}\pi\gamma\rho_0^2)U + \rho_0\frac{dW}{dr} = 0 \quad \ldots\ldots\ldots\ldots(54).$$

Also equation (11) of p. 92 reduces to

$$\frac{1}{r^2}\frac{d}{dr}\left(r^2\frac{dW}{dr}\right) = 4\pi\gamma\rho_0\Delta.$$

On eliminating W between these two equations we find the equation

$$(\lambda + 2\mu)\left(\frac{d^2\Delta}{dr^2} + \frac{2}{r}\frac{d\Delta}{dr}\right) + (p^2\rho_0 + \tfrac{16}{3}\pi\gamma\rho_0^2)\Delta = 0 \quad \ldots\ldots\ldots(55).$$

The relevant solution of this equation is

$$\Delta = A_0\psi_0(\alpha r) = A_0\frac{\sin\alpha r}{\alpha r} \quad \ldots\ldots\ldots\ldots\ldots\ldots\ldots\ldots(56),$$

where

$$\alpha^2 = (p^2\rho_0 + \tfrac{16}{3}\pi\gamma\rho_0^2)/(\lambda + 2\mu) \quad \ldots\ldots\ldots\ldots\ldots\ldots\ldots(57);$$

and the corresponding relevant form for U is

$$U = A_0 \frac{\sin \alpha r - \alpha r \cos \alpha r}{\alpha^3 r^2} \quad \text{.......................(58).}$$

The condition that the traction across the bounding surface vanishes is expressed by the equation

$$\lambda \Delta + 2\mu \frac{dU}{dr} = 0,$$

which must hold at $r = a$. This gives the equation

$$(\lambda + 2\mu)\, \alpha^2 a^2 \sin \alpha a - 4\mu (\sin \alpha a - \alpha a \cos \alpha a) = 0,$$

or

$$\alpha a \cot \alpha a = 1 - \frac{\lambda + 2\mu}{4\mu} \alpha^2 a^2 \quad \text{.......................(59).}$$

The general analysis in §§ 112—117 has been worked out for the case where equation (28) on p. 97 has one negative root and one positive root. When the frequency of vibration ($p/2\pi$) is great enough both the roots are negative, and the analysis requires some extension. The consideration of this extension will be postponed to Chapter X.

CHAPTER VIII

EFFECT OF COMPRESSIBILITY ON EARTH TIDES

119. We shall now apply the analysis developed in the previous Chapter to the problem of corporeal tides in the earth, regarded as a homogeneous sphere composed of solid material which has a finite modulus of compression and a finite rigidity. We shall assume that the problem is a statical one, so that $p=0$, and we shall take the spherical solid harmonic W_n to be the tide-generating potential, and shall write it W_2, as it is of the second degree.

The disturbing potential W consists of (1) the tide-generating potential W_2, (2) the potential due to the volume distribution of density $-\rho_0\Delta$, (3) the potential due to the surface distribution $\rho_0 U_a$; and we have

$$W = K_2(r)\, W_2$$
$$= A_2\psi_2(\alpha r) + B_2\chi_2(\beta r) + C_2 \quad \text{......................(1)},$$

where $-\alpha^2$ and β^2 are the roots of the equation

$$\mu(\lambda+2\mu)\,\xi^2 + \tfrac{16}{3}\pi\gamma\rho_0{}^2\mu\xi - 6\,(\tfrac{4}{3}\pi\gamma\rho_0{}^2)^2 = 0 \quad \text{..............(2)}.$$

From the general form of solution we find

$$\Delta = -\frac{1}{4\pi\gamma\rho_0}\{\alpha^2 A_2\psi_2(\alpha r) - \beta^2 B_2\chi_2(\beta r)\}\, W_2 \quad \text{...............(3)}$$

and
$$rU = -\left[\left\{\frac{3A_2'}{\alpha^2}\psi_2(\alpha r) + \frac{A_2}{4\pi\gamma\rho_0}\psi_1(\alpha r)\right\}\right.$$
$$\left. + \left\{\frac{3B_2'}{\beta^2}\chi_2(\beta r) - \frac{B_2}{4\pi\gamma\rho_0}\chi_1(\beta r)\right\} - 2C_2'\right] W_2 \quad \text{...(4)},$$

where the six constants $A_2, \ldots, C_2'$ are connected by the three equations

$$\left.\begin{aligned} A_2' &= \frac{\alpha^2 A_2}{4\pi\gamma\rho_0}\left(1 + \frac{8\pi\gamma\rho_0{}^2}{3\mu\alpha^2}\right) \\ B_2' &= \frac{\beta^2 B_2}{4\pi\gamma\rho_0}\left(1 - \frac{8\pi\gamma\rho_0{}^2}{3\mu\beta^2}\right) \\ C_2 &= \tfrac{8}{3}\pi\gamma\rho_0 C_2' \end{aligned}\right\} \quad \text{.........................(5)}.$$

120. These constants are also connected by the equations furnished by the boundary conditions. The first of these conditions is the surface characteristic equation for the potential. At points within the sphere $r=a$, the potential due to the volume distribution of density $-\rho_0\Delta$ and the surface distribution $\rho_0 U_a$ is $W-W_2$, or it is

$$K_2(r)\,W_2 - W_2.$$

At points outside the surface $r=a$ the potential due to the same volume and surface distributions of matter is

$$\{K_2(a)-1\}\frac{a^5}{r^5}W_2.$$

Hence the surface characteristic equation is

$$\left[\{K_2(a)-1\}\frac{\partial}{\partial r}\left(\frac{a^5}{r^5}W_2\right)\right]_{r=a} - \left[\frac{\partial}{\partial r}\{K_2(r)\,W_2 - W_2\}\right]_{r=a} = -4\pi\gamma\rho_0 U_a,$$

or it is
$$a\frac{d}{da}K_2(a) + 5\{K_2(a)-1\} = 4\pi\gamma\rho_0\left(\frac{rU}{W_2}\right)_{r=a}.$$

Since for all values of r

$$r\frac{d}{dr}K_2(r) + 5K_2(r) = -A_2\psi_1(\alpha r) + B_2\chi_1(\beta r) + 5C_2,$$

the above equation becomes, by (53) of p. 103,

$$5(C_2-1) = 4\pi\gamma\rho_0\left[2C_2' - 3\left\{\frac{A_2'}{\alpha^2}\psi_2(\alpha a) + \frac{B_2'}{\beta^2}\chi_2(\beta a)\right\}\right] \quad \text{......(6).}$$

121. The remaining boundary conditions are to be written down by means of equations (51) and (52) on p. 102. We have

$$\frac{A_2'}{\alpha^2}\left\{\left(\frac{\alpha^2a^2}{2}-8\right)\psi_2(\alpha a) - \psi_1(\alpha a)\right\} - \frac{A_2}{4\pi\gamma\rho_0}\left\{\frac{\alpha^2a^2}{2}\psi_2(\alpha a) + \psi_1(\alpha a)\right\}$$
$$-\frac{B_2'}{\beta^2}\left\{\left(\frac{\beta^2a^2}{2}+8\right)\chi_2(\beta a) - \chi_1(\beta a)\right\} + \frac{B_2}{4\pi\gamma\rho_0}\left\{\frac{\beta^2a^2}{2}\chi_2(\beta a) + \chi_1(\beta a)\right\}$$
$$+2C_2' = 0 \quad \text{.........(7)}$$

and
$$A_2'\{8\psi_3(\alpha a) + \psi_2(\alpha a)\} + \left(1+\frac{\lambda}{\mu}\right)\frac{\alpha^2 A_2}{4\pi\gamma\rho_0}\psi_2(\alpha a)$$
$$+B_2'\{8\chi_3(\beta a) - \chi_2(\beta a)\} - \left(1+\frac{\lambda}{\mu}\right)\frac{\beta^2 B_2}{4\pi\gamma\rho_0}\chi_2(\beta a) = 0 \quad \text{...........(8).}$$

122. Now equation (2) gives

$$\alpha^2-\beta^2 = \frac{16}{3}\frac{\pi\gamma\rho_0^2}{\lambda+2\mu}, \quad \alpha^2\beta^2 = \frac{32}{3}\frac{(\pi\gamma\rho_0^2)^2}{\mu(\lambda+2\mu)} \quad \text{...............(9),}$$

so that
$$\frac{\alpha^2\beta^2}{\alpha^2-\beta^2} = \frac{2\pi\gamma\rho_0^2}{\mu}, \quad \frac{\lambda+2\mu}{\mu} = \frac{8\alpha^2\beta^2}{3(\alpha^2-\beta^2)^2} \quad \text{................(10).}$$

Hence the first two of equations (5) become

$$A_2' = \frac{\alpha^2 A_2}{4\pi\gamma\rho_0}\frac{3\alpha^2+\beta^2}{3(\alpha^2-\beta^2)}, \quad B_2' = -\frac{\beta^2 B_2}{4\pi\gamma\rho_0}\frac{\alpha^2+3\beta^2}{3(\alpha^2-\beta^2)} \quad \text{.........(11).}$$

We may now re-write equation (6) in the form

$$\tfrac{4}{3}C_2' + \frac{A_2}{4\pi\gamma\rho_0}\frac{3\alpha^2+\beta^2}{\alpha^2-\beta^2}\psi_2 - \frac{B_2}{4\pi\gamma\rho_0}\frac{3\beta^2+\alpha^2}{\alpha^2-\beta^2}\chi_2 = \frac{5}{4\pi\gamma\rho_0} \quad \text{.......(12),}$$

where the arguments αa and βa of the ψ and χ functions need no longer be expressed. On using (11) to eliminate A_2' and B_2' and (12) to eliminate C_2', we obtain instead of equations (7) and (8) the two equations

$$A_2\left[\frac{3\alpha^2+\beta^2}{3(\alpha^2-\beta^2)}\left(\frac{25-\alpha^2a^2}{2}\psi_2+\psi_1\right)+\frac{\alpha^2a^2}{2}\psi_2+\psi_1\right]$$
$$-B_2\left[\frac{\alpha^2+3\beta^2}{3(\alpha^2-\beta^2)}\left(\frac{25+\beta^2a^2}{2}\chi_2-\chi_1\right)+\frac{\beta^2a^2}{2}\chi_2+\chi_1\right]=\frac{15}{2} \quad \text{.........(13)}$$

and

$$A_2\alpha^2\left\{\frac{3\alpha^2+\beta^2}{3(\alpha^2-\beta^2)}(\psi_2+8\psi_3)+\left(1+\frac{\lambda}{\mu}\right)\psi_2\right\}$$
$$+B_2\beta^2\left\{\frac{3\beta^2+\alpha^2}{3(\alpha^2-\beta^2)}(\chi_2-8\chi_3)-\left(1+\frac{\lambda}{\mu}\right)\chi_2\right\}=0 \quad \text{.........(14).}$$

Again we may simplify (14) by writing

$$\psi_3 = -\frac{5\psi_2+\psi_1}{\alpha^2a^2}, \quad \chi_3 = -\frac{5\chi_2-\chi_1}{\beta^2a^2};$$

it becomes

$$A_2\left[\frac{3\alpha^2+\beta^2}{3(\alpha^2-\beta^2)}(40\psi_2+8\psi_1-\alpha^2a^2\psi_2)-\frac{\lambda+\mu}{\mu}\alpha^2a^2\psi_2\right]$$
$$-B_2\left[\frac{3\beta^2+\alpha^2}{3(\alpha^2-\beta^2)}(40\chi_2-8\chi_1+\beta^2a^2\chi_2)-\frac{\lambda+\mu}{\mu}\beta^2a^2\chi_2\right]=0,$$

which is the same as

$$A_2\left[\frac{3\alpha^2+\beta^2}{3(\alpha^2-\beta^2)}(40\psi_2+8\psi_1-\alpha^2a^2\psi_2)+\alpha^2a^2\psi_2-\frac{\lambda+2\mu}{\mu}\alpha^2a^2\psi_2\right]$$
$$=B_2\left[\frac{3\beta^2+\alpha^2}{3(\alpha^2-\beta^2)}(40\chi_2-8\chi_1+\beta^2a^2\chi_2)+\beta^2a^2\chi_2-\frac{\lambda+2\mu}{\mu}\beta^2a^2\chi_2\right]$$

or, by the second of equations (10),

$$A_2\left[(3\alpha^2+\beta^2)(40\psi_2+8\psi_1)-4\alpha^2\beta^2a^2\psi_2-8\frac{\alpha^2}{\alpha^2-\beta^2}\alpha^2\beta^2a^2\psi_2\right]$$
$$=B_2\left[(3\beta^2+\alpha^2)(40\chi_2-8\chi_1)+4\alpha^2\beta^2a^2\chi_2-8\frac{\beta^2}{\alpha^2-\beta^2}\alpha^2\beta^2a^2\chi_2\right]$$

or $$A_2[(3\alpha^2+\beta^2)(\alpha^2-\beta^2)(10\psi_2+2\psi_1)-(3\alpha^2-\beta^2)\alpha^2\beta^2a^2\psi_2]$$
$$=B_2[(3\beta^2+\alpha^2)(\alpha^2-\beta^2)(10\chi_2-2\chi_1)-(3\beta^2-\alpha^2)\alpha^2\beta^2a^2\chi_2] \quad \text{...........(15)}$$

The two equations (13) and (15) determine A_2 and B_2.

123. When A_2 and B_2 are known C_2' is known from (12), and then the remaining constants are known from (5). The solution is therefore complete. The numbers h and k introduced (p. 53) in the general theory of Chapter IV are expressed by the equations

$$\left.\begin{aligned} h &= \frac{5}{2} - \frac{5}{6}\frac{3\alpha^2+\beta^2}{\alpha^2-\beta^2} A_2\psi_2 - \frac{1}{3}A_2\psi_1 + \frac{5}{6}\frac{\alpha^2+3\beta^2}{\alpha^2-\beta^2} B_2\chi_2 + \frac{1}{3}B_2\chi_1 \\ k &= A_2\psi_2 + B_2\chi_2 + C_2 - 1 \end{aligned}\right\} \quad \text{......(16).}$$

By way of verification it seemed to be worth while to work out the limiting case in which μ is finite and μ/λ tends to zero as a limit, that is to say the case of incompressible material. The numbers α and β both tend to zero, the quotient β/α tends to unity, $\psi_n(\alpha a)$ and $\chi_n(\beta a)$ tend to

$$\frac{(-1)^n}{1.3.5\ldots(2n+1)} \quad \text{and} \quad \frac{1}{1.3.5\ldots(2n+1)},$$

also $(\alpha^2-\beta^2)/\alpha^2\beta^2$ tends to $\mu/2\pi\gamma\rho_0^2$. It can then be shown that h tends to the limit

$$\frac{5}{2}\Big/\left(1+\frac{19}{2}\frac{\mu}{\frac{4}{3}\pi\gamma\rho_0^2a^2}\right),$$

which is in accordance with Lord Kelvin's solution as recorded on p. 62 *ante*. In this case (incompressibility) $k=\frac{3}{5}h$ for all values of μ, the material being homogeneous.

124. In order to discover the sense of the correction for compressibility, and its order of magnitude, it seems to be best to work out two particular numerical examples, chosen so as to simplify the values of αa and βa. Now from (2) we have

$$\alpha^2a^2 = \frac{g\rho_0 a}{\lambda+2\mu}\left[\sqrt{\left\{4+\frac{6(\lambda+2\mu)}{\mu}\right\}}+2\right],$$

$$\beta^2a^2 = \frac{g\rho_0 a}{\lambda+2\mu}\left[\sqrt{\left\{4+\frac{6(\lambda+2\mu)}{\mu}\right\}}-2\right],$$

where g is written for $\frac{4}{3}\pi\gamma\rho_0 a$. To get simple values for αa and βa the expression under the square root should be a perfect square, and the ratio of the two expressions in the square brackets should also be a perfect square. To assimilate the properties of the material to those of known materials the ratio $\lambda:\mu$ should lie between 1 and 2, the former value making Poisson's ratio equal to $\frac{1}{4}$, and the latter making it equal to $\frac{1}{3}$.

125. A first simple example of values which satisfy these conditions is afforded by taking

$$\alpha a = 3, \quad \beta a = 2.$$

This makes $$\frac{\lambda}{\mu}=\frac{46}{25},$$

and $$\frac{g\rho_0 a}{\mu}=\frac{24}{5}.$$

For a sphere of the size and mass of the earth this gives for μ the value $7{\cdot}16\times10^{11}$ dynes per square cm., which is a little less than the rigidity of steel. The rigidity of the earth, as computed by Lord Kelvin, is given by the equation $g\rho_0 a/\mu=\frac{19}{4}$, which would give for μ the value $7{\cdot}23\times10^{11}$ dynes per square cm.

The functions ψ_1, ... are given by the formulae

$$\left.\begin{aligned}\psi_1&=(\alpha a\cos\alpha a-\sin\alpha a)/\alpha^3a^3\\ \psi_2&=\{(3-\alpha^2a^2)\sin\alpha a-3\alpha a\cos\alpha a\}/\alpha^5a^5\\ \chi_1&=(\beta a\cosh\beta a-\sinh\beta a)/\beta^3a^3\\ \chi_2&=\{(3+\beta^2a^2)\sinh\beta a-3\beta a\cosh\beta a\}/\beta^5a^5\end{aligned}\right\}\quad\text{.........(17).}$$

Hence we find*

$$\begin{aligned}\psi_1(3)&=-0{\cdot}1152,\\ \psi_2(3)&=0{\cdot}0332,\\ \chi_1(2)&=0{\cdot}4872,\\ \chi_2(2)&=0{\cdot}0880;\end{aligned}$$

and thence by equations (14) and (15)

$$A_2=-10{\cdot}37,\quad B_2=-6{\cdot}27.$$

Hence we find the values of h and k to be

$$h=0{\cdot}932,\quad k=0{\cdot}513.$$

With the same value of μ we should find, on assuming incompressibility,

$$h=0{\cdot}839,\quad k=0{\cdot}503.$$

Thus if λ is nearly equal to 2μ, the computed value of h is increased by about 10 per cent. of itself on account of the compressibility, while the computed value of k is but slightly increased.

126. A second fairly simple example of values for αa and βa which satisfy the conditions stated above is afforded by taking

$$\alpha a=3{\cdot}3,\quad \beta a=2{\cdot}1.$$

This makes $$\frac{\lambda}{\mu}=\frac{2041}{1944},$$

so that λ/μ is but slightly greater than unity. We then find for μ the value

* In computing the values of the functions ψ_1,... I used the tables published by C. Burrau, "Tables of cosines and sines of real and imaginary angles expressed in radians," Berlin, 1907.

$6{\cdot}955 \times 10^{11}$ dynes per square cm., a slightly smaller rigidity than that found in the previous example. In this case we find

$$\psi_1(3{\cdot}3) = -\,0{\cdot}0863,$$
$$\psi_2(3{\cdot}3) = \,0{\cdot}0282,$$
$$\chi_1(2{\cdot}1) = \,0{\cdot}5055,$$
$$\chi_2(2{\cdot}1) = \,0{\cdot}0904,$$

and thence by equations (14) and (15)

$$A_2 = -\,15{\cdot}24, \quad B_2 = -\,6{\cdot}82.$$

Hence we find the values of h and k to be

$$h = 1{\cdot}044, \quad k = 0{\cdot}523.$$

With the same value of μ, we should find, on assuming incompressibility,

$$h = 0{\cdot}855, \quad k = 0{\cdot}513.$$

Thus if λ is nearly equal to μ, the computed value of h is increased by nearly 20 per cent. of itself on account of the compressibility, while the computed value of k is but slightly increased.

127. We have seen in Chapter IV that the first attempts which were made to estimate the height of earth tides were based on the simplifying assumptions of homogeneity and incompressibility, together with the observed height of the fortnightly tide. We saw also how the yielding of the earth to tidal forces could be expressed by the two numbers which we have denoted by h and k. Further we found that the first estimates were in excess of the true values, for we saw that both numbers could be determined very approximately by combining the results of two kinds of observations, viz. those of the lunar deflexion of gravity and the periodic variation of latitude. We noted also that it had been made out that heterogeneity of the material would tend to diminish the computed values of the two numbers. In this Chapter we have proved by two examples, which may fairly be regarded as typical, that compressibility tends to increase the computed values of the two numbers. Another way of expressing the result is to say that any estimate of the rigidity of the earth, based on a theory in which the earth is regarded as homogeneous, is likely to be too great, while any estimate, based on a theory in which the earth is regarded as incompressible, is likely to be too small. On a survey of the whole question it seems that the correction for heterogeneity is rather more important than the correction for compressibility.

CHAPTER IX

THE PROBLEM OF GRAVITATIONAL INSTABILITY

128. In an elastic solid body slightly strained by external forces, and held by them in a state which differs but little from a state of zero stress, there can be no question of instability. The solution of the equations of equilibrium is, in fact, uniquely determinate. In particular if there are no external forces there is no displacement*. All this is different for a large gravitating body in a state of initial stress. If the resistance to compression and the rigidity are small enough, the body may be capable of being held in a strained state by the inequalities in the gravitational attraction that are caused by the strain. Any change in the density at a point is accompanied by changes of attraction. Now, as the body passes from a homogeneous state of aggregation, or from a state in which the mass is distributed symmetrically round the centre, to some other state of aggregation, the gravitational potential energy may be diminished, but a certain amount of strain energy will be stored in the body. If the gravitational energy lost exceeds the strain energy gained, the body in the unstrained state is unstable. The critical condition separating stable from unstable states is such that the gain of strain energy corresponding to the small displacement is just equal to the loss of gravitational energy corresponding to the same displacement. In order that this may be so, it is evidently necessary that the equations of equilibrium under no external forces should be satisfied by displacements which do not vanish, although the external forces vanish. This comes to the same thing as saying that the body must admit of vibrations the frequency of which is zero.

129. The chief interest of the problem arises from the theory propounded by J. H. Jeans† to the effect that the earth was at one time in such a state, as regards resistance to compression and rigidity, that it would have been unstable if it had been homogeneous, or if its mass had been distributed symmetrically about a centre. Traces of this past state were supposed to be

* A displacement which would be possible in a rigid body is, of course, disregarded, as there is no strain answering to it.

† *Loc. cit.*, *ante* p. 89.

manifested in the existing distribution of land and water on the surface of the globe. Jeans worked out the problem for a gravitating sphere in which, in the homogeneous state, gravitation is supposed to be balanced by body-forces of external origin. The problem for a body in a state of initial stress was afterwards solved* by adopting the first of the two alternative hypotheses (as regards initial pressure) which have been explained at the beginning of Chapter VII. The second alternative being more consonant with physical reality, it seems to be appropriate to obtain a new solution by applying the analysis developed in that Chapter.

In the formulae for the displacement and the inequality of potential we have simply to put $p=0$. Then the six constants A_n, B_n, C_n, A_n', B_n', C_n' are connected by the equations (41) of p. 99, (45) of p. 100, (51) and (52) of p. 102, and a sixth equation which results from the surface characteristic equation for the potential.

130. The potential W, $=K_n(r)\,W_n$, is due to the volume distribution of density $-\rho_0\Delta$ and the distribution of superficial density $\rho_0 U_a$ on the surface $r=a$; and the potential at external points due to the same volume density and surface density is

$$K_n(a)\frac{a^{2n+1}}{r^{2n+1}}W_n.$$

The surface characteristic equation for the potential is therefore

$$\left[\frac{\partial}{\partial r}\left\{K_n(a)\frac{a^{2n+1}}{r^{2n+1}}W_n\right\}\right]_{r=a}-\left[\frac{\partial}{\partial r}\{K_n(r)\,W_n\}\right]_{r=a}=-4\pi\gamma\rho_0 U_a,$$

or it is

$$a\frac{dK_n(a)}{da}+(2n+1)K_n(a)=4\pi\gamma\rho_0\left(\frac{rU}{W_n}\right)_{r=a}.$$

By equations (33), (36), (39) of pp. 98, 99 we have

$$a\frac{dK_n(a)}{da}+(2n+1)K_n(a)=-A_n\psi_{n-1}(\alpha a)+B_n\chi_{n-1}(\beta a)+(2n+1)C_n,$$

and hence, using the result (53) of p. 103, we find that the surface characteristic equation for the potential becomes

$$(2n+1)\frac{C_n}{4\pi\gamma\rho_0}=nC_n'-(n+1)\left\{\frac{A_n'}{\alpha^2}\psi_n(\alpha a)+\frac{B_n'}{\beta^2}\chi_n(\beta a)\right\},$$

or, by equation (47) of p. 100, it becomes

$$\frac{2n(n-1)}{3}C_n'=-(n+1)\left\{\frac{A_n'}{\alpha^2}\psi_n(\alpha a)+\frac{B_n'}{\beta^2}\chi_n(\beta a)\right\}\;\ldots\ldots\ldots(1).$$

131. Now, p being zero, $-\alpha^2$ and β^2 are the roots of the equation

$$\mu(\lambda+2\mu)\,\xi^2+\tfrac{16}{3}\pi\gamma\rho_0^2\mu\xi-n(n+1)(\tfrac{4}{3}\pi\gamma\rho_0^2)^2=0\;\ldots\ldots\ldots(2),$$

* A. E. H. Love, *loc. cit.*, *ante* p. 89.

so that we have

$$\alpha^2 - \beta^2 = \frac{16\pi\gamma\rho_0^2}{3(\lambda + 2\mu)}, \quad \frac{\alpha^2\beta^2}{\alpha^2 - \beta^2} = \frac{n(n+1)\pi\gamma\rho_0^2}{3\mu} \quad \ldots\ldots\ldots\ldots(3),$$

and the equations (41) of p. 99 and (45) of p. 100 can be written

$$\left.\begin{aligned} A_n' &= \frac{A_n\alpha^2}{4\pi\gamma\rho_0}\left\{1 + \frac{4\beta^2}{(n+1)(\alpha^2 - \beta^2)}\right\} \\ B_n' &= \frac{B_n\beta^2}{4\pi\gamma\rho_0}\left\{1 - \frac{4\alpha^2}{(n+1)(\alpha^2 - \beta^2)}\right\} \end{aligned}\right\} \quad \ldots\ldots\ldots\ldots\ldots\ldots(4).$$

When any particular value is assigned to n, the condition that the initially homogeneous sphere may be gravitationally unstable for harmonic disturbances of the nth degree is to be obtained by eliminating the undetermined constants from the equations (51) and (52) of p. 102 and the equations (1) and (4) above. The special value zero for n is best treated by a distinct method, as was explained at the end of Chapter VII.

132. In the problem of purely radial displacements the condition of gravitational instability is obtained from equations (57) and (59) of pp. 103, 104 by putting 0 for p. If the ratio of λ to μ is taken to be given, α is to be found from the equation

$$\frac{\tan \alpha a}{\alpha a} = 1 \Big/ \left(1 - \frac{\lambda + 2\mu}{4\mu}\alpha^2 a^2\right) \ldots\ldots\ldots\ldots\ldots\ldots\ldots\ldots(5),$$

and then λ and μ will be known from the equation

$$\alpha^2 = \frac{16\pi\gamma\rho_0^2}{3(\lambda + 2\mu)} \quad \ldots\ldots\ldots\ldots\ldots\ldots\ldots\ldots\ldots\ldots(6).$$

In the following table the numbers in the first row are selected values for the ratio λ/μ, the particular value in the last column being intended to represent the case where the ratio is large, that is to say either the substance is very incompressible or of very small rigidity. The results for this particular value have been worked out for the sake of comparison with the results answering to spherical harmonics of the first degree, for which, as will be seen later, the results can be worked out most easily by assuming certain special values for the ratio $\lambda : \mu$, and 95918/441 is one of these special values. In the second row are given the corresponding smallest roots of equation (5). Some of these are adapted from the results given by H. Lamb*. In the third row are given, as multiples of 10^{12} dynes per square cm., the corresponding values of $\lambda + 2\mu$, as determined by equation (6). In the fourth row are given, in km. per second, the corresponding values of $\sqrt{\{(\lambda + 2\mu)/\rho_0\}}$, the velocity of compressional waves in the material. In the fifth row are given,

* *Loc. cit., ante* p. 50.

as multiples of 10^{11} dynes per square cm., the corresponding values of μ, the rigidity. The values assumed for ρ_0 and a are 5·5 grammes per cubic cm. and $6{\cdot}37 \times 10^8$ cm.

λ/μ	1	2	95918/441
αa	2·564	2·578	3·136
$\lambda + 2\mu$	2·10	2·07	1·40
$\sqrt{\{(\lambda+2\mu)/\rho_0\}}$	6·2	6·13	5·0
μ	7·0	5·17	0·0637

133. An example will make it clear how the table is to be interpreted. From the first column we learn that a homogeneous sphere of the size and mass of the earth made of a material nearly as rigid as steel and nearly as incompressible, the Poisson's ratio of the material being $\frac{1}{4}$, could not exist. It would be unstable as regards radial displacement. If such a sphere existed for an instant it would at once begin to condense towards the centre. If it were as rigid and as incompressible as steel, and homogeneous, it would be stable.

The velocity of transmission of the preliminary tremors (first phase) that are observed when a great earthquake occurs at a place which is a long way from the observing station is about 9·2 km. per second. This is greater than any of the values in the fourth row of the table. Assuming that these tremors are correctly described as waves of compression travelling through the body of the earth, and emerging at the surface, we appear to be justified in concluding that the resistance to compression of the materials composing the earth is, on the average, so great that the earth would be stable, as regards radial displacements, if it were homogeneous.

It appears further from the table that a body in which the rigidity is small compared with the resistance to compression is stable, as regards radial displacements, for a smaller rigidity than would be required to render stable a body, in which the ratio of the two elastic constants is of the order observed in most hard solids. If we pass to the limit by making the substance incompressible the body is gravitationally stable however small the rigidity may be.

134. We next take up the problem for harmonic disturbances of the first degree. Equations (4) become

$$A_1' = \frac{\alpha^2+\beta^2}{\alpha^2-\beta^2}\frac{A_1\alpha^2}{4\pi\gamma\rho_0}, \quad B_1' = -\frac{\alpha^2+\beta^2}{\alpha^2-\beta^2}\frac{B_1\beta^2}{4\pi\gamma\rho_0} \quad \text{..........(7).}$$

Equation (1) becomes

$$\frac{A_1'}{\alpha^2}\psi_1 + \frac{B_1'}{\beta^2}\chi_1 = 0 \quad \text{..........(8),}$$

where the arguments αa and βa of the ψ and χ functions are suppressed. Equations (51) and (52) of p. 102 become

$$\frac{A_1'}{\alpha^2}\left\{(\alpha^2 a^2 - 6)\psi_1 - 2\psi_0\right\} - \frac{A_1}{4\pi\gamma\rho_0}\alpha^2 a^2 \psi_1$$
$$- \frac{B_1'}{\beta^2}\left\{(\beta^2 a^2 + 6)\chi_1 - 2\chi_0\right\} + \frac{B_1}{4\pi\gamma\rho_0}\beta^2 a^2 \chi_1 = 0 \quad \text{........(9),}$$

and

$$A_1'(6\psi_2 + \psi_1) + \left(1 + \frac{\lambda}{\mu}\right)\frac{\alpha^2 A_1}{4\pi\gamma\rho_0}\psi_1$$
$$+ B_1'(6\chi_2 - \chi_1) - \left(1 + \frac{\lambda}{\mu}\right)\frac{\beta^2 B_1}{4\pi\gamma\rho_0}\chi_1 = 0 \quad \text{..........(10).}$$

The terms in C_1' have disappeared through the vanishing of the factor $n-1$ in the general formulae. In fact it is easy to see that the solution corresponding to the constant term C_1 in the formula for $K_1(r)$ represents a displacement which would be possible in a rigid body, and is therefore irrelevant. Equations (7), (8), (9), and (10) appear to be too many, but it will be found that (10) is equivalent to a combination of (8) and (9)*.

On substituting from (7) in (8) we get

$$A_1\psi_1 = B_1\chi_1 \quad \text{..........(11).}$$

On substituting from (7) in (9), and using (11), we get

$$\frac{\alpha^2+\beta^2}{\alpha^2-\beta^2}\left(\alpha^2 a^2 - 6 - 2\frac{\psi_0}{\psi_1}\right) - \alpha^2 a^2$$
$$+ \frac{\alpha^2+\beta^2}{\alpha^2-\beta^2}\left(\beta^2 a^2 + 6 - 2\frac{\chi_0}{\chi_1}\right) + \beta^2 a^2 = 0,$$

or

$$\frac{\psi_0}{\psi_1} + \frac{\chi_0}{\chi_1} = \frac{2\alpha^2\beta^2 a^2}{\alpha^2+\beta^2} \quad \text{..........(12).}$$

On substituting from (7) in (10), and using (11) and the appropriate form of (3) which gives

$$\frac{\lambda + 2\mu}{\mu} = \frac{8\alpha^2\beta^2}{(\alpha^2-\beta^2)^2},$$

* Some peculiarity was to be expected to occur when $n=1$. See the papers by Jeans and Love cited on p. 89, *ante*.

we find
$$\alpha^2\left[\frac{\alpha^2+\beta^2}{\alpha^2-\beta^2}\frac{6\psi_2}{\psi_1}+\frac{2\beta^2}{\alpha^2-\beta^2}+\frac{8\alpha^2\beta^2}{(\alpha^2-\beta^2)^2}\right]$$
$$-\beta^2\left[\frac{\alpha^2+\beta^2}{\alpha^2-\beta^2}\frac{6\chi_2}{\chi_1}-\frac{2\alpha^2}{\alpha^2-\beta^2}+\frac{8\alpha^2\beta^2}{(\alpha^2-\beta^2)^2}\right]=0,$$

and, on simplifying this by means of the equations
$$\psi_2=-\frac{3\psi_1+\psi_0}{\alpha^2a^2},\quad \chi_2=-\frac{3\chi_1-\chi_0}{\beta^2a^2},$$

we find that it reduces to equation (12).

135. Now from equation (2) we have
$$\left.\begin{aligned}\alpha^2a^2&=\frac{4\pi\gamma\rho_0{}^2a^2}{3(\lambda+2\mu)}\left\{\sqrt{\left(4+2\frac{\lambda+2\mu}{\mu}\right)}+2\right\}\\ \beta^2a^2&=\frac{4\pi\gamma\rho_0{}^2a^2}{3(\lambda+2\mu)}\left\{\sqrt{\left(4+2\frac{\lambda+2\mu}{\mu}\right)}-2\right\}\end{aligned}\right\}\ldots\ldots\ldots\ldots(13),$$

and equation (12) becomes
$$-\frac{\alpha^2a^2\sin\alpha a}{\sin\alpha a-\alpha a\cos\alpha a}+\frac{\beta^2a^2\sinh\beta a}{\beta a\cosh\beta a-\sinh\beta a}-\frac{2\alpha^2\beta^2a^2}{\alpha^2+\beta^2}=0$$

or
$$-\frac{\alpha^2}{\beta^2}\frac{\sin\alpha a}{\sin\alpha a-\alpha a\cos\alpha a}+\frac{\sinh\beta a}{\beta a\cosh\beta a-\sinh\beta a}-\frac{2\alpha^2}{\alpha^2+\beta^2}=0\ldots(14),$$

where, as appears from (13), the ratio $\lambda:\mu$ determines the ratio $\beta:\alpha$, and, when this ratio is known, (14) becomes an equation for determining αa. When we have found the smallest value of αa by which this equation can be satisfied, (13) gives us the greatest value of $\lambda+2\mu$ for which the sphere can be gravitationally unstable in respect of harmonic inequalities of the first degree.

We select values of λ/μ so as to make $\alpha a/\beta a$, as given by (13), the ratio of two small integers, and at the same time to be either between 1 and 2, or very large. The first case is that where Poisson's ratio is between $\frac{1}{4}$ and $\frac{1}{3}$, the second that where the rigidity is small compared with the resistance to compression. It is easiest to begin by selecting a value for $\alpha a/\beta a$ which shall secure what is desired. In the following table the numbers in the first row are the selected values of $\alpha a/\beta a$, those in the second row the corresponding values of λ/μ. In the third row are given the smallest roots of the equation (14) for αa which answer to these selected values of $\alpha a/\beta a$. In the fourth row are given, as multiples of 10^{12} dynes per square cm., the corresponding values of $\lambda+2\mu$; these are obtained from the first of equations (13). In the fifth row are given in km. per second the corresponding values of $\sqrt{\{(\lambda+2\mu)/\rho_0\}}$, the velocity of waves of compression. In the sixth row are given, as multiples of 10^{11} dynes per square cm., the corresponding values of μ, the rigidity.

$\alpha a/\beta a$	2	1·1
λ/μ	14/9	95918/441 = 217·5...
αa	3·45	4·14
$\lambda+2\mu$	1·54	4·61
$\sqrt{\{(\lambda+2\mu)/\rho_0\}}$	5·29	9·16
μ	4·33	0·210

136. On comparing this table with that given on p. 114 for radial disturbances, we see that, if the value of λ/μ is such as is found in ordinary solid materials, a rigidity and resistance to compression great enough to secure stability as regards radial disturbances would be amply sufficient to secure stability in regard to disturbances represented by spherical harmonics of the first degree. But, on comparing the last columns of the two tables we find the interesting result that, if the rigidity is small enough in comparison with the resistance to compression, a homogeneous sphere may be stable as regards radial disturbances but unstable as regards disturbances specified by spherical harmonics of the first degree. This would happen if the velocity of waves of compression were that actually deduced from seismic observations, and the rigidity were intermediate between one-tenth of that of sandstone and one-tenth of that of granite.

137. If the constitution of the body were such that a spherically symmetrical configuration would be unstable for disturbances of the type in question, the state in which the body could exist would be one in which the density would be greater in one hemisphere than in the other, and the excess density at a point would be proportional to the product of the distance of the point from the bounding plane of the two hemispheres and a certain function of its distance from the centre. With a view to criticising the suggestion that the observed fact of the land and water hemispheres may be the effect of a survival from a past state of the earth, in which a spherically symmetrical configuration would have been unstable, it seems to be desirable to ascertain the value of the excess density at a point, as determined by the theory of Chapter VII. The excess density in question is represented by the expression $-\rho_0\Delta$, and we have

$$-\rho_0\Delta = \frac{1}{4\pi\gamma}\left[\alpha^2 A_1\psi_1(\alpha r) - \beta^2 B_1\chi_1(\beta r)\right] W_1,$$

and by equation (11) this is proportional to

$$\left[\alpha^2\psi_1(\alpha r)/\psi_1(\alpha a) - \beta^2\chi_1(\beta r)/\chi_1(\beta a)\right] r\cos\theta,$$

where θ is the angle which the radius vector drawn from the centre makes with the axis of the harmonic. The way in which the excess density is distributed along any diameter may be shown graphically by tracing the curve whose equation is

$$y = x\left[\alpha^2\psi_1(\alpha x)/\psi_1(\alpha a) - \beta^2\chi_1(\beta x)/\chi_1(\beta a)\right]$$

for values of x between $-a$ and a. Taking $\alpha/\beta = 1{\cdot}1$ and $\alpha a = 4{\cdot}14$, I find a curve resembling the arc of the sine curve $y = \sin x$ between $x = -3$ and $x = 3$. From this figure we should conclude that, if the inequality of the shape of the earth, which is manifested by the distinction between the land and water hemispheres, is really a survival from a past state in which a spherically symmetrical configuration would have been unstable, the correlated inequalities of density would be likely to be deep-seated. The hypothesis of isostasy, on the other hand, makes out that the inequalities of density which are correlated with the continental elevations and oceanic depressions are superficial. So far as it goes this discussion is rather unfavourable to the view that the existing continents and oceans are survivals of such a past state as has been described. It is possible that new light could be thrown on the question if we could solve the problem of gravitational instability for a heterogeneous sphere; but even the simplest example, that of a nucleus of greater density enclosed in a shell of smaller density, has so far proved intractable.

138. We consider next disturbances which are expressed by harmonic inequalities of the second degree. Equations (4) become

$$A_2' = \frac{A_2\alpha^2}{4\pi\gamma\rho_0}\,\frac{3\alpha^2+\beta^2}{3(\alpha^2-\beta^2)},\qquad B_2' = -\frac{B_2\beta^2}{4\pi\gamma\rho_0}\,\frac{\alpha^2+3\beta^2}{3(\alpha^2-\beta^2)}\quad\ldots\ldots(15),$$

and equation (1) becomes

$$C_2' = -\frac{9}{4}\left(\frac{A_2'}{\alpha^2}\psi_2 + \frac{B_2'}{\beta^2}\chi_2\right)\ldots\ldots\ldots\ldots\ldots\ldots\ldots\ldots(16),$$

where the arguments αa and βa of the ψ and χ functions are suppressed. Also, by putting $n = 2$ in equations (3), we find

$$\frac{\lambda+2\mu}{\mu} = \frac{8\alpha^2\beta^2}{3(\alpha^2-\beta^2)^2}.$$

Further, equations (51) and (52) of p. 102 take the forms

$$\frac{A_2'}{\alpha^2}\{(\tfrac{1}{2}\alpha^2 a^2 - 8)\,\psi_2 - \psi_1\} - \frac{A_2}{4\pi\gamma\rho_0}(\tfrac{1}{2}\alpha^2 a^2 \psi_2 + \psi_1)$$
$$-\frac{B_2'}{\beta^2}\{(\tfrac{1}{2}\beta^2 a^2 + 8)\,\chi_2 - \chi_1\} + \frac{B_2}{4\pi\gamma\rho_0}(\tfrac{1}{2}\beta^2 a^2 \chi_2 + \chi_1) + 2C_2' = 0 \quad \text{...(17)}$$

and

$$A_2'(8\psi_3 + \psi_2) + \left\{\frac{8\alpha^2\beta^2}{3(\alpha^2-\beta^2)^2} - 1\right\}\frac{A_2\alpha^2}{4\pi\gamma\rho_0}\psi_2$$
$$+ B_2'(8\chi_3 - \chi_2) - \left\{\frac{8\alpha^2\beta^2}{3(\alpha^2-\beta^2)^2} - 1\right\}\frac{B_2\beta^2}{4\pi\gamma\rho_0}\chi_2 = 0 \quad \text{...(18)}.$$

On eliminating C_2' between equations (16) and (17), substituting from (15), and substituting in (18) from the formulae

$$\alpha^2 a^2 \psi_3 = -(5\psi_2 + \psi_1), \quad \beta^2 a^2 \chi_3 = -(5\chi_2 - \chi_1),$$

we obtain the equations

$$A_2[\{4\alpha^2\beta^2 a^2 - 25(3\alpha^2+\beta^2)\}\,\psi_2 - 4(3\alpha^2-\beta^2)\,\psi_1]$$
$$+ B_2[\{4\alpha^2\beta^2 a^2 + 25(3\beta^2+\alpha^2)\}\,\chi_2 - 4(3\beta^2-\alpha^2)\,\chi_1] = 0 \quad \text{...(19)}$$

and

$$A_2\left[\left\{10(3\alpha^2+\beta^2) - \frac{3\alpha^2-\beta^2}{\alpha^2-\beta^2}\alpha^2\beta^2 a^2\right\}\psi_2 + 2(3\alpha^2+\beta^2)\,\psi_1\right]$$
$$- B_2\left[\left\{10(3\beta^2+\alpha^2) - \frac{3\beta^2-\alpha^2}{\alpha^2-\beta^2}\alpha^2\beta^2 a^2\right\}\chi_2 - 2(3\beta^2+\alpha^2)\,\chi_1\right] = 0 \quad \text{...(20)}.$$

Hence the condition of gravitational instability as regards disturbances represented by spherical harmonics of the second degree is

$$\frac{\left\{10(3\alpha^2+\beta^2) - \frac{3\alpha^2-\beta^2}{\alpha^2-\beta^2}\alpha^2\beta^2 a^2\right\}\psi_2 + 2(3\alpha^2+\beta^2)\,\psi_1}{\{4\alpha^2\beta^2 a^2 - 25(3\alpha^2+\beta^2)\}\,\psi_2 - 4(3\alpha^2-\beta^2)\,\psi_1}$$
$$+ \frac{\left\{10(3\beta^2+\alpha^2) - \frac{3\beta^2-\alpha^2}{\alpha^2-\beta^2}\alpha^2\beta^2 a^2\right\}\chi_2 - 2(3\beta^2+\alpha^2)\,\chi_1}{\{4\alpha^2\beta^2 a^2 + 25(3\beta^2+\alpha^2)\}\,\chi_2 - 4(3\beta^2-\alpha^2)\,\chi_1} = 0 \quad \text{...(21)}.$$

139. Just as in the case where $n = 1$, when the ratio λ/μ is assigned the ratio $\alpha a/\beta a$ is known, and equation (21) becomes an equation to determine αa. As in Chapter VIII we have

$$\alpha^2 a^2 = \frac{g\rho_0 a}{\lambda + 2\mu}\left[\sqrt{\left\{4 + \frac{6(\lambda+2\mu)}{\mu}\right\}} + 2\right],$$
$$\beta^2 a^2 = \frac{g\rho_0 a}{\lambda + 2\mu}\left[\sqrt{\left\{4 + \frac{6(\lambda+2\mu)}{\mu}\right\}} - 2\right].$$

In order to approximate, by means of tables of circular and hyperbolic functions, to the smallest root of equation (21), it is necessary to assign to the ratio λ/μ such a value as will make the ratio $\alpha a/\beta a$ rational. It is desirable also that $\alpha a/\beta a$ should be the ratio of two *small* whole numbers. The two cases of greatest interest are those in which λ/μ either lies between 1 and 2, or is a large number. The first case can be illustrated by taking $\alpha a/\beta a = 3 : 2$, the second by taking $\alpha a/\beta a = 18 : 17$.

When $\alpha a/\beta a = \frac{3}{2}$, we find that

$$\lambda/\mu = \tfrac{46}{25} = 1{\cdot}84,$$

and equation (21) becomes

$$\frac{(1550 - 92\alpha^2 a^2)\,\psi_2 + 310\psi_1}{(80\alpha^2 a^2 - 3875)\,\psi_2 - 460\psi_1} + \frac{(350 - 9\beta^2 a^2)\,\chi_2 - 70\chi_1}{(60\beta^2 a^2 + 875)\,\chi_2 - 20\chi_1} = 0.$$

The smallest value of αa by which this equation can be satisfied is found to be about 4·56.

When $\alpha a/\beta a = \frac{18}{17}$, we find that

$$\frac{\lambda}{\mu} = \frac{247246}{1225} = 201{\cdot}8\ldots,$$

and equation (21) becomes

$$\frac{(441350 - 197387\alpha^2 a^2)\,\psi_2 + 88270\psi_1}{(1156\alpha^2 a^2 - 31525)\,\psi_2 - 2732\psi_1} + \frac{(416850 - 175932\beta^2 a^2)\,\chi_2 - 83370\chi_1}{(1296\beta^2 a^2 + 29775)\,\chi_2 - 2172\chi_1} = 0.$$

The smallest value of αa by which this equation can be satisfied is found to be about 5·45.

In the following table we record the two values of λ/μ, and the corresponding values of $\lambda + 2\mu$, as a multiple of 10^{12} dynes per square cm., the values of $\sqrt{\{(\lambda + 2\mu)/\rho_0\}}$, as a multiple of 1 km. per second, and those of μ, as a multiple of 10^{11} dynes per square cm.

λ/μ	$\lambda+2\mu$	$\sqrt{\{(\lambda+2\mu)/\rho_0\}}$	μ
1·84	1·19	4·65	3·10
201·8...	4·28	8·82	0·210

On comparing the results in this table with those given in the table on p. 117, we note that the critical value of μ answering to the large value of λ/μ is nearly the same for $n = 1$ and $n = 2$; but it is to be observed that the large value adopted in the second case is smaller than that adopted in the first. It would therefore appear that the critical rigidity answering to $n=2$ is a little smaller than that answering to $n=1$ even for large values of the ratio λ/μ.

140. We consider next disturbances which are expressed by harmonic inequalities of the third degree. Equations (4) become

$$A_3' = \frac{A_3\alpha^2}{4\pi\gamma\rho_0}\frac{\alpha^2}{\alpha^2-\beta^2}, \qquad B_3' = -\frac{B_3\beta^2}{4\pi\gamma\rho_0}\frac{\beta^2}{\alpha^2-\beta^2} \quad \text{.........(22)},$$

and equation (1) becomes

$$C_3' = -\left(\frac{A_3'}{\alpha^2}\psi_3 + \frac{B_3'}{\beta^2}\chi_3\right) \quad \text{......................(23)},$$

where the arguments αa and βa of the ψ and χ functions are suppressed. Also, by putting $n=3$ in equations (3), we find

$$\frac{\lambda+2\mu}{\mu} = \frac{4\alpha^2\beta^2}{3(\alpha^2-\beta^2)^2}.$$

Further, equations (51) and (52) of p. 102 take the forms

$$\frac{A_3'}{\alpha^2}\left(\frac{\alpha^2a^2}{3}\psi_3 - 10\psi_3 - \tfrac{2}{3}\psi_2\right) - \frac{A_3}{4\pi\gamma\rho_0}\left(\frac{\alpha^2a^2}{3}\psi_3 + \tfrac{4}{3}\psi_2\right)$$
$$-\frac{B_3'}{\beta^2}\left(\frac{\beta^2a^2}{3}\chi_3 + 10\chi_3 - \tfrac{2}{3}\chi_2\right) + \frac{B_3}{4\pi\gamma\rho_0}\left(\frac{\beta^2a^2}{3}\chi_3 + \tfrac{4}{3}\chi_2\right) + 4C_3' = 0 \quad \text{...(24)}$$

and

$$A_3'(10\psi_4 + \psi_3) + \left\{\frac{4\alpha^2\beta^2}{3(\alpha^2-\beta^2)^2} - 1\right\}\frac{A_3\alpha^2}{4\pi\gamma\rho_0}\psi_3$$
$$+ B_3'(10\chi_4 - \chi_3) - \left\{\frac{4\alpha^2\beta^2}{3(\alpha^2-\beta^2)^2} - 1\right\}\frac{B_3\beta^2}{4\pi\gamma\rho_0}\chi_3 = 0 \quad \text{...(25)}.$$

On eliminating C_3' between equations (23) and (24), substituting from (22), and substituting in (25) from the formulae

$$\alpha^2a^2\psi_4 = -(7\psi_3+\psi_2), \qquad \beta^2a^2\chi_4 = -(7\chi_3-\chi_2),$$

we obtain the equations

$$A_3\{(42-\beta^2a^2)\alpha^2\psi_3 + 2(3\alpha^2-2\beta^2)\psi_2\}$$
$$-B_3\{(42+\alpha^2a^2)\beta^2\chi_3 - 2(3\beta^2-2\alpha^2)\chi_2\} = 0 \quad \text{......(26)}$$

and

$$A_3\left\{\left(210\alpha^2 - \beta^2\frac{7\alpha^2-3\beta^2}{\alpha^2-\beta^2}\alpha^2a^2\right)\psi_3 + 30\alpha^2\psi_2\right\}$$
$$-B_3\left\{\left(210\beta^2 - \alpha^2\frac{7\beta^2-3\alpha^2}{\alpha^2-\beta^2}\beta^2a^2\right)\chi_3 - 30\beta^2\chi_2\right\} = 0 \quad \text{...(27)}.$$

By substituting in (26) and (27) from the formulae

$$\alpha^2a^2\psi_3 = -(5\psi_2+\psi_1), \qquad \beta^2a^2\chi_3 = -(5\chi_2-\chi_1),$$

we obtain the condition of gravitational instability, in regard to disturbances expressed by spherical harmonics of the third degree, in the form

$$\frac{\left\{\left(30\alpha^2+5\beta^2\frac{7\alpha^2-3\beta^2}{\alpha^2-\beta^2}\right)\alpha^2a^2-1050\alpha^2\right\}\psi_2-\left(210\alpha^2-\beta^2\frac{7\alpha^2-3\beta^2}{\alpha^2-\beta^2}.\alpha^2a^2\right)\psi_1}{\{(6\alpha^2+\beta^2)\alpha^2a^2-210\alpha^2\}\psi_2-(42\alpha^2-\beta^2.\alpha^2a^2)\psi_1}$$

$$+\frac{\left\{\left(30\beta^2-5\alpha^2\frac{7\beta^2-3\alpha^2}{\alpha^2-\beta^2}\right)\beta^2a^2+1050\beta^2\right\}\chi_2-\left(210\beta^2-\alpha^2\frac{7\beta^2-3\alpha^2}{\alpha^2-\beta^2}.\beta^2a^2\right)\chi_1}{(42\beta^2+\alpha^2.\beta^2a^2)\chi_1-\{(6\beta^2+\alpha^2)\beta^2a^2+210\beta^2\}\chi_2}=0 \quad \text{......(28).}$$

141. As in previous cases we solve this equation for selected values of λ/μ. When any value is assigned to this ratio, the ratio $\alpha a/\beta a$ is known from the formulae

$$\alpha^2a^2=\frac{g\rho_0a}{\lambda+2\mu}\left[\sqrt{\left\{4+\frac{12(\lambda+2\mu)}{\mu}\right\}}+2\right],$$

$$\beta^2a^2=\frac{g\rho_0a}{\lambda+2\mu}\left[\sqrt{\left\{4+\frac{12(\lambda+2\mu)}{\mu}\right\}}-2\right],$$

and the equation (28) becomes an equation to determine αa. We require the smallest root of this equation, and when this root is found either of the above equations determines the greatest values of $\lambda+2\mu$ and μ for which the homogeneous sphere can be unstable in respect of disturbances expressed by spherical harmonics of the third degree. As before, it is convenient to begin by assigning to the ratio $\alpha a/\beta a$ a value which shall be the ratio of two small whole numbers, and shall make the ratio λ/μ either lie between 1 and 2 or be rather large. The first condition is satisfied by taking $\alpha a/\beta a$ to be $\frac{4}{3}$, the second by taking it to be $\frac{26}{25}$.

When $\alpha a/\beta a=\frac{4}{3}$, we find that

$$\lambda/\mu=\tfrac{94}{49}=1{\cdot}918...,$$

and equation (28) becomes

$$\frac{(479\alpha^2a^2-7840)\psi_2+(51\alpha^2a^2-1568)\psi_1}{(35\alpha^2a^2-1120)\psi_2+(3\alpha^2a^2-224)\psi_1}+\frac{(69\beta^2a^2+6615)\chi_2+(24\beta^2a^2-1323)\chi_1}{(8\beta^2a^2+189)\chi_1-(35\beta^2a^2+945)\chi_2}=0.$$

The smallest value of αa by which this equation can be satisfied is found to be approximately 5·47.

When $\alpha a/\beta a=\frac{26}{25}$, we find that

$$\frac{\lambda}{\mu}=\frac{1674394}{7803}=214{\cdot}58...,$$

and equation (28) becomes

$$\frac{[\{20280+3125\times(2857/51)\}\,\alpha^2a^2-709800]\,\psi_2+\{625\times(2857/51)\,\alpha^2a^2-141960\}\,\psi_1}{(4681\alpha^2a^2-141960)\,\psi_2+(625\alpha^2a^2-28392)\,\psi_1}$$
$$+\frac{[\{18750-3380\times(2347/51)\}\,\beta^2a^2+656250]\,\chi_2+\{676\times(2347/51)\,\beta^2a^2-131250\}\,\chi_1}{(676\beta^2a^2+26250)\,\chi_1-(4426\beta^2a^2+131250)\,\chi_2}=0.$$

The smallest value of αa by which this equation can be satisfied is found to be approximately 6·72.

In the following table we record the two values of λ/μ, and the corresponding values of $\lambda+2\mu$, as a multiple of 10^{12} dynes per square cm., the values of $\sqrt{\{(\lambda+2\mu)/\rho_0\}}$, as a multiple of 1 km. per second, and those of μ, as a multiple of 10^{11} dynes per square cm.

λ/μ	$\lambda+2\mu$	$\sqrt{\{(\lambda+2\mu)/\rho_0\}}$	μ
1·918...	1·05	4·37	2·68
214·58...	4·03	8·56	0·186

142. On comparing the results which have been found in the cases:— $n=0$ (radial disturbances), $n=1$ (hemispherical disturbances), $n=2$ (ellipsoidal disturbances), $n=3$ (disturbances expressed by spherical harmonics of the third degree), we observe, in the first place, that, when the ratio of rigidity to incompressibility is like those met with in experiments performed upon ordinary materials at the earth's surface, the critical value of the rigidity steadily diminishes as n increases. We infer that, if a homogeneous sphere composed of ordinary solid material had so small a rigidity and incompressibility as would make it gravitationally unstable at all, it would be in respect of radial disturbances that the instability would manifest itself. Such a sphere could not exist, but the body composed of these materials could have its mass distributed symmetrically about a centre, with a density diminishing, according to some law, as the distance from the centre increases.

But if, pursuing the comparison of our results, we examine the problem for a homogeneous sphere composed of such material that the rigidity is small in comparison with the incompressibility, we find that, if the rigidity were just small enough to make such a sphere gravitationally unstable at all, it would be in respect of hemispherical disturbances, that is to say such as are specified by spherical harmonics of the first degree, that the instability would manifest itself. The homogeneous sphere could not exist, and the body could exist in a state in which the mass of one hemisphere would be greater than that of the other.

The results which have been obtained in this Chapter show the importance of the part played by rigidity in securing gravitational stability. A sphere of homogeneous fluid, subject to its own gravitation, but free from surface tension, would be gravitationally unstable, and therefore could not exist, for the fluid could not be absolutely incompressible, and some degree of rigidity would be necessary to stability if the sphere is to be homogeneous.

In those previous discussions of the problem of gravitational instability to which reference has already been made it is taken as probable that, if a homogeneous sphere with certain elastic constants is proved to be unstable in regard to displacements specified by spherical harmonics of an assigned degree, a sphere with a spherically symmetrical arrangement of the mass, and average values of the elastic constants which differ but slightly from the values found, would be unstable in respect of the same type of displacements. If this argument is sound, we should seem to be justified in concluding from the results which were found in § 135 that, if a large part of the earth's mass were now in a fluid state, so that its average rigidity would be small, it would exhibit a much more decided displacement of the centre of gravity away from the centre of figure than it actually does.

143. The theory of gravitational instability derives its chief interest, as has been explained above, from the speculation which suggested that the existing distribution of continent and ocean might be a survival from a past state in which the earth would have been gravitationally unstable if the distribution of its mass had been spherically symmetrical. The present investigation throws some light on this speculation. The result that, if the rigidity were small enough in comparison with the incompressibility, the instability would be first manifested in regard to hemispherical disturbances, shows that it is quite possible that the inequality which we recognise in the land and water hemispheres may have originated in the way suggested. In previous solutions of the problem it seemed that instability would always be first manifested in respect of radial disturbances. The new result is favourable to the hypothesis. We have seen, however, that the hemispherical distribution of density which an otherwise homogeneous sphere would tend to take up, if, in the homogeneous state, it were unstable in regard to hemispherical disturbances, would not be easily reconcilable with the distribution that accords with the hypothesis of isostasy, and is supported by geodetic observation. It is not easy to see why if the traces, which undoubtedly exist, of a hemispherical distribution of density are survivals from such a past state as has been described, they should be confined to a superficial layer instead of being deep-seated. In the present state of our knowledge we cannot assert that the existence of land and water hemispheres is really a survival from such a past state.

In Chapter I it was pointed out that harmonic inequalities of the third degree are somewhat more prominent in the existing distribution of continent and ocean than those of the first degree. The theory of gravitational instability, as worked out here, does not suggest any origin for these inequalities, unless they may arise through hemispherical disturbances existing in a rotating body*. In Chapters V and VI we saw that, if a rotating spheroid is subjected to forces derived from a potential which, at any distance from the centre, is proportional to a spherical surface harmonic of the second degree, the displacement which these forces would set up in a sphere at rest must be supplemented by an additional displacement. The displacement which would be set up in the sphere at rest is proportional to the spherical surface harmonic of the second degree, and the supplementary displacement would be compounded of two: one proportional to this surface harmonic, and the other proportional to a surface harmonic of the fourth degree. Now in a body having a hemispherical distribution of density, and a corresponding harmonic inequality of the first degree in the equation of its surface, gravity would be derived from a potential compounded of two: one spherically symmetrical, the other proportional to a spherical surface harmonic of the first degree. If the body were set in rotation, so that its figure approximated to an oblate spheroid, the second of these terms in the expression for the potential would give rise to a displacement, again compounded of two: one proportional to this surface harmonic of the first degree and the other to a surface harmonic of the third degree. Another way of expressing this result is to say that, to the kind of unsymmetrical configuration which would be stable in a body at rest, and so constituted that a spherically symmetrical configuration would be unstable, there would correspond, in a rotating body, a configuration expressed by means of harmonic inequalities of the first, second and third degrees. This suggested explanation of the origin of the harmonic inequality of the third degree may seem rather remote; but the fact that the inequality is prominent is undeniable, and, so far as I am aware, no other explanation of it has ever been proposed.

* As suggested by Love, *loc. cit.*, *ante* p. 89.

CHAPTER X

VIBRATIONS OF A GRAVITATING COMPRESSIBLE PLANET

144. The theory of the free vibrations of a homogeneous isotropic elastic solid sphere was studied very completely by H. Lamb* in 1882. At that time very little was known about the propagation of seismic waves, but, as observations concerning these were accumulated, it became increasingly desirable to discover the modifications that should be made in the theory in order to take into account the effects that might be due to the mutual gravitation of the parts of the sphere and those that might be due to the compressibility of its substance. The effects due to mutual gravitation were first investigated by T. J. I'A. Bromwich†, but his investigation was incomplete in the sense that he took the material to be incompressible. Apart from their importance in connexion with the propagation of earthquake shocks, the free vibrations of the earth, considered as a deformable body, have a bearing on the theory of earth tides. As we saw in Chapter IV, one of the reasons why a statical theory of earth tides may be presumed to be adequate is that all the tidal periods are very long compared with the periods of free vibration, so far as these have been computed. From this point of view the most important vibrations are such that the surface becomes an harmonic spheroid of the second degree, and, among the modes of vibration which have this character, the most important are those which have the longest period. In this Chapter we shall first complete the general theory which was partially developed in Chapter VII, and then discuss in detail the period of the gravest mode of vibration which is such that the surface becomes an harmonic spheroid of the second degree, reserving the application of the theory to the propagation of seismic disturbances for the following Chapter.

The necessity for a further development of the analysis in Chapter VII arises from the circumstance that the equation (28) of p. 97 was there assumed to have one positive root and one negative root, as it certainly

* *Loc. cit., ante* p. 50.

† T. J. I'A. Bromwich, "On the influence of gravity on elastic waves, and, in particular, on the vibrations of an elastic globe," *Proc. London Math. Soc.*, vol. xxx. 1898.

has if the frequency $(p/2\pi)$ is small enough. But, whatever the degree of the spherical harmonic by which the surface inequality is specified may be, there will be a series of modes of vibration which can be arranged in order of increasing frequency, and there must be a place in the series at which the frequency first becomes so great that the equation in question has two negative roots. We must therefore add to what was done in Chapter VII an investigation of the types of displacement that occur when both the roots of the equation in question are negative. This is quite simple; but the possibility of a change from the conditions in which the two roots have opposite signs to those in which they have the same sign involves the possibility that one root of the equation may be zero. The type of displacement which occurs when the equation has a zero root requires an independent investigation.

145. In the notation of Chapter VII the equations of vibration are three of the type

$$(\lambda+\mu)\frac{\partial\Delta}{\partial x}+\mu\nabla^2 u+\rho_0 p^2 u-\tfrac{4}{3}\pi\gamma\rho_0^2\frac{\partial}{\partial x}(rU)+\tfrac{4}{3}\pi\gamma\rho_0^2 x\Delta+\rho_0\frac{\partial W}{\partial x}=0 \quad\ldots(1),$$

where $p/2\pi$ is the frequency, and we have also the equations

$$\Delta=\frac{\partial u}{\partial x}+\frac{\partial v}{\partial y}+\frac{\partial w}{\partial z} \quad\ldots\ldots(2),$$

$$rU=xu+yv+zw \quad\ldots\ldots(3),$$

$$\nabla^2 W=4\pi\gamma\rho_0\Delta \quad\ldots\ldots(4).$$

The boundary conditions which hold at the surface $r=a$ are the surface characteristic equation for the potential and the stress-conditions. The latter are three equations of the type

$$\lambda x\Delta+\mu\left(\frac{\partial(rU)}{\partial x}+r\frac{\partial u}{\partial r}-u\right)=0 \quad\ldots\ldots(5).$$

We obtain a typical solution by putting

$$\left.\begin{aligned} W=K_n(r)W_n,\quad \Delta=f_n(r)W_n \\ u=F_n(r)\frac{\partial W_n}{\partial x}+G_n(r)\,xW_n,\quad v=\ldots,\quad w=\ldots \end{aligned}\right\} \quad\ldots\ldots(6),$$

and then we have

$$f_n=\frac{n}{r}\frac{dF_n}{dr}+r\frac{dG_n}{dr}+(n+3)\,G_n=\frac{1}{4\pi\gamma\rho_0}\vartheta K_n \quad\ldots\ldots(7),$$

where ϑ denotes the operator

$$\frac{d^2}{dr^2}+\frac{2(n+1)}{r}\frac{d}{dr}.$$

The equations (1) are then satisfied provided the functions f_n, ... are connected by the additional relations

$$(\lambda+\mu)f_n+\mu\left(\frac{d^2F_n}{dr^2}+\frac{2n}{r}\frac{dF_n}{dr}+2G_n\right)-\tfrac{4}{3}\pi\gamma\rho_0^2(nF_n+r^2G_n)$$
$$+\rho_0K_n+\rho_0p^2F_n=0\text{......(8)},$$

and

$$(\lambda+\mu)\frac{1}{r}\frac{df_n}{dr}+\mu\left(\frac{d^2G_n}{dr^2}+\frac{2(n+2)}{r}\frac{dG_n}{dr}\right)-\tfrac{4}{3}\pi\gamma\rho_0^2\frac{1}{r}\frac{d}{dr}(nF_n+r^2G_n)$$
$$+\tfrac{4}{3}\pi\gamma\rho_0^2f_n+\rho_0\frac{1}{r}\frac{dK_n}{dr}+\rho_0p^2G_n=0\text{...(9)}.$$

From equations (7), (8) and (9) we find that K_n satisfies the equation

$$(\vartheta+\alpha^2)(\vartheta-\beta^2)\vartheta K_n=0\text{......................(10)},$$

where $-\alpha^2$ and β^2 are the roots of the equation

$$\mu(\lambda+2\mu)\xi^2+\{\tfrac{16}{3}\pi\gamma\rho_0^2\mu+(\lambda+3\mu)p^2\rho_0\}\xi-\{n(n+1)(\tfrac{4}{3}\pi\gamma\rho_0^2)^2$$
$$-\tfrac{16}{3}\pi\gamma\rho_0^2\cdot p^2\rho_0-p^4\rho_0^2\}=0\text{...(11)}$$

supposed to have one negative root and one positive root. When this is the case the solution takes the form

$$\left.\begin{aligned}
K_n&=A_n\psi_n(\alpha r)+B_n\chi_n(\beta r)+C_n\\
G_n&=A_n'\psi_{n+1}(\alpha r)+B_n'\chi_{n+1}(\beta r)\\
F_n&=\frac{A_n'}{\alpha^2}\psi_n(\alpha r)+\left(\frac{A_n'}{n\alpha^2}-\frac{A_n}{4\pi\gamma\rho_0 n}\right)\psi_{n-1}(\alpha r)\\
&\quad-\frac{B_n'}{\beta^2}\chi_n(\beta r)-\left(\frac{B_n'}{n\beta^2}-\frac{B_n}{4\pi\gamma\rho_0 n}\right)\chi_{n-1}(\beta r)+C_n'\\
f_n&=-\frac{A_n\alpha^2}{4\pi\gamma\rho_0}\psi_n(\alpha r)+\frac{B_n\beta^2}{4\pi\gamma\rho_0}\chi_n(\beta r)
\end{aligned}\right\}\text{......(12)},$$

where A_n, ... are constants connected by the equations

$$A_n'=\frac{A_n\alpha^2}{4\pi\gamma\rho_0}\left(1+\frac{\tfrac{4}{3}\pi\gamma\rho_0^2n}{\mu\alpha^2-p^2\rho_0}\right),\quad B_n'=\frac{B_n\beta^2}{4\pi\gamma\rho_0}\left(1-\frac{\tfrac{4}{3}\pi\gamma\rho_0^2n}{\mu\beta^2+p^2\rho_0}\right),$$
$$C_n=\tfrac{4}{3}\pi\gamma\rho_0\left(n-\frac{p^2}{\tfrac{4}{3}\pi\gamma\rho_0}\right)C_n'\text{...(13)}.$$

These constants are also connected by the three equations

$$\frac{A_n'}{\alpha^2}\left\{\frac{\alpha^2a^2}{n}\psi_n(\alpha a)-2(n+2)\psi_n(\alpha a)-\frac{2}{n}\psi_{n-1}(\alpha a)\right\}$$
$$-\frac{A_n}{4\pi\gamma\rho_0}\left\{\frac{\alpha^2a^2}{n}\psi_n(\alpha a)+\frac{2(n-1)}{n}\psi_{n-1}(\alpha a)\right\}$$

$$-\frac{B_n'}{\beta^2}\left\{\frac{\beta^2 a^2}{n}\chi_n(\beta a)+2(n+2)\chi_n(\beta a)-\frac{2}{n}\chi_{n-1}(\beta a)\right\}$$

$$+\frac{B_n}{4\pi\gamma\rho_0}\left\{\frac{\beta^2 a^2}{n}\chi_n(\beta a)+\frac{2(n-1)}{n}\chi_{n-1}(\beta a)\right\}$$

$$+2(n-1)C_n'=0 \quad\text{......(14)},$$

$$A_n'\{2(n+2)\psi_{n+1}(\alpha a)+\psi_n(\alpha a)\}+\left(1+\frac{\lambda}{\mu}\right)\frac{A_n\alpha^2}{4\pi\gamma\rho_0}\psi_n(\alpha a)$$

$$+B_n'\{2(n+2)\chi_{n+1}(\beta a)-\chi_n(\beta a)\}-\left(1+\frac{\lambda}{\mu}\right)\frac{B_n\beta^2}{4\pi\gamma\rho_0}\chi_n(\beta a)=0 \quad\text{...(15)},$$

$$\frac{2n+1}{4\pi\gamma\rho_0}C_n-nC_n'=-(n+1)\left\{\frac{A_n'}{\alpha^2}\psi_n(\alpha a)+\frac{B_n'}{\beta^2}\chi_n(\beta a)\right\} \quad\text{......(16)},$$

where (14) and (15) are the stress-conditions formed like (51) and (52) of p. 102, and (16) is the surface characteristic equation for the potential formed like (1) of p. 112.

All this theory has been written down to save the reader trouble; it is all included in the general theory of Chapter VII. and in the special investigation at the beginning of Chapter IX.

146. In the theory recapitulated above it is assumed that the equation (11) has one negative root and one positive root. As has been pointed out already, this is not necessarily the case, and the frequency may be so great that both roots are negative. This happens if

$$p^4+4p^2\cdot\tfrac{4}{3}\pi\gamma\rho_0>n(n+1)(\tfrac{4}{3}\pi\gamma\rho_0)^2 \quad\text{......(17)}.$$

We shall now suppose that the inequality (17) is satisfied, and shall proceed to obtain the corresponding form of solution. Equations (1) to (9) are unaltered. Equation (10) becomes

$$(\vartheta+\alpha^2)(\vartheta+\delta^2)\vartheta K_n=0 \quad\text{......(18)},$$

where $-\alpha^2$ and $-\delta^2$ are the roots of the equation (11), supposed to have two negative roots. The solution takes the form

$$\left.\begin{aligned}
K_n&=A_n\psi_n(\alpha r)+D_n\psi_n(\delta r)+C_n\\
G_n&=A_n'\psi_{n+1}(\alpha r)+D_n'\psi_{n+1}(\delta r)\\
F_n&=\frac{A_n'}{\alpha^2}\psi_n(\alpha r)+\left(\frac{A_n'}{n\alpha^2}-\frac{A_n}{4\pi\gamma\rho_0 n}\right)\psi_{n-1}(\alpha r)\\
&\quad+\frac{D_n'}{\delta^2}\psi_n(\delta r)+\left(\frac{D_n'}{n\delta^2}-\frac{D_n}{4\pi\gamma\rho_0 n}\right)\psi_{n-1}(\delta r)+C_n'\\
f_n&=-\frac{A_n\alpha^2}{4\pi\gamma\rho_0}\psi_n(\alpha r)-\frac{D_n\delta^2}{4\pi\gamma\rho_0}\psi_n(\delta r)
\end{aligned}\right\}\quad\text{...(19)},$$

where the constants A_n, ... are connected by the six equations

$$\left.\begin{aligned}
&A_n' = \frac{A_n\alpha^2}{4\pi\gamma\rho_0}\left(1+\frac{\frac{4}{3}\pi\gamma\rho_0^2 n}{\mu\alpha^2 - p^2\rho_0}\right), \qquad D_n' = \frac{D_n\delta^2}{4\pi\gamma\rho_0}\left(1+\frac{\frac{4}{3}\pi\gamma\rho_0^2 n}{\mu\delta^2 - p^2\rho_0}\right),\\
&C_n = \tfrac{4}{3}\pi\gamma\rho_0\left(n - \frac{p^2}{\frac{4}{3}\pi\gamma\rho_0}\right)C_n',\\
&\frac{A_n'}{\alpha^2}\left\{\frac{\alpha^2 a^2}{n}\psi_n(\alpha a) - 2(n+2)\psi_n(\alpha a) - \frac{2}{n}\psi_{n-1}(\alpha a)\right\}\\
&\qquad - \frac{A_n}{4\pi\gamma\rho_0}\left\{\frac{\alpha^2 a^2}{n}\psi_n(\alpha a) + \frac{2(n-1)}{n}\psi_{n-1}(\alpha a)\right\}\\
&\quad + \frac{D_n'}{\delta^2}\left\{\frac{\delta^2 a^2}{n}\psi_n(\delta a) - 2(n+2)\psi_n(\delta a) - \frac{2}{n}\psi_{n-1}(\delta a)\right\}\\
&\qquad - \frac{D_n}{4\pi\gamma\rho_0}\left\{\frac{\delta^2 a^2}{n}\psi_n(\delta a) + \frac{2(n-1)}{n}\psi_{n-1}(\delta a)\right\}\\
&\quad + 2(n-1)C_n' = 0,\\
&A_n'\{2(n+2)\psi_{n+1}(\alpha a) + \psi_n(\alpha a)\} + \left(1+\frac{\lambda}{\mu}\right)\frac{A_n\alpha^2}{4\pi\gamma\rho_0}\psi_n(\alpha a)\\
&\quad + D_n'\{2(n+2)\psi_{n+1}(\delta a) + \psi_n(\delta a)\}\\
&\quad + \left(1+\frac{\lambda}{\mu}\right)\frac{D_n\delta^2}{4\pi\gamma\rho_0}\psi_n(\delta a) = 0,\\
&\frac{2n+1}{4\pi\gamma\rho_0}C_n - nC_n' = -(n+1)\left\{\frac{A_n'}{\alpha^2}\psi_n(\alpha a) + \frac{D_n'}{\delta^2}\psi_n(\delta a)\right\}
\end{aligned}\right\} \text{...(20).}$$

We shall return hereafter to the method of determining the frequency by means of this system of equations.

147. At this point we note that there is an intermediate case, which arises if the equation (11) has a zero root. This happens if the frequency satisfies the equation

$$p^4 + 4p^2 \cdot \tfrac{4}{3}\pi\gamma\rho_0 - n(n+1)(\tfrac{4}{3}\pi\gamma\rho_0)^2 = 0 \text{ ....(21).}$$

When this is so the equation (10) becomes

$$(\vartheta + \alpha^2)\vartheta^2 K_n = 0 \text{ ....(22),}$$

where α^2 is given by the formula

$$\mu(\lambda + 2\mu)\alpha^2 = \tfrac{16}{3}\pi\gamma\rho_0^2\mu + p^2\rho_0(\lambda + 3\mu) \text{ ....(23).}$$

The relevant solution of equation (22) is of the form

$$K_n = A_n\psi_n(\alpha r) + C_n + E_n r^2 \text{ ....(24).}$$

Just as in Chapter VII, to the three terms in the expression for K_n there correspond three forms for f_n, ... The forms answering to the first two terms have been already obtained, and we may find the forms answering to the third term by proceeding as if this term constituted the complete expression for K_n. We have at once from (7) on p. 127

$$f_n = \frac{2(2n+3)}{4\pi\gamma\rho_0} E_n.$$

Now equation (23) of p. 96 gives at once

$$G_n = E_n',$$

where E_n' is a constant expressed in terms of E_n by the equation

$$E_n' = \left(1 - \frac{\frac{4}{3}\pi\gamma\rho_0 n}{p^2}\right)\frac{E_n}{2\pi\gamma\rho_0} \quad \text{.....................(25).}$$

To obtain the corresponding form for F_n we have equation (7) in the form

$$\frac{n}{r}\frac{dF_n}{dr} = (2n+3)\frac{E_n}{2\pi\gamma\rho_0} - (n+3)E_n',$$

and hence we find

$$F_n = \left\{\frac{2n+3}{4\pi\gamma\rho_0 n} E_n - \frac{n+3}{2n} E_n'\right\} r^2 + E_n'',$$

where E_n'' is a constant. This may be written

$$F_n = \left\{1 + (n+3)\frac{\frac{4}{3}\pi\gamma\rho_0}{p^2}\right\}\frac{E_n r^2}{4\pi\gamma\rho_0} + E_n''.$$

To determine the constant E_n'' we use equation (8), and find after slight reduction by help of equation (21)

$$E_n'' = -(2n+3)\left\{\lambda + 2\mu + \frac{\mu}{n}\left(\frac{p^2}{\frac{4}{3}\pi\gamma\rho_0} + 4\right)\right\}\frac{E_n}{2\pi\gamma\rho_0^2(p^2 - \frac{4}{3}\pi\gamma\rho_0 n)} \quad \text{...(26).}$$

148. We have next to find the contribution of this solution to the expression

$$\lambda x\Delta + \mu\left\{\frac{\partial(rU)}{\partial x} + r\frac{\partial u}{\partial r} - u\right\}.$$

We can write down the formulae

$$\Delta = 2(2n+3)\frac{E_n}{4\pi\gamma\rho_0} W_n,$$

$$rU = (nF_n + r^2 G_n) W_n$$

$$= \left\{\left(\frac{2n+3}{4\pi\gamma\rho_0} E_n - \frac{n+1}{2} E_n'\right) r^2 + nE_n''\right\} W_n,$$

$$\frac{\partial(rU)}{\partial x} = \left\{\left(\frac{2n+3}{4\pi\gamma\rho_0} E_n - \frac{n+1}{2} E_n'\right) r^2 + nE_n''\right\}\frac{\partial W_n}{\partial x}$$

$$+ \left\{\frac{2n+3}{2\pi\gamma\rho_0} E_n - (n+1) E_n'\right\} x W_n,$$

$$r\frac{\partial u}{\partial r} - u = \left\{\left(\frac{2n+3}{4\pi\gamma\rho_0} E_n - \frac{n+3}{2} E_n'\right) r^2 + (n-2) E_n''\right\}\frac{\partial W_n}{\partial x} + nE_n' x W_n,$$

in all of which those terms only are expressed which arise from the term $E_n r^2$ in K_n. The corresponding terms of $\lambda x\Delta + \ldots$ are

$$\mu\left[\left\{\frac{2n+3}{2\pi\gamma\rho_0}E_n - (n+2)E_n'\right\}r^2 + 2(n-1)E_n''\right]\frac{\partial W_n}{\partial x}$$
$$+\left[(\lambda+\mu)\frac{2n+3}{2\pi\gamma\rho_0}E_n - \mu E_n'\right]xW_n.$$

Hence the stress-conditions at the boundary $r = a$ become

$$\frac{A_n'}{\alpha^2}\left\{\frac{\alpha^2a^2}{n}\psi_n(\alpha a) - 2(n+2)\psi_n(\alpha a) - \frac{2}{n}\psi_{n-1}(\alpha a)\right\}$$
$$-\frac{A_n}{4\pi\gamma\rho_0}\left\{\frac{\alpha^2a^2}{n}\psi_n(\alpha a) + \frac{2(n-1)}{n}\psi_{n-1}(\alpha a)\right\}$$
$$+\left\{\frac{2n+3}{2\pi\gamma\rho_0}E_n - (n+2)E_n'\right\}a^2 + 2(n-1)E_n'' + 2(n-1)C_n' = 0 \quad \ldots(27)$$

and

$$-A_n'\{2(n+2)\psi_{n+1}(\alpha a) + \psi_n(\alpha a)\} - \left(1+\frac{\lambda}{\mu}\right)\frac{A_n\alpha^2}{4\pi\gamma\rho_0}\psi_n(\alpha a)$$
$$- E_n' + \left(1+\frac{\lambda}{\mu}\right)\frac{2n+3}{2\pi\gamma\rho_0}E_n = 0 \ldots(28).$$

Again the terms contributed to

$$a\frac{dK_n(a)}{da} + (2n+1)K_n(a)$$

by the term $E_n r^2$ of $K_n(r)$ amount to $(2n+3)E_n a^2$, and therefore the surface characteristic equation for the potential becomes

$$\frac{2n+1}{4\pi\gamma\rho_0}C_n - nC_n' = -(n+1)\left\{\frac{A_n'}{\alpha^2}\psi_n(\alpha a) + \tfrac{1}{2}E_n'a^2\right\} + nE_n'',$$

and, on simplifying this by the third of (13), which is unaffected by the zero root of (11), we find

$$C_n'\left\{\frac{2n+1}{3}\frac{p^2}{\frac{4}{3}\pi\gamma\rho_0} - \frac{2n(n-1)}{3}\right\} = (n+1)\left\{\frac{A_n'}{\alpha^2}\psi_n(\alpha a) + \tfrac{1}{2}E_n'a^2\right\} - nE_n''$$
$$\ldots\ldots(29).$$

149. The typical solution which holds in case p^2 satisfies equation (21) is therefore expressed by equations (6) and (24) and the equations

$$\left.\begin{aligned}
f_n &= -\frac{A_n\alpha^2}{4\pi\gamma\rho_0}\psi_n(\alpha r) + \frac{2n+3}{2\pi\gamma\rho_0}E_n\\
G_n &= A_n'\psi_{n+1}(\alpha r) + E_n'\\
F_n &= \frac{A_n'}{\alpha^2}\psi_n(\alpha r) + \left(\frac{A_n'}{n\alpha^2} - \frac{A_n}{4\pi\gamma\rho_0 n}\right)\psi_{n-1}(\alpha r)\\
&\quad + \left\{1 + (n+3)\frac{\frac{4}{3}\pi\gamma\rho_0}{p^2}\right\}\frac{E_n r^2}{4\pi\gamma\rho_0} + E_n'' + C_n'
\end{aligned}\right\} \ldots(30).$$

The seven constants A_n, A_n', C_n, C_n', E_n, E_n', E_n'' are connected by the following equations:—the first and third of (13), (25), (26), (27), (28) and (29). From these equations the constants can be eliminated and there results an equation to determine αa.

150. In order to obtain the equation in question it is convenient to introduce the notation

$$q = p^2/\tfrac{4}{3}\pi\gamma\rho_0 \quad \text{.............................(31).}$$

Then q is the positive root of the quadratic

$$q^2 + 4q - n(n+1) = 0 \quad \text{........................(32),}$$

so that q is known when n is chosen. Then (29) becomes

$$C_n' = \frac{3}{(2n+1)q - 2n(n-1)}\left[(n+1)\left\{\frac{A_n'}{\alpha^2}\psi_n(\alpha a) + \tfrac{1}{2}E_n'a^2\right\} - nE_n''\right] \text{...(33).}$$

Also (23) gives
$$\mu\alpha^2 = \tfrac{4}{3}\pi\gamma\rho_0^2\left(q\frac{\lambda+3\mu}{\lambda+2\mu} + \frac{4\mu}{\lambda+2\mu}\right) \quad \text{.................(34),}$$

and we find by the first of (13)

$$A_n' = \frac{A_n\alpha^2}{4\pi\gamma\rho_0}\left(1 + \frac{n}{4+q}\frac{\lambda+2\mu}{\mu}\right) \text{.....................(35).}$$

Also (25) is
$$E_n' = \frac{E_n}{2\pi\gamma\rho_0}\left(1 - \frac{n}{q}\right),$$

and this becomes, by (32),

$$E_n' = -\frac{E_n}{2\pi\gamma\rho_0}\frac{q-n+3}{n+1} \quad \text{.......................(36).}$$

Further, on substituting for μ from (34), we find (26) taking the form

$$E_n'' = m\frac{E_n}{2\pi\gamma\rho_0 a^2} \quad \text{.........................(37),}$$

where m is given by the equation

$$m = -\frac{2n+3}{q-n}\left(q\frac{\lambda+3\mu}{\lambda+2\mu} + \frac{4\mu}{\lambda+2\mu}\right)\left(\frac{q+4}{n} + \frac{\lambda+2\mu}{\mu}\right) \quad \text{......(38),}$$

so that m is known when n and λ/μ are chosen.

When these substitutions are made in equations (27) and (28) and the constants $\boldsymbol{A_n}$, E_n are eliminated, there results the equation

$$\frac{+\dfrac{\lambda+2\mu}{\mu}\dfrac{n}{4+q}\Big)\left[\left\{\dfrac{\alpha^2a^2}{n} - 2(n+2) + \dfrac{6(n^2-1)}{(2n+1)q-2n(n-1)}\right\}\psi_n - \dfrac{2}{n}\psi_{n-1}\right] - \left(\dfrac{\alpha^2a^2}{n}\psi_n + 2\dfrac{n-1}{n}\psi_{n-1}\right)}{\left[\left(1+\dfrac{\lambda+2\mu}{\mu}\dfrac{n}{4+q}\right)\{\psi_n + 2(n+2)\psi_{n+1}\} + \dfrac{\lambda+\mu}{\mu}\psi_n\right]\alpha^2a^2}$$
$$+\frac{2n+3+\dfrac{n+2}{n+1}(q-n+3) - \dfrac{3(n-1)(q-n+3)}{(2n+1)q-2n(n-1)} + \dfrac{2m(n-1)}{\alpha^2a^2}\left\{1 - \dfrac{3n}{(2n+1)q-2n(n-1)}\right\}}{\dfrac{q-n+3}{n+1} + \dfrac{\lambda+\mu}{\mu}(2n+3)} = 0$$

......(39),

where the argument αa of the ψ-functions has been suppressed.

Equation (39) will be satisfied by a series of values of αa, and to each of these there corresponds, in accordance with equation (34), a value of μ. Hence, when n and λ/μ are chosen, there are a certain series of values of μ for each of which vibrations of the type here investigated can occur, but such vibrations cannot occur for any value of μ which is not a member of the series. The greatest of these special values of μ corresponds to the smallest of the values of αa by which the equation (39) can be satisfied.

151. In addition to the types of vibration which have been investigated in this Chapter, there are others which involve no dilatation and no radial displacement. For these Δ, U, and W all vanish. These vibrations are independent of gravity and initial stress, and are identical with those vibrations of a solid homogeneous sphere free from gravitation which have been described by Lamb* as "vibrations of the first class." The types of vibration so far discussed in this Chapter are all analogues, under different conditions, of vibrations which he described as being of the "second class." The types investigated in § 145 and expressed by equations (12) may be described as "slow," those investigated in § 146 and expressed by equations (19) may be described as "quick," and those investigated in §§ 147—150 may be described as "intermediate." If the degree n of the spherical harmonic that is involved is given, and likewise the ratio λ/μ, vibrations of a slow type cannot occur unless the rigidity μ is less than a certain critical value. The method by which this critical value is to be determined has been explained already; it is the value of μ which is determined by equation (34) when αa has the smallest value by which equation (39) can be satisfied. If μ exceeds this critical value all the vibrations of the second class which answer to the chosen values of n and λ/μ are of quick types.

Now let us suppose that n and λ/μ remain fixed, and that μ continually diminishes. After passing the critical value corresponding to the smallest root of (39) the value of μ is such that vibrations of a slow type can occur, provided the condition of gravitational stability is satisfied. At first only one such type can occur, and this will be the type with the longest period; all the remaining types will be quick. The value of μ for which instability sets in may or may not exceed that corresponding to the second root of equation (39); if it is smaller than this value, then, as μ diminishes, it can assume values for which there are two vibrations of slow types while the rest are of quick types. In general it would be a question of some mathematical interest to determine the number of roots of equation (39) which can occur before the value of μ corresponding to the largest of them becomes less than the value of μ at which instability sets in. The physical interest of the question, however, seems to be but slight.

* *Loc. cit.*, *ante* p. 50.

152. We shall now form the frequency equation for vibrations of quick types. Using q as before to denote $p^2/\frac{4}{3}\pi\gamma\rho_0$, we find from the third and sixth of equations (20)

$$C_n' = \frac{3(n+1)}{(2n+1)q - 2n(n-1)}\left\{\frac{A_n'}{\alpha^2}\psi_n(\alpha a) + \frac{D_n'}{\delta^2}\psi_n(\delta a)\right\} \quad \text{...(40).}$$

Also, writing g for $\frac{4}{3}\pi\gamma\rho_0 a$, we find from the first and second of equations (20)

$$A_n' = \frac{A_n\alpha^2}{4\pi\gamma\rho_0}\left(1 + \frac{ng\rho_0/a}{\mu\alpha^2 - p^2\rho_0}\right), \qquad D_n' = \frac{D_n\delta^2}{4\pi\gamma\rho_0}\left(1 + \frac{ng\rho_0/a}{\mu\delta^2 - p^2\rho_0}\right) \text{...(41).}$$

Hence we can write down the fourth and fifth of equations (20) in the forms

$$\frac{A_n}{4\pi\gamma\rho_0}\left[\left(1 + \frac{ng\rho_0/a}{\mu\alpha^2 - p^2\rho_0}\right)\left\{\left(\frac{\alpha^2a^2}{n} - 2(n+2) + \frac{6(n^2-1)}{(2n+1)q - 2n(n-1)}\right)\psi_n(\alpha a)\right.\right.$$
$$\left.\left. - \frac{2}{n}\psi_{n-1}(\alpha a)\right\} - \left\{\frac{\alpha^2a^2}{n}\psi_n(\alpha a) + 2\frac{n-1}{n}\psi_{n-1}(\alpha a)\right\}\right]$$
$$+ \frac{D_n}{4\pi\gamma\rho_0}\left[\left(1 + \frac{ng\rho_0/a}{\mu\delta^2 - p^2\rho_0}\right)\left\{\left(\frac{\delta^2a^2}{n} - 2(n+2) + \frac{6(n^2-1)}{(2n+1)q - 2n(n-1)}\right)\psi_n(\delta a)\right.\right.$$
$$\left.\left. - \frac{2}{n}\psi_{n-1}(\delta a)\right\} - \left\{\frac{\delta^2a^2}{n}\psi_n(\delta a) + 2\frac{n-1}{n}\psi_{n-1}(\delta a)\right\}\right] = 0 \quad \text{...(42)}$$

and

$$\frac{A_n\alpha^2}{4\pi\gamma\rho_0}\left[\left(1 + \frac{ng\rho_0/a}{\mu\alpha^2 - p^2\rho_0}\right)\{\psi_n(\alpha a) + 2(n+2)\psi_{n+1}(\alpha a)\} + \left(1 + \frac{\lambda}{\mu}\right)\psi_n(\alpha a)\right]$$
$$+ \frac{D_n\delta^2}{4\pi\gamma\rho_0}\left[\left(1 + \frac{ng\rho_0/a}{\mu\delta^2 - p^2\rho_0}\right)\{\psi_n(\delta a) + 2(n+2)\psi_{n+1}(\delta a)\} + \left(1 + \frac{\lambda}{\mu}\right)\psi_n(\delta a)\right] = 0$$
$$\text{......(43).}$$

Before eliminating the constants it is convenient to transform the equations by putting

$$\frac{d}{d(\alpha r)}\psi_n(\alpha r) = \psi_n'(\alpha r), \qquad \psi_{n+1}(\alpha r) = \frac{1}{\alpha r}\psi_n'(\alpha r),$$
$$\psi_{n-1}(\alpha r) = -\alpha r\psi_n'(\alpha r) - (2n+1)\psi_n(\alpha r).$$

Then the two equations (42) and (43) can be written

$$\frac{A_n\psi_n(\alpha a)}{4\pi\gamma\rho_0}\left[\frac{ng\rho_0/a}{\mu\alpha^2 - p^2\rho_0}\left\{\frac{\alpha^2a^2}{n} - 2\frac{n^2-1}{n} + \nu + \frac{2}{n}\alpha a\frac{\psi_n'(\alpha a)}{\psi_n(\alpha a)}\right\}\right.$$
$$\left. + 2(n-1) + \nu + 2\alpha a\frac{\psi_n'(\alpha a)}{\psi_n(\alpha a)}\right]$$
$$+ \frac{D_n\psi_n(\delta a)}{4\pi\gamma\rho_0}\left[\frac{ng\rho_0/a}{\mu\delta^2 - p^2\rho_0}\left\{\frac{\delta^2a^2}{n} - 2\frac{n^2-1}{n} + \nu + \frac{2}{n}\delta a\frac{\psi_n'(\delta a)}{\psi_n(\delta a)}\right\}\right.$$
$$\left. + 2(n-1) + \nu + 2\delta a\frac{\psi_n'(\delta a)}{\psi_n(\delta a)}\right] = 0$$

and

$$\alpha^2 \frac{A_n \psi_n(\alpha a)}{4\pi\gamma\rho_0} \left[\frac{ng\rho_0/a}{\mu\alpha^2 - p^2\rho_0} \left\{1 + 2\frac{n+2}{\alpha a}\frac{\psi_n'(\alpha a)}{\psi_n(\alpha a)}\right\} + \frac{\lambda+2\mu}{\mu} + 2\frac{n+2}{\alpha a}\frac{\psi_n'(\alpha a)}{\psi_n(\alpha a)} \right]$$

$$+ \delta^2 \frac{D_n \psi_n(\delta a)}{4\pi\gamma\rho_0} \left[\frac{ng\rho_0/a}{\mu\delta^2 - p^2\rho_0} \left\{1 + 2\frac{n+2}{\delta a}\frac{\psi_n'(\delta a)}{\psi_n(\delta a)}\right\} + \frac{\lambda+2\mu}{\mu} + 2\frac{n+2}{\delta a}\frac{\psi_n'(\delta a)}{\psi_n(\delta a)} \right] = 0,$$

where ν is written for $6(n^2-1)/\{(2n+1)q - 2n(n-1)\}$. The general frequency equation can now be written down in the form

$$\frac{\dfrac{ng\rho_0/a}{\mu\alpha^2 - p^2\rho_0}\left\{\dfrac{\alpha^2 a^2}{n} - 2\dfrac{n^2-1}{n} + \nu + \dfrac{2}{n}\alpha a \dfrac{\psi_n'(\alpha a)}{\psi_n(\alpha a)}\right\} + 2(n-1) + \nu + 2\alpha a \dfrac{\psi_n'(\alpha a)}{\psi_n(\alpha a)}}{\alpha^2\left[\dfrac{ng\rho_0/a}{\mu\alpha^2 - p^2\rho_0}\left\{1 + 2\dfrac{n+2}{\alpha a}\dfrac{\psi_n'(\alpha a)}{\psi_n(\alpha a)}\right\} + \dfrac{\lambda+2\mu}{\mu} + 2\dfrac{n+2}{\alpha a}\dfrac{\psi_n'(\alpha a)}{\psi_n(\alpha a)}\right]}$$
$$- \frac{\dfrac{ng\rho_0/a}{\mu\delta^2 - p^2\rho_0}\left\{\dfrac{\delta^2 a^2}{n} - 2\dfrac{n^2-1}{n} + \nu + \dfrac{2}{n}\delta a \dfrac{\psi_n'(\delta a)}{\psi_n(\delta a)}\right\} + 2(n-1) + \nu + 2\delta a \dfrac{\psi_n'(\delta a)}{\psi_n(\delta a)}}{\delta^2\left[\dfrac{ng\rho_0/a}{\mu\delta^2 - p^2\rho_0}\left\{1 + 2\dfrac{n+2}{\delta a}\dfrac{\psi_n'(\delta a)}{\psi_n(\delta a)}\right\} + \dfrac{\lambda+2\mu}{\mu} + 2\dfrac{n+2}{\delta a}\dfrac{\psi_n'(\delta a)}{\psi_n(\delta a)}\right]} = 0 \quad \text{......(44).}$$

Here α^2 and δ^2 are the roots of the equation

$$\mu(\lambda+2\mu)\xi^2 - \left\{(\lambda+3\mu)p^2 + 4\frac{g}{a}\mu\right\}\rho_0\xi + \left\{p^4 + 4\frac{g}{a}p^2 - n(n+1)\left(\frac{g}{a}\right)^2\right\}\rho_0^2 = 0 \quad \text{......(45),}$$

and we shall take α^2 to be the greater of the two roots.

153. We get a certain verification by treating gravity as very small, and passing to the limit by allowing $g\rho_0 a/\mu$ to tend to zero. The limiting values of α^2 and δ^2 are respectively $p^2\rho_0/\mu$ and $p^2\rho_0/(\lambda+2\mu)$, and we find from equation (45) that $\mu\alpha^2 - p^2\rho_0$ is small of the second order in g, while $\mu\delta^2 - p^2\rho_0$ has a finite non-zero limit. Hence we shall have to take $\dfrac{A_n}{4\pi\gamma\rho_0}$ to have the limit zero, but $\dfrac{A_n}{4\pi\gamma\rho_0}\dfrac{ng\rho_0/a}{\mu\alpha^2 - p^2\rho_0}$ to have a finite limit. Also we have to take $\dfrac{D_n}{4\pi\gamma\rho_0}$ to have a finite limit, but $\dfrac{D_n}{4\pi\gamma\rho_0}\dfrac{ng\rho_0/a}{\mu\delta^2 - p^2\rho_0}$ to have the limit zero. Further ν has the limit zero. Thus the frequency equation becomes

$$\frac{\dfrac{\alpha^2 a^2}{n} - 2\dfrac{n^2-1}{n} + \dfrac{2}{n}\alpha a\dfrac{\psi_n'(\alpha a)}{\psi_n(\alpha a)}}{\alpha^2\left\{1 + 2\dfrac{n+2}{\alpha a}\dfrac{\psi_n'(\alpha a)}{\psi_n(\alpha a)}\right\}} - \frac{2(n-1) + 2\delta a\dfrac{\psi_n'(\delta a)}{\psi_n(\delta a)}}{\delta^2\left\{\dfrac{\lambda+2\mu}{\mu} + 2\dfrac{n+2}{\delta a}\dfrac{\psi_n'(\delta a)}{\psi_n(\delta a)}\right\}} = 0 \quad \text{...(46),}$$

and this can be identified without difficulty with the frequency equation given by Lamb for a homogeneous sphere free from gravitation.

The above method of passing to a limit enables us to correlate with each mode of vibration of a gravitating sphere a corresponding mode of vibration of a sphere free from gravitation. As these modes have been very completely discussed, a comprehensive discussion of the vibrations of a gravitating sphere may be dispensed with.

154. The problem of determining the modes of vibration of a gravitating *incompressible* sphere might also perhaps be treated as a limiting case of the general problem, but it seems best to investigate it independently*. The equations of motion can be written down at once from equations (1) of p. 127, by taking Δ to vanish except when multiplied by λ, and taking the product $\lambda\Delta$ to have a finite limit. We shall denote this limit by Π. Then the equations of motion can be written in such forms as

$$\frac{\partial \Pi'}{\partial x} + \mu\nabla^2 u + \rho_0 p^2 u + \rho_0 \frac{\partial W}{\partial x} = 0 \quad \text{.................(47)},$$

where

$$\Pi' = \Pi - \tfrac{4}{3}\pi\gamma\rho_0{}^2 r U \quad \text{..........................(48)},$$

and W is the potential due to the superficial distribution of density $\rho_0 U_a$ on the surface $r = a$. The boundary conditions are the surface characteristic equation for the potential and the conditions that the disturbed surface is free from traction. The latter conditions can, just as in Chapter VII, be expressed in such forms as

$$x\Pi + \mu\left\{\frac{\partial (rU)}{\partial x} + r\frac{\partial u}{\partial r} - u\right\} = 0 \quad \text{.................(49)}.$$

155. To obtain a typical solution we put

$$W = W_n \quad \text{................................(50)},$$

where W_n denotes a spherical solid harmonic of the nth degree. Then we observe that, since $\Delta = 0$, it follows from the equations of type (47) that Π' satisfies the equation

$$\nabla^2 \Pi' = 0,$$

and we may put

$$\Pi' = \alpha_n W_n \quad \text{................................(51)},$$

where α_n denotes a constant which is at present undetermined. Nothing would be gained by assuming a more complicated form for Π'. Again, for u, v, w, we assume such forms as

$$u = F_n(r)\frac{\partial W_n}{\partial x} + G_n(r)\, x W_n \quad \text{.....................(52)}.$$

* This has been done by Bromwich, *loc. cit.*, *ante* p. 126. The method in the text, which differs from that used by him, is in accordance with the general method of Chapter VII.

Then to make $\Delta = 0$ we must have

$$\frac{n}{r}\frac{dF_n}{dr} + r\frac{dG_n}{dr} + (n+3)\,G_n = 0 \quad \text{.................(53)};$$

and the equations of motion become three equations of the type

$$\left\{\mu\left(\frac{d^2F_n}{dr^2} + \frac{2n}{r}\frac{dF_n}{dr} + 2G_n\right) + \rho_0 p^2 F_n + \alpha_n + \rho_0\right\}\frac{\partial W_n}{\partial x}$$
$$+\left[\mu\left\{\frac{d^2G_n}{dr^2} + \frac{2(n+2)}{r}\frac{dG_n}{dr}\right\} + \rho_0 p^2 G_n\right] x W_n = 0 \quad \text{...(54)},$$

and these are satisfied if G_n and F_n satisfy the two equations

$$\frac{d^2G_n}{dr^2} + \frac{2(n+2)}{r}\frac{dG_n}{dr} + \kappa^2 G_n = 0 \quad \text{.................(55)}$$

and

$$\frac{d^2F_n}{dr^2} + \frac{2n}{r}\frac{dF_n}{dr} + \kappa^2 F_n + 2G_n + \frac{\alpha_n + \rho_0}{\mu} = 0 \quad \text{...........(56)},$$

where

$$\kappa^2 = p^2\rho_0/\mu \quad \text{..............................(57)}.$$

The relevant solution of equation (55) is of the form

$$G_n = A_n \psi_{n+1}(\kappa r) \quad \text{..........................(58)},$$

and the relevant solution of equation (56) is of the form

$$F_n = \frac{A_n}{\kappa^2}\psi_n(\kappa r) + A_n'\psi_{n-1}(\kappa r) - \frac{\alpha_n + \rho_0}{\rho_0 p^2} \quad \text{..............(59)},$$

and, to satisfy (53), we must have

$$n\kappa^2 A_n' = A_n \quad \text{..............................(60)},$$

so that

$$F_n = \frac{A_n}{\kappa^2}\left\{\psi_n(\kappa r) + \frac{1}{n}\psi_{n-1}(\kappa r)\right\} - \frac{\alpha_n + \rho_0}{\rho_0 p^2} \quad \text{..............(61)}.$$

From these forms we find

$$rU = -\left\{\frac{A_n}{\kappa^2}(n+1)\,\psi_n(\kappa r) + \frac{n(\alpha_n + \rho_0)}{\rho_0 p^2}\right\} W_n \quad \text{........(62)}.$$

156. The surface characteristic equation for the potential is

$$\left[\frac{\partial}{\partial r}\left(\frac{a^{2n+1}}{r^{2n+1}}W_n\right)\right]_{r=a} - \left[\frac{\partial W_n}{\partial r}\right]_{r=a} = -4\pi\gamma\rho_0 U_a,$$

and this gives

$$-(2n+1) = 4\pi\gamma\rho_0\left\{\frac{A_n}{\kappa^2}(n+1)\,\psi_n(\kappa a) + \frac{n(\alpha_n + \rho_0)}{\rho_0 p^2}\right\},$$

or, as it may be written,

$$n(\alpha_n + \rho_0) + \mu A_n (n+1)\,\psi_n(\kappa a) = -\frac{2n+1}{3}\rho_0 q \quad \text{........(63)},$$

where q is written, as before, for $p^2/\tfrac{4}{3}\pi\gamma\rho_0$.

To form the conditions that the boundary is free from traction we note the formulae

$$\frac{\partial (rU)}{\partial x} = -\left\{\frac{(n+1)A_n}{\kappa^2}\psi_n(\kappa r) + \frac{n(\alpha_n+\rho_0)}{\rho_0 p^2}\right\}\frac{\partial W_n}{\partial x} - (n+1)A_n\psi_{n+1}(\kappa r)\,xW_n$$

and

$$r\frac{\partial u}{\partial r} - u = \left[\frac{A_n}{\kappa^2}\left\{\frac{\kappa^2 r^2}{n}\psi_n(\kappa r) - (n+3)\psi_n(\kappa r) - \frac{2}{n}\psi_{n-1}(\kappa r)\right\}\right.$$

$$\left. - (n-2)\frac{\alpha_n+\rho_0}{\rho_0 p^2}\right]\frac{\partial W_n}{\partial x} - A_n\{\psi_n(\kappa r) + (n+3)\psi_{n+1}(\kappa r)\}\,xW_n.$$

In obtaining these some reductions have been effected by using the relations connecting ψ-functions with consecutive suffixes (p. 98 *ante*). Now equation (49) can be written

$$x(\Pi' + \tfrac{4}{3}\pi\gamma\rho_0^2 rU) + \mu\left\{\frac{\partial(rU)}{\partial x} + r\frac{\partial u}{\partial r} - u\right\} = 0,$$

and there are three equations of this type which hold at $r = a$. On using the above formulae, and equating separately to zero the coefficients of $\partial W_n/\partial x$ and xW_n, we find the two conditions

$$\mu A_n\left\{\frac{\kappa^2 a^2}{n}\psi_n(\kappa a) - 2(n+2)\psi_n(\kappa a) - \frac{2}{n}\psi_{n-1}(\kappa a)\right\} - 2(n-1)(\alpha_n+\rho_0) = 0 \qquad \text{......(64)}$$

and

$$\alpha_n - \frac{n}{q}(\alpha_n+\rho_0) - \frac{\mu}{q}A_n(n+1)\psi_n(\kappa a) - \mu A_n\{\psi_n(\kappa a) + 2(n+2)\psi_{n+1}(\kappa a)\} = 0 \qquad \text{......(65).}$$

On combining (63) and (65) we obtain the equation

$$\mu A_n\{\psi_n(\kappa a) + 2(n+2)\psi_{n+1}(\kappa a)\} - (\alpha_n+\rho_0) = \tfrac{2}{3}(n-1)\rho_0 \text{ ...(66).}$$

From this equation and the equations (63) and (64) we can eliminate A_n and α_n, and thus obtain the frequency equation in the form

$$\begin{vmatrix} (n+1)\psi_n & n & (2n+1)q \\ \left\{2(n+2) - \frac{\kappa^2 a^2}{n}\right\}\psi_n + \frac{2}{n}\psi_{n-1} & 2(n-1) & 0 \\ -\{\psi_n + 2(n+2)\psi_{n+1}\} & 1 & 2(n-1) \end{vmatrix} = 0,$$

where the argument κa of the ψ-functions has been suppressed. On substituting for q its value, which is equivalent to $\kappa^2 a\mu/g\rho_0$, and multiplying out, we obtain the frequency equation in the form

$$\kappa^2 a\mu\,.\,(2n+1)\{2\psi_{n-1} - \kappa^2 a^2\psi_n + 2n(2n+1)\psi_n + 4n(n-1)(n+2)\psi_{n+1}\}$$

$$- g\rho_0 a\,.\,2n(n-1)\{2\psi_{n-1} - \kappa^2 a^2\psi_n + 2(2n+1)\psi_n\} = 0 \text{ ...(67),}$$

or, as it may be written,

$$\frac{2\psi_n'(\kappa a)}{\kappa a\psi_n(\kappa a)}+\frac{(2n+1)+ng\rho_0 a/(2n+1)\mu-\kappa^2a^2/2(n-1)}{n(n+2)+ng\rho_0 a/(2n+1)\mu-\kappa^2a^2/2(n-1)} \quad \text{....(68).}$$

Equation (68) is the frequency equation found by Bromwich. If we suppose μ to become very small, so that κa becomes very great, the most important terms in the coefficients that multiply $\kappa^2 a\mu(2n+1)$ and $-g\rho_0 a\,.\,2n(n-1)$ in (67) are identical, and therefore, as Bromwich pointed out, the equation passes over into the well-known frequency equation

$$p^2=\frac{2n(n-1)}{2n+1}\frac{g}{a} \quad \text{..........................(69),}$$

which was given in 1863 by Lord Kelvin as determining the periods for a sphere of homogeneous incompressible fluid.

157. We shall now exemplify the theory of §§ 147—150 by working out the rigidity which a homogeneous sphere of the same size and mass as the earth must have in order that the gravest mode of those vibrations which are specified by spherical harmonics of the second degree may be of intermediate type. We shall take λ to be equal to μ.

Equation (32) gives $$q=\sqrt{10}-2,$$

and, with this value of q, equation (31) gives the period as 4697 seconds nearly, or about 1 hr. 18 mins. Again, equation (38) gives

$$m=-\frac{14(q+1)(q+10)}{3(q-2)},$$

and equation (39), which gives αa, can be written

$$\{14+\tfrac{1}{3}(q+1)\}\left[\frac{q+10}{q+4}\left\{\left(\frac{\alpha^2a^2}{2}-8+\frac{18}{5q-4}\right)\psi_2-\psi_1\right\}-\left(\frac{\alpha^2a^2}{2}\psi_2+\psi_1\right)\right]$$
$$+\left[\left\{7+\frac{5(4q-5)(q+1)}{3(5q-4)}\right\}\alpha^2a^2-\frac{140(q+1)(q+10)}{3(5q-4)}\right]$$
$$\times\left\{\frac{q+10}{q+4}(8\psi_3+\psi_2)+2\psi_2\right\}=0.$$

On introducing the value of q and replacing ψ_3 by $-(5\psi_2+\psi_1)/\alpha^2a^2$, we find after some reduction that the above equation for αa becomes

$$\{33\sqrt{10}\,.\,\alpha^4a^4-(3570+1785\sqrt{10})\alpha^2a^2+(72800+28000\sqrt{10})\}\psi_2(\alpha a)$$
$$-\{(122+109\sqrt{10})\alpha^2a^2-(14560+5600\sqrt{10})\}\psi_1(\alpha a)=0 \quad \text{...(70).}$$

The smallest positive root of this equation is found to lie between 4 and 4·1. The critical value of the rigidity is then found from (34) to lie between $6{\cdot}19\times10^{11}$ and $5{\cdot}89\times10^{11}$ dynes per square cm. According to a result given on p. 114 *ante*, the sphere with this rigidity would be unstable as regards radial displacements. Hence it appears that all the vibrations which a homogeneous body representing the earth can execute, if they are of types specified by spherical harmonics of the second degree, are of what we have called quick types. In particular, the period of the gravest of them is less than 4697 seconds.

158. It seems to be worth while to find this period more exactly. According to the results obtained in Lamb's paper*, the period of the gravest mode of this type which a homogeneous sphere of the same size and mass as the earth can execute is 66 minutes, the rigidity being that of steel, taken as $8{\cdot}19 \times 10^{11}$ dynes per square cm. In this calculation gravity is omitted, and the material treated as incompressible. Bromwich† found that, if gravity is taken into account, but the material is still treated as incompressible, the period is reduced to about 55 minutes. The effect of compressibility must be to lengthen the period. We therefore proceed to form the period equation for vibrations of quick types which are specified by spherical harmonics of the second degree. We shall take λ to be equal to μ.

In obtaining this equation it is most convenient to start from equations (42) and (43) of p. 135, putting 2 for n, and putting λ equal to μ. Equation (45) gives

$$\left.\begin{aligned} \mu\alpha^2 a^2 &= \tfrac{1}{3} g\rho_0 a \{2(1+q) + \sqrt{(q^2 - 4q + 22)}\} \\ \mu\delta^2 a^2 &= \tfrac{1}{3} g\rho_0 a \{2(1+q) - \sqrt{(q^2 - 4q + 22)}\} \end{aligned}\right\} \quad \text{..........(71)},$$

and hence $$\frac{ng\rho_0/a}{\mu\alpha^2 - p^2\rho_0} = \frac{6}{2-q+R}, \quad \frac{ng\rho_0/a}{\mu\delta^2 - p^2\rho_0} = \frac{6}{2-q-R},$$

where $$R = \sqrt{(q^2 - 4q + 22)} \quad \text{..........(72)}.$$

As before we replace $\psi_3(\alpha a)$ by

$$-\{5\psi_2(\alpha a) + \psi_1(\alpha a)\}/\alpha^2 a^2$$

and $\psi_3(\delta a)$ by the corresponding expression in terms of δa. Then equation (42) becomes

$$\begin{aligned} &\frac{A_2}{4\pi\gamma\rho_0}\left[\frac{8-q+R}{2-q+R}\left\{\left(\frac{\alpha^2 a^2}{2} - \frac{10(4q-5)}{5q-4}\right)\psi_2(\alpha a) - \psi_1(\alpha a)\right\}\right. \\ &\qquad\qquad \left. - \left\{\frac{\alpha^2 a^2}{2}\psi_2(\alpha a) + \psi_1(\alpha a)\right\}\right] \\ &+ \frac{D_2}{4\pi\gamma\rho_0}\left[\frac{8-q-R}{2-q-R}\left\{\left(\frac{\delta^2 a^2}{2} - \frac{10(4q-5)}{5q-4}\right)\psi_2(\delta a) - \psi_1(\delta a)\right\}\right. \\ &\qquad\qquad \left. - \left\{\frac{\delta^2 a^2}{2}\psi_2(\delta a) + \psi_1(\delta a)\right\}\right] = 0, \end{aligned}$$

and equation (43) becomes

$$\begin{aligned} &\frac{A_2}{4\pi\gamma\rho_0}\left[\frac{12-3q+3R}{2-q+R}\alpha^2 a^2 \psi_2(\alpha a) - 8\frac{8-q+R}{2-q+R}\{5\psi_2(\alpha a) + \psi_1(\alpha a)\}\right] \\ &+ \frac{D_2}{4\pi\gamma\rho_0}\left[\frac{12-3q-3R}{2-q-R}\delta^2 a^2 \psi_2(\delta a) - 8\frac{8-q-R}{2-q-R}\{5\psi_2(\delta a) + \psi_1(\delta a)\}\right] = 0. \end{aligned}$$

* H. Lamb, *loc. cit.*, *ante* p. 50.

† T. J. I'A. Bromwich, *loc. cit.*, *ante* p. 126.

Hence the frequency equation can be written

$$\frac{\{3\alpha^2a^2-10(8-q+R)(4q-5)/(5q-4)\}\,\psi_2(\alpha a)-(10-2q+2R)\,\psi_1(\alpha a)}{\{(12-3q+3R)\,\alpha^2a^2-40(8-q+R)\}\,\psi_2(\alpha a)-8(8-q+R)\,\psi_1(\alpha a)}$$

$$-\frac{\{3\delta^2a^2-10(8-q-R)(4q-5)/(5q-4)\}\,\psi_2(\delta a)-(10-2q-2R)\,\psi_1(\delta a)}{\{(12-3q-3R)\,\delta^2a^2-40(8-q-R)\}\,\psi_2(\delta a)-8(8-q-R)\,\psi_1(\delta a)}$$

$$=0 \quad\ldots\ldots(73).$$

We cannot solve this equation until some value is assigned to the ratio $\alpha a/\delta a$; but, as soon as this ratio is assigned, equations (71) show that q becomes determinate, that is to say the period becomes determinate, before the equation (73) is solved for αa. If the ratio $\alpha a/\delta a$ is assigned, and the equation (73) solved for αa, or δa, and the result substituted in equations (71), there results a definite value for μ. In order to determine the period of the gravest mode for a sphere of given rigidity it seems to be best to find the values of μ which correspond to a suitably chosen series of values of the ratio $\alpha a/\delta a$. We have seen that periods between 3300 and 3960 seconds are the most interesting. In the following table are given a series of values of the ratio

$\alpha a/\delta a$	q	period	αa	μ
2	2·5670	3161	3·53	10·5
2·1	2·3789	3283	3·61	9·7
2·2	2·2309	3390	3·68	9·1
2·3	2·1114	3485	3·72	8·7
2·4	2·0126	3570	3·75	8·3
2·5	1·9298	3645	3·79	8·0
2·6	1·8595	3714	3·82	7·8
2·7	1·7990	3776	3·84	7·6
2·8	1·7465	3832	3·86	7·5
2·9	1·7006	3883	3·87	7·4
3	1·6601	3930	3·88	7·3

$\alpha a/\delta a$, the corresponding values of q and of the period in seconds, the smallest values of αa by which in each case the equation (73) can be satisfied, and the corresponding values of μ as multiples of 10^{11} dynes per square cm.

It appears from the table that for a homogeneous sphere of the same size and mass as the earth, having a rigidity equal to that of steel and a Poisson's ratio equal to $\frac{1}{4}$, the period of the slowest vibration of the type in question is almost exactly 60 min. We see that the period is diminished by gravity but not so much as it would be if the substance were incompressible.

CHAPTER XI

THEORY OF THE PROPAGATION OF SEISMIC WAVES

159. We shall begin this Chapter with a statement of the leading features of seismic records and of the most important steps that have been taken in their interpretation.

As long ago as 1830 it was proved by Poisson* that a homogeneous isotropic elastic solid body of unlimited extent can transmit two kinds of waves with different velocities, and that, at a great distance from the source of disturbance, the motion transmitted by the quicker wave is longitudinal, that is to say the displacement is parallel to the direction of propagation, and the motion transmitted by the slower wave is transverse, that is to say the displacement is at right angles to the direction of propagation. It was afterwards proved by Stokes† that the quicker wave is a wave of irrotational dilatation, and the slower wave is a wave of equivoluminal distortion characterized by differential rotation of the elements of the body, the velocities of the two waves being $\sqrt{\{(\lambda+2\mu)/\rho\}}$ and $\sqrt{(\mu/\rho)}$, where ρ denotes the density, μ the rigidity, and $\lambda+\frac{2}{3}\mu$ the modulus of compression. These two velocities will be denoted by $\mathbf{a}$ and $\mathbf{b}$. Stokes proved also that, if any disturbance takes place within a limited volume of the body, waves spread out from the disturbed region in the following way:—At a distant point no movement occurs until sufficient time has elapsed for the travelling of the disturbance with velocity $\mathbf{a}$ from the nearest point of the initially disturbed region, and again no movement occurs after a sufficient time has elapsed for the travelling of the disturbance with velocity $\mathbf{b}$ from the furthest point of the initially disturbed region. If the point is sufficiently distant for the $\mathbf{a}$-disturbance, travelling from the furthest point of the initially disturbed region, to reach it before the $\mathbf{b}$-disturbance, travelling from the nearest point of the initially disturbed region, reaches it, the motion that takes place at the point has three stages. In the first stage there is change of volume without any

* S. D. Poisson, "Mémoire sur la propagation du mouvement dans les milieux élastiques," Paris, *Mém. de l'Acad.*, t. x. 1831.

† G. G. Stokes, "On the dynamical theory of diffraction," Cambridge, *Trans. Phil. Soc.*, vol. IX. 1849; reprinted in Stokes's *Math. and Phys. Papers*, vol. II. p. 243.

rotation, in the last stage there is rotation without any change of volume, in the intermediate stage there is neither dilatation nor rotation, but the substance moves like an incompressible fluid in which there are no vortices. Thus at a sufficiently great distance from the initially disturbed region the two waves are separated completely. At shorter distances they are superposed for part of the time.

Systematic records, made by self-registering instruments, of the disturbances that are transmitted to distant stations when a great earthquake takes place, began to be made about the year 1889. It was very soon noticed that the records showed two very distinct stages, the first characterized by a very feeble movement, the second by a much larger movement. These are the so-called "preliminary tremor" and "main shock*." The idea that these might be dilatational and distortional waves, emerging at the surface, took firm root among seismologists for a time. In the light of increasing knowledge this idea had to be abandoned.

160. The theory of the dilatational and distortional waves takes no account of the existence of a boundary. When the waves from a source of disturbance within a body reach the boundary they are reflected, but in general the dilatational wave gives rise on reflexion to both kinds of waves, and the same is true of the distortional wave. Any subsequent state of the body can, of course, be represented as the result of superposing waves of the two kinds reflected one or more times at the boundary, with an allowance for the motions that take place between the two waves, but this mode of representation is very difficult to follow in detail. In particular it is not easy to see without mathematical analysis how such waves can combine to form a disturbance travelling with a definite velocity, less than either $\mathbf{a}$ or $\mathbf{b}$, over the surface. Yet such is the case. Lord Rayleigh† showed in 1885 that an irrotational displacement involving dilatation and an equivoluminal displacement involving rotation can be such that (1) neither of them penetrates far beneath the surface, (2) when they are combined the surface is free from traction. Such displacements may take the form of standing simple harmonic waves of a definite wave-length and period, or they may take the form of progressive simple harmonic waves of a definite wave-length and wave-velocity. In Lord Rayleigh's work the surface is regarded as an unlimited plane, and the waves may be of any length. Gravity is neglected, and it is found that the wave-velocity is independent of the wave-length. Such waves have since been called "Rayleigh-waves."

* The part of the motion here called the "main shock" is often described by the term "large waves," sometimes as the "principal portion." For many details in regard to the observed facts about earthquake shocks, and their transmission to great distances, the author is indebted to the treatise by C. G. Knott, "The physics of earthquake phenomena," Oxford, 1908.

† Lord Rayleigh, "On waves propagated along the plane surface of an elastic solid," London, *Proc. Math. Soc.*, vol. XVII., 1887; reprinted in *Scientific Papers*, vol. II., p. 441.

Besides the features of Rayleigh-waves which have been mentioned above, it is to be remarked that the displacement involved in them is two-dimensional. If we think of the plane boundary as horizontal, the components of displacement are a vertical component, and a horizontal component, and it is important to notice that the horizontal component is parallel to the direction of propagation. A second noteworthy feature is that the vertical component at the surface is larger than the horizontal component. The ratio of the two is nearly 2 : 1, if the material is incompressible; it is nearly 3 : 2, if the Poisson's ratio is $\frac{1}{4}$.

161. In the paper cited Lord Rayleigh suggested that waves of the type in question might play an important part in earthquakes. Since they do not penetrate far beneath the surface, they diverge practically in two dimensions only, and so acquire a continually increasing preponderance at a great distance from the source. This suggestion was not at first well received by seismologists, mainly because the records did not show a preponderance of vertical motion in the main shock. It was first systematically applied to the interpretation of seismic records by R. D. Oldham* in 1900. He pointed out that the preliminary tremors show two distinct phases, and that these are received at distant stations at times which correspond to the passage *through the body* of the earth of waves travelling with practically constant velocities; but the main shock is received at times which correspond to the passage *over the surface* of the earth of waves travelling with a different nearly constant velocity. He therefore proposed to identify the first and second phases of the preliminary tremors respectively with dilatational and distortional waves, generated at the source of disturbance, travelling by nearly straight paths through the body of the earth, and emerging at the surface; and he proposed to regard the main shock as propagated by Rayleigh-waves. The suggestion that the first and second phases of the preliminary tremors should be regarded as dilatational and distortional waves, transmitted through the body of the earth, has been very generally accepted, but the proposed identification of the main shock with Rayleigh-waves has been less favourably received, partly on account of the difficulty already mentioned in regard to the relative magnitudes of the horizontal and vertical displacements, and partly because observation has shown that a large part of the motion transmitted in the main shock is a horizontal movement at right angles to the direction of propagation.

162. Lord Rayleigh's investigation indicates the way in which waves of a certain type travel over the surface when they have already arrived at such a distance from the source that they can be treated as straight-crested, and it also shows that this type of waves is the only one in which the motion is

* R. D. Oldham, "On the propagation of earthquake motion to great distances," London, *Phil. Trans. R. Soc.*, A, vol. 194 (1900).

confined to the region near the surface, the body being homogeneous. The propagation of an arbitrary disturbance setting out from a limited region of a homogeneous body bounded by an infinite plane has been discussed very fully by H. Lamb*. He considered in detail the waves produced by impulsive pressure suddenly applied at a point of the surface. The motion received at a distant point begins suddenly at a time corresponding to the advent of the **a**-waves. The surface rises rather sharply, and then subsides very gradually without oscillation. At a time corresponding to the advent of the **b**-waves a slight jerk occurs; and this is followed, at a time corresponding to the advent of Rayleigh-waves, by a much larger jerk, after which the movement gradually subsides without oscillation. The subsidence is indefinitely prolonged. This peculiarity of an indefinitely prolonged "tail" to the waves has been shown by Lamb† to be a characteristic feature of the propagation of waves which diverge in two dimensions, even for the simplest imaginable medium with a single wave-velocity independent of the wave-length. Lamb's theory accounts easily for some of the most prominent features of seismic records, viz. the first and second phases of the preliminary tremors and the larger disturbance of the main shock, each with its appropriate velocity of chordal or arcual transmission, as the case may be, and it also accounts for the gradual subsidence of the movement. It does not account for the existence of horizontal movements at right angles to the direction of the propagation. Such movements are observed both in the second phase of the preliminary tremors and in the main shock. The existence of such movements in the second phase of the preliminary tremors could be accounted for easily by assuming a different kind of initial disturbance, such, for example, as would be caused by a couple applied locally, or by a sudden shearing movement in a horizontal direction. But no assumption as to the nature of the disturbance at the source will enable us to account for the relatively large horizontal displacements, transverse to the direction of propagation, which accompany the main shock; for, in a homogeneous body, there are no waves of transverse disturbance which are practically confined to the superficial regions. Again, the theory does not account for the approximately periodic oscillations which are a prominent feature in all seismic records, and Lamb suggested that these might be due to a succession of primitive shocks. A different explanation will be proposed presently.

163. It is now recognized that the large waves of the main shock, like the preliminary tremors, show more than one phase. The first phase is characterized by relatively long periods and a preponderance of transverse movement, the second phase by shorter periods with again a preponderance

* H. Lamb, "The propagation of tremors over the surface of an elastic solid," London, *Phil. Trans. R. Soc.*, A, vol. 203 (1904).

† H. Lamb, "On wave-propagation in two dimensions," London, *Proc. Math. Soc.*, vol. xxxv., 1903.

of transverse movement; the distinction between these two seems not to be very important. In the third phase the horizontal movement is mainly in the direction of propagation, the periods are shorter than those which occur in the two preceding phases, and these periods gradually diminish. This phase brings the largest movements, and, although various phases have been recognized in the subsequent parts of the train of waves, these three appear to be the most important. Observation has also shown that the first phase of the preliminary tremors is characterized by shorter periods than the second phase. C. G. Knott* and E. Wiechert† have both proposed to account for the preponderant transverse movement in the earlier phases of the large waves, by assuming that it is an effect of the transmission of waves through the "crust of the earth." Knott supposes that these waves are produced by successive reflexions of ordinary dilatational and distortional waves at the inner and outer boundaries of the crust and at the bounding surfaces of the various heterogeneous materials of which it is composed; and he emphasizes the results (1) that dilatational waves incident on a surface give rise on reflexion to distortional waves as well as dilatational waves, and (2) that, when the angle of incidence is high, the greater part of the energy is transferred to the distortional waves. Presumably, reflexions at oblique rock-faces must be supposed to be involved; for there is no such thing as a generation by reflexion of waves with displacement at right angles to the plane of incidence from waves with displacement parallel to the plane of incidence. But there seems to be no reason why waves with horizontal displacement at right angles to the direction of propagation should not travel through the crust, even if it were homogeneous, without penetrating far into the subjacent material, and this is, in fact, assumed to be the case by Wiechert, who supposes the crust to rest upon a sheet of magma, in such a way as to be practically free at the inner surface. I shall return presently to the discussion of these ideas.

Wiechert has also suggested that the existence of definite periods in the seismic records may be due to the setting up by the shock of the natural free vibrations of tracts of country; and Knott has pointed out, after Omori, that the records of Japanese earthquakes always show a preponderance of vibrations of period 4·6 seconds in the preliminary tremors, and that this period is characteristic also of the minute pulsations of the ground which are constantly observed at Tokyo. He suggests that this is a period of vibration natural to the plain in which Tokyo lies.

164. Besides the method of investigating the transmission of movements by determining the kinds of waves that can be propagated and their velocities, there is another—the method of normal functions. The earth being a body of limited extent, the movements which ensue upon any disturbance can be

* See especially p. 256 of Knott's treatise cited on p. 145 *ante*.

† E. Wiechert and K. Zöppritz, "Ueber Erdbebenwellen," *Göttingen Nachrichten*, 1907.

analysed into simple harmonic vibrations in normal modes. Lord Rayleigh* pointed out that his theory of the superficial waves must be included in Lamb's theory† of the vibrations of an elastic sphere; and the deduction of the equation giving the velocity of Rayleigh-waves from the period equation for the vibrations of a sphere was afterwards effected by Bromwich‡ in the case where the sphere is incompressible, and the modified equation in which gravity is taken into account, the substance being still treated as incompressible, was also obtained by him.

Just as all the movements that can take place may be regarded as the result of dilatational and distortional waves, transmitted with the appropriate velocities through the various materials of which the earth is composed, and reflected at the bounding surface and at the interfaces between materials of different properties (with a proper allowance for the motions that take place between the two waves), so also all the movements that can take place may be regarded as the result of superposed vibrations in normal modes. Sometimes one method yields results which are not easily obtained by the other.

We shall now consider a series of illustrative problems, with the object of throwing fresh light upon some of the questions that have been raised in the preceding statement; and we shall avail ourselves sometimes of one method and sometimes of another, as may appear most appropriate.

Transmission of waves through a gravitating compressible body.

165. Our first problem will be to determine the laws of wave-propagation in the interior of a gravitating compressible planet. The equations of wave-propagation are to be formed in the same way as equations (9) of p. 92, but without introducing the assumption that the components of displacement are proportional to simple harmonic functions of the time. We shall assume that the undisturbed body is homogeneous. The equations are three of the type

$$\rho_0 \frac{\partial^2 u}{\partial t^2} = (\lambda + \mu)\frac{\partial \Delta}{\partial x} + \mu \nabla^2 u - \tfrac{4}{3}\pi\gamma\rho_0^2 \frac{\partial}{\partial x}(rU) + \tfrac{4}{3}\pi\gamma\rho_0^2 x\Delta + \rho_0 \frac{\partial W}{\partial x} \quad \text{......(1)},$$

with

$$\Delta = \frac{\partial u}{\partial x} + \frac{\partial v}{\partial y} + \frac{\partial w}{\partial z} \quad \text{......(2)},$$

$$rU = xu + yv + zw \quad \text{......(3)},$$

$$\nabla^2 W = 4\pi\gamma\rho_0 \Delta \quad \text{......(4)}.$$

* *Loc. cit., ante* p. 145. † *Loc. cit., ante* p. 50.

‡ *Loc. cit., ante* p. 126.

By differentiating both members of the third of the equations of type (1) with respect to y, and both members of the second with respect to z, and subtracting the results, we obtain an equation which can be written

$$\rho_0 \frac{\partial^2 \varpi_x}{\partial t^2} = \mu \nabla^2 \varpi_x + \tfrac{2}{3}\pi\gamma\rho_0^2 \left\{\frac{\partial}{\partial y}(z\Delta) - \frac{\partial}{\partial z}(y\Delta)\right\} \quad \text{..........(5)},$$

where

$$\varpi_x = \frac{1}{2}\left(\frac{\partial w}{\partial y} - \frac{\partial v}{\partial z}\right) \quad \text{..........(6)}.$$

There are three equations of the type (5), and they show that, if Δ vanishes, waves of distortion involving rotation can be propagated in exactly the same way as in an elastic solid medium supposed to be free from gravitation and initial stress. This result is in accordance with the result noted in § 151, viz. that the vibrations of the first class are unaffected by gravity and initial stress.

The result would probably need to be modified if we could take proper account of the heterogeneity of the materials within the earth and of the inequalities of its figure. The modification would, in all likelihood, take the form of a dependence of the wave-velocity of a train of distortional waves upon the locality and the wave-length. Cf. § 168 *infra*.

166. By differentiating both members of the three equations of type (1) with respect to x, y, z in order, adding the results, and using (4) to eliminate W, we obtain the equation

$$\rho_0 \frac{\partial^2 \Delta}{\partial t^2} = (\lambda + 2\mu)\nabla^2\Delta - \tfrac{4}{3}\pi\gamma\rho_0^2 \nabla^2 (rU) + \tfrac{4}{3}\pi\gamma\rho_0^2 r \frac{\partial \Delta}{\partial r} + 8\pi\gamma\rho_0^2\Delta \quad \text{......(7)}.$$

By multiplying both members of the same three equations by x, y, z in order, and adding the results, we obtain the equation

$$\rho_0 \frac{\partial^2 (rU)}{\partial t^2} = (\lambda + \mu) r \frac{\partial \Delta}{\partial r} + \mu\{\nabla^2 (rU) - 2\Delta\} - \tfrac{4}{3}\pi\gamma\rho_0^2 r \frac{\partial (rU)}{\partial r}$$
$$+ \tfrac{4}{3}\pi\gamma\rho_0^2 r^2 \Delta + \rho_0 r \frac{\partial W}{\partial r} \quad \text{......(8)}.$$

Now we have the formulae

$$\nabla^2 \left\{r \frac{\partial (rU)}{\partial r}\right\} = r \frac{\partial}{\partial r} \nabla^2 (rU) + 2\nabla^2 (rU),$$

$$\nabla^2 (r^2\Delta) = r^2\nabla^2\Delta + 4r \frac{\partial \Delta}{\partial r} + 6\Delta,$$

$$\nabla^2 \left(r \frac{\partial W}{\partial r}\right) = 4\pi\gamma\rho_0 \left(r \frac{\partial \Delta}{\partial r} + 2\Delta\right),$$

in the last of which use has been made of equation (4). On operating with

∇^2 on both members of (8), and eliminating $\nabla^2(rU)$ by means of (7), we find an equation which can be written

$$\left(\mu\nabla^2 - \rho_0 \frac{\partial^2}{\partial t^2}\right)\left\{(\lambda + 2\mu)\nabla^2 - \rho_0 \frac{\partial^2}{\partial t^2} + \tfrac{16}{3}\pi\gamma\rho_0^2\right\}\Delta$$

$$+ (\tfrac{4}{3}\pi\gamma\rho_0^2)^2 r^2 \left(\nabla^2 - \frac{\partial^2}{\partial r^2} - \frac{2}{r}\frac{\partial}{\partial r}\right)\Delta = 0 \quad \ldots(9).$$

This equation gives the law according to which waves of dilatation are propagated through the body. The equations of type (5) show that in general the motion transmitted by such waves is not strictly irrotational, but the dilatation must be accompanied by rotational strain. Thus the separate existence of waves of irrotational dilatation and waves of equivoluminal distortion is not maintained when gravity is taken into account. In the case of the earth $\frac{4}{3}\pi\gamma\rho_0^2/\mu$ is $(g\rho_0 a/\mu)\, a^{-2}$, where a is the radius of the earth; and therefore the rotation, which the equations of type (5) show must accompany the dilatation, is very small, the quantity $(g\rho_0 a/\mu)$ being comparable with unity. The quantity $(g\rho_0 a/\mu)$ is about 5 if the rigidity is that of steel.

A similar argument can be used to deduce from equation (7) the result that, to a first approximation, Δ satisfies the equation

$$\rho_0 \frac{\partial^2 \Delta}{\partial t^2} = (\lambda + 2\mu)\nabla^2\Delta.$$

It follows that the law of propagation of waves of dilatation is nearly the same as it would be if gravity and initial stress were neglected, and the effect due to these influences can be treated as a small correction.

167. To determine the nature of this correction we assume for Δ a formula of the type

$$A\cos\{f(x - Vt)\},$$

in which A, f, and V are constants, and substitute in the left-hand member of equation (9). The result can be written

$$\{f^4(\mu - V^2\rho_0)(\lambda + 2\mu - V^2\rho_0) - \tfrac{4}{3}\pi\gamma\rho_0^2 \,.\, 4f^2(\mu - V^2\rho_0)$$

$$- (\tfrac{4}{3}\pi\gamma\rho_0^2)^2 f^2(r^2 - x^2)\}\cos\{f(x - Vt)\}$$

$$+ (\tfrac{4}{3}\pi\gamma\rho_0^2)^2\, 2fx \sin\{f(x - Vt)\} \quad \ldots\ldots(10).$$

It is impossible to adjust V so that this expression shall vanish for all values of x and t, and therefore simple harmonic plane waves of dilatation cannot be propagated through the body without change of type. We observe, however, that, if the wave-length $2\pi/f$ is small compared with the radius, the quantity fx is in general small compared with $f^2(r^2 - x^2)$, while this quantity is in general of the same order as $f^2\mu/\frac{4}{3}\pi\gamma\rho_0^2$. Hence the sine term in the above expression (10) is in general small compared with the cosine term.

To make the cosine term vanish when the first power of a quantity of the order $(g\rho_0 a/\mu)\times(1/a^2f^2)$ is retained, but the second power is neglected, we put

$$V = V_0 + \delta V,$$

where $V_0^2 = (\lambda + 2\mu)/\rho_0$. Then we find after a little reduction

$$2\rho_0 V_0 \delta V = -\frac{g\rho_0 a}{f^2 a^2}\left(4 - \frac{g\rho_0 a}{\lambda+\mu}\frac{r^2 - x^2}{a^2}\right) \quad \text{..............(11).}$$

This value of V is a function of y and z, though not of x, and therefore, in strictness, differential coefficients of V should be introduced into the expression (10). It would, however, be found that the terms containing them are small of a higher order than those here retained.

168. A first approximation to the law of propagation of dilatational waves is expressed in the statement that such waves travel with the uniform velocity V_0; this is the velocity denoted by **a** in § 159. A second approximation shows (1) that the velocity depends to some extent on the locality, and (2) that it depends to some extent on the wave-length. The effect of dependence on the locality would be shown in a curvature of the paths by which the first phase of the preliminary tremors is propagated through the earth. Even if the earth were homogeneous, gravity and initial stress would cause these paths to deviate slightly from straightness.

According to what has been said here and in § 165, it might be expected that the paths of the second phase tremors would be straighter, and their rate of transmission more regular, than those of the first. Actually the reverse holds. This discrepancy between theory and observation is, of course, to be attributed to the heterogeneity of the materials composing the earth.

169. Dependence of the rate of transmission upon the wave-length indicates dispersion, analogous to optical dispersion*. The only example of waves in a dispersive medium for which the effects produced by an initial disturbance, confined to a limited region, have been worked out at all fully is that of waves on deep water†, treated as incompressible and free from viscosity. In that example the wave-velocity of a simple harmonic wave-train increases as the wave-length increases. Owing to the assumed incompressi-

* The result that in a gravitating compressible planet the velocity of waves which are mainly dilatational should depend upon the locality and the wave-length was obtained by Love in the paper cited on p. 89. On p. 251 of the treatise cited on p. 145 Knott suggests that the wave-velocity of compressional waves may depend on the wave-length, although the theory of elasticity, as ordinarily developed, does not admit the possibility of such dependence. He also suggests that the longer periods associated with the second phase preliminary tremors may be due to the intermingling of the distortional waves with the compressional waves of longer periods.

† See the revision, in Lamb's *Hydrodynamics* (3rd edition), pp. 364—374, of Cauchy and Poisson's investigations of this problem.

bility, the motion received at a distant place begins at once. In the early stages it is not even approximately periodic, but the surface rises and falls at intervals which diminish rather rapidly. When the initial disturbance is concentrated at a point the motion in its later stages becomes much more nearly periodic, as if a regular simple harmonic wave-train were passing the place. The wave-length of this wave-train, and therefore also the period of the motion that is being executed at the place and time, is determined as that to which there corresponds, as group-velocity (not wave-velocity), the velocity required to travel from the initially disturbed spot to the place in the time. In the problem of water-waves the period continually diminishes. If the initially disturbed region is of finite extent, the motion in the later stages exhibits phenomena of "interference," the superposed waves due to different parts of the initially disturbed region alternately reinforcing each other and opposing each other, so that the surface shows a series of bands of disturbed water separated by bands of smooth water, and the bands appear to pass a place with the group-velocity described above. In the earlier stages of the motion the amplitudes of the alternate elevations and depressions which occur at a place increase rather rapidly. In the later stages they diminish gradually. In any other problem of wave-motion in a dispersive medium we can do little more than argue by analogy to the special problem of waves on deep water, allowing, so far as we can, for such modifications as may be necessary if the wave-velocity of simple harmonic wave-trains diminishes as the wave-length increases, and if these wave-velocities are restricted to lie between particular limiting velocities, instead of being capable of taking all positive values. We may expect, although we cannot prove strictly, that the disturbance received at a place will be oscillatory, though not strictly periodic, the intervals between successive maxima changing from time to time. We may expect also that these intervals will increase or diminish according as the wave-velocity of a simple harmonic wave-train diminishes or increases as the wave-length increases.

Now we have seen that, apart from any effect of heterogeneity, gravity and initial stress should cause dispersion of the dilatational waves, and we should expect therefore that such waves would emerge at the surface in the form of oscillatory disturbances. In equation (11) the wave-velocity of a simple harmonic wave-train increases or diminishes as the wave-length increases, according as the second factor in the right-hand member is negative or positive. Now if the rigidity is taken to be that of steel, and if the Poisson's ratio is taken to be $\frac{1}{4}$, the quantity $g\rho_0 a/(\lambda+\mu)$ is about $\frac{5}{2}$, and the factor in question is certainly positive. We should expect, therefore, that the periods, or rather the intervals between maxima, of the oscillatory displacement that can be observed at the surface during the passage of the first phase preliminary tremors, should gradually increase. These results are in accordance with observation.

170. The above theory of a local velocity of propagation, depending on the wave-length, is a very rough approximation, and the particular law of dependence of wave-velocity upon wave-length and locality which is expressed by equation (11) can hardly be regarded as more than an indication of possibilities. It certainly cannot be regarded as the true law by which this dependence should be expressed in the case of the earth. One defect of the theory is that it represents waves which are mainly dilatational as being propagated with a definite velocity, which cannot exceed that of simple **a**-waves in the material. In strictness there is no such finite velocity. This can be seen without analysis. Let any disturbance involving a change of density occur in the neighbourhood of a place A. The attraction of the earth at any other place B is immediately altered by an amount depending upon the change of density at A, and therefore a feeble motion with a very small finite acceleration begins at once at B. This result would be expressed in our equations (1)—(4) by observing that the potential due to the change of density at A is included in the value of W at B. The theory may, however, be relied upon in so far as it shows that a much more important disturbance should begin at a time corresponding approximately to that at which simple **a**-waves would arrive, and it suggests an explanation of some of the features by which the first phase preliminary tremors are found to be characterized.

TRANSMISSION OF WAVES OVER THE SURFACE OF A SPHERE.

171. Our second problem will be to investigate the effect of gravity on superficial waves. For this purpose we shall have recourse to the frequency equations obtained in §§ 152 and 156. Before proceeding, it may be in place to give an illustration, taken from the theory of the transverse vibrations of strings, of the way in which standing vibrations in normal modes may combine to form progressive waves travelling with a definite front*.

Let a uniform string of length l, fixed at both ends, be thrown into transverse vibration by an impulse applied at its middle at the instant $t=0$. According to a result obtained in Lord Rayleigh's *Theory of Sound*, § 129, the displacement at a distance x from one end at any subsequent time t is given by the formula

$$y = 2A \sum_{n=0}^{n=\infty} \frac{(-1)^n}{2n+1} \sin \frac{(2n+1)\pi x}{l} \sin \frac{(2n+1)\pi V t}{l} \quad \text{.........(12)},$$

* The Cauchy-Poisson problem for waves on deep water illustrates the combination of standing simple harmonic waves to form progressive waves, but in that problem the period of a simple harmonic wave may be any whatever. The object here in view is to illustrate the case where only certain definite periods can occur.

where A is a constant depending on the magnitude of the initial impulse, and V^2 is equal to T/ρ, T denoting the tension, and ρ the mass per unit of length. Now if we take $t < \frac{1}{2}l/V$, and expand, in a Fourier's series of sines of multiples of $\pi x/l$, a function which has the value

$$\tfrac{1}{2}\pi A \text{ when } \tfrac{1}{2}l + Vt > x > \tfrac{1}{2}l - Vt,$$

and the value

$$0 \text{ when } l > x > \tfrac{1}{2}l + Vt,$$

$$\text{and when } \tfrac{1}{2}l - Vt > x > 0,$$

we find that the series is precisely that which stands on the right-hand side of (12). Hence, at any instant before the disturbance setting out from the middle at the time $t=0$, and travelling with the velocity V, reaches the ends, the displacement is equal to $\frac{1}{2}\pi A$ within a length Vt on either side of the middle, and vanishes in the remaining parts of the string. The awkwardness of a discontinuous displacement at the front of the wave could be avoided, at the expense of greater complexity, by taking the initial impulse to be diffused over a short length instead of being concentrated at one point.

In the above example the normal functions are simple harmonic functions of position. In the problem of the vibrations of a sphere they are proportional to spherical surface harmonics. Combinations of such functions suitable to express displacements in progressive waves are more difficult to work out in detail. But the facts (1) that zonal harmonics of high degrees (near their equatorial plane) tend to a limiting form, which is a simple harmonic function of the meridional arc, and (2) that sectorial harmonics (at their equatorial plane) are actually simple harmonic functions of the equatorial arc, suggest that the analytical principles on which the combination of standing vibrations in normal modes to form progressive waves depend, in the case of a string, could be adapted to give a formal proof in the case of a sphere. They also suggest that, in the latter case, displacements represented by spherical harmonics of high degrees would be important elements in the combination, or, in other words, short waves would be largely involved. For the purpose in hand a wave is to be regarded as "short" if the wave-length is small compared with the radius of the sphere.

172. As in Chapter X, let a denote the radius of the sphere, and n the degree of the spherical harmonic to which any normal mode of vibration corresponds. Then $2\pi a/n$ takes the place of the wave-length. We shall denote it by $2\pi/f$, so that

$$f = n/a \qquad \text{..................................(13).}$$

Also let $2\pi/p$ denote the period corresponding to the same normal mode.

Then p/f represents the wave-velocity for waves of length $2\pi/f$. We shall put

$$V = p/f \quad \text{..............................(14)}.$$

We have to consider modes of vibration in which n and a are both large. The frequency-equation obtained in § 152 passes over into a limiting form, which is a relation between V and f.

In order that this equation may be applicable to the transmission of superficial waves over the surface of the earth it is necessary that the vibrations in question should be of types which were described in § 151 as "quick." According to (17) of p. 129 the condition for this is in the limit

$$p^4 > f^2 g^2,$$

or

$$V > \sqrt{(g/f)} \quad \text{..............................(15)}.$$

Now the large waves of earthquakes are transmitted with a velocity of about 3 km. per second, and, if V has this value, the shortest wave-length for which the inequality (15) is not satisfied is about 6000 km. We may therefore conclude that all short waves which can be propagated with any such velocity as this correspond to vibrations of quick types.

173. In order to find the limiting form to which equation (44) of p. 136 tends, we begin by re-writing this equation in the form

$$\frac{\dfrac{\alpha^2}{f^2} - 2 + \dfrac{2}{n^2} + \dfrac{\nu}{n} + \dfrac{2\alpha}{nf}\dfrac{\psi_n'(\alpha a)}{\psi_n(\alpha a)} + \dfrac{\alpha^2-\kappa^2}{\kappa^2}\dfrac{p^2}{gf}\left\{2 - \dfrac{2}{n} + \dfrac{\nu}{n} + \dfrac{2\alpha}{f}\dfrac{\psi_n'(\alpha a)}{\psi_n(\alpha a)}\right\}}{\alpha^2\left[1 + \dfrac{2f}{\alpha}\left(1+\dfrac{2}{n}\right)\dfrac{\psi_n'(\alpha a)}{\psi_n(\alpha a)} + \dfrac{\alpha^2-\kappa^2}{\kappa^2}\dfrac{p^2}{gf}\left\{\dfrac{\kappa^2}{h^2} + \dfrac{2f}{\alpha}\left(1+\dfrac{2}{n}\right)\dfrac{\psi_n'(\alpha a)}{\psi_n(\alpha a)}\right\}\right]}$$
$$- \frac{-\dfrac{\kappa^2}{\kappa^2-\delta^2}\dfrac{gf}{p^2}\left\{\dfrac{\delta^2}{f^2} - 2 + \dfrac{2}{n^2} + \dfrac{\nu}{n} + \dfrac{2\delta}{nf}\dfrac{\psi_n'(\delta a)}{\psi_n(\delta a)}\right\} + 2 - \dfrac{2}{n} + \dfrac{\nu}{n} + \dfrac{2\delta}{f}\dfrac{\psi_n'(\delta a)}{\psi_n(\delta a)}}{\delta^2\left[-\dfrac{\kappa^2}{\kappa^2-\delta^2}\dfrac{gf}{p^2}\left\{1 + \dfrac{2f}{\delta}\left(1+\dfrac{2}{n}\right)\dfrac{\psi_n'(\delta a)}{\psi_n(\delta a)}\right\} + \dfrac{\kappa^2}{h^2} + \dfrac{2f}{\delta}\left(1+\dfrac{2}{n}\right)\dfrac{\psi_n'(\delta a)}{\psi_n(\delta a)}\right]} = 0$$
$$\text{............(16)},$$

where, in accordance with a usual notation, we have put

$$\kappa^2 = p^2\rho_0/\mu, \quad h^2 = p^2\rho_0/(\lambda + 2\mu) \quad \text{....................(17)};$$

and then we proceed to approximate to the various expressions which occur on the understanding that $1/n$ tends to zero as a limit, while gf/p^2 is a small quantity of which the square may be neglected.

Now the quantities α^2 and δ^2 are the roots of the equation

$$\mu(\lambda+2\mu)\xi^2 - \left\{(\lambda+3\mu)p^2 + 4\mu\frac{g}{a}\right\}\rho_0\xi + \left\{p^4 + 4\frac{g}{a}p^2 - \frac{n(n+1)g^2}{a^2}\right\}\rho_0^2 = 0,$$

or, as it may be written,

$$\xi^2 - \left(\kappa^2 + h^2 + 4h^2\frac{gf}{p^2}\frac{1}{n}\right)\xi + \kappa^2 h^2\left\{1 + 4\frac{gf}{p^2}\frac{1}{n} - \frac{g^2f^2}{p^4}\left(1+\frac{1}{n}\right)\right\} = 0 \quad \text{...(18)};$$

and we see that, to a first approximation, we may write κ for α and h for δ, as it has been understood all along in the theory which led to equation (16) that α^2 is the greater root. For a second approximation, we substitute $\kappa^2+\eta$ for ξ in (18), and find, on neglecting η^2,

$$\kappa^4 + 2\kappa^2\eta - \left(\kappa^2 + h^2 + 4h^2 \frac{gf}{p^2}\frac{1}{n}\right)(\kappa^2+\eta) + \kappa^2 h^2 \left\{1 + 4\frac{gf}{p^2}\frac{1}{n} - \frac{g^2f^2}{p^4}\left(1+\frac{1}{n}\right)\right\},$$

or

$$\eta\left(\kappa^2 - h^2 - 4h^2\frac{gf}{p^2}\frac{1}{n}\right) = \kappa^2 h^2 \frac{g^2f^2}{p^4}\left(1+\frac{1}{n}\right).$$

Hence, neglecting $1/n$, we have, correctly to the second order in gf/p^2,

$$\alpha^2 = \kappa^2 + \frac{\kappa^2 h^2}{\kappa^2 - h^2}\left(\frac{gf}{p^2}\right)^2 \quad\text{.........................(19).}$$

To the same order we should find

$$\delta^2 = h^2 - \frac{\kappa^2 h^2}{\kappa^2 - h^2}\left(\frac{gf}{p^2}\right)^2.$$

We see that the corrections to the values κ and h for α and δ are of the order which we propose to neglect, and therefore, in general, we may replace α by κ and δ by h. The only expression in which these substitutions may not be made is

$$\frac{\alpha^2-\kappa^2}{\kappa^2}\frac{p^2}{gf},$$

and, from the value for α^2 given in (19), we see that we may put

$$\frac{\alpha^2-\kappa^2}{\kappa^2}\frac{p^2}{gf} = \frac{h^2}{\kappa^2-h^2}\frac{gf}{p^2} \quad\text{.........................(20),}$$

and this equation is correct to the first order in gf/p^2, when $1/n$ tends to zero as a limit.

The equation defining ν may be written

$$\nu = \frac{3gf}{p^2}\left(1-\frac{1}{n^2}\right)\Big/\left\{1+\frac{1}{2n} - \left(1-\frac{1}{n}\right)\frac{gf}{p^2}\right\},$$

and therefore we have, correctly to the same order,

$$\nu = \frac{3gf}{p^2} \quad\text{..............................(21),}$$

so that ν/n is a quantity of the order which we omit.

Again it has been proved by Bromwich* that, when n and κa are both very great, the expression $\psi_n'(\kappa a)/\psi_n(\kappa a)$ tends asymptotically to the value $(s-f)/\kappa$, in which $f = \lim. n/a$, and

$$s = \sqrt{(f^2-\kappa^2)} \quad\text{.............................(22).}$$

* *Loc. cit., ante* p. 126.

We shall therefore take, as sufficient approximations,

$$\frac{\psi_n'(\alpha a)}{\psi_n(\alpha a)} = \frac{s-f}{\kappa}, \quad \frac{\psi_n'(\delta a)}{\psi_n(\delta a)} = \frac{r-f}{h} \quad \text{.................(23)},$$

where

$$r = \sqrt{(f^2 - h^2)} \quad \text{.............................(24)}.$$

When these substitutions are made in equation (16) it becomes

$$\frac{\dfrac{\kappa^2}{f^2} - 2 + \dfrac{h^2}{\kappa^2 - h^2}\dfrac{gf}{p^2}\left(2 + 2\dfrac{s-f}{f}\right)}{\kappa^2 + 2f(s-f) + \dfrac{h^2}{\kappa^2 - h^2}\dfrac{gf}{p^2}\left\{\dfrac{\kappa^4}{h^2} + 2f(s-f)\right\}}$$

$$- \frac{2 + 2\dfrac{r-f}{f} - \dfrac{\kappa^2}{\kappa^2 - h^2}\dfrac{gf}{p^2}\left(\dfrac{h^2}{f^2} - 2\right)}{\kappa^2 + 2f(r-f) - \dfrac{\kappa^2}{\kappa^2 - h^2}\dfrac{gf}{p^2}\left\{h^2 + 2f(r-f)\right\}} = 0.$$

On multiplying up, and neglecting the square of gf/p^2, we obtain the equation

$$\left(\frac{\kappa^2}{f^2} - 2\right)^2 - \frac{4rs}{f^2} + \frac{4gf}{p^2}\left[\frac{s}{f}\left\{\frac{\kappa^2 h^2}{(\kappa^2 - h^2)f^2} - \frac{\kappa^2 + h^2}{\kappa^2 - h^2}\right\}\right.$$

$$\left. - \frac{r}{f}\left\{\frac{\kappa^4}{(\kappa^2 - h^2)f^2} - \frac{\kappa^2 + h^2}{\kappa^2 - h^2}\right\}\right] = 0 \quad \text{...(25)}.$$

This equation gives κ in terms of f, and therefore the velocity of waves of length $2\pi/f$ in terms of f. If gf/p^2 is neglected, it passes over into the equation

$$\left(\frac{\kappa^2}{f^2} - 2\right)^2 - \frac{4rs}{f^2} = 0 \quad \text{.........................(26)},$$

which gives the velocity of Rayleigh-waves. The equation (25) therefore gives the means of finding a correction to this velocity on account of gravity.

It may be noted that, if h vanishes, that is to say, if the material is incompressible, equation (25) becomes

$$\left(\frac{\kappa^2}{f^2} - 2\right)^2 - \frac{4s}{f} - \frac{4gf}{p^2}\left(\frac{\kappa^2}{f^2} - 1 + \frac{s}{f}\right) = 0 \quad \text{..............(27)}.$$

Now in this case, if we neglected gf/p^2 altogether, the equation giving the velocity would be

$$\left(\frac{\kappa^2}{f^2} - 2\right)^2 - \frac{4s}{f} = 0 \quad \text{.........................(28)};$$

and therefore, if the square of gf/p^2 is neglected, equation (27) can be written

$$\left(\frac{\kappa^2}{f^2} - 2\right)^2 - \frac{4s}{f} - \frac{gf}{p^2}\frac{\kappa^4}{f^4} = 0 \text{.......................(29)}.$$

Equation (29) has been obtained by Bromwich by two distinct methods, one of which consists in a passage to the limit from equation (68) on p. 140 *ante*.

174. Now let V and V_0 denote the wave-velocity and the value that it would have if g were neglected, and let b stand for $\sqrt{(\mu/\rho)}$, the velocity of simple distortional waves. Then κ/f is the same as V/b, and equation (26) can be written

$$\left(2-\frac{V_0^2}{b^2}\right)^2=4\sqrt{\left\{\left(1-\frac{V_0^2}{b^2}\right)\left(1-\frac{\mu}{\lambda+2\mu}\frac{V_0^2}{b^2}\right)\right\}} \quad \text{.........(30)},$$

from which it appears that V_0 is independent of the wave-length. Equation (30) is the equation found, and solved, by Lord Rayleigh*. Equation (25) shows that, on account of gravity, V differs a little from V_0, and it gives approximately

$$\frac{V_0(V-V_0)}{b^2}\left[4\left(\frac{\lambda+3\mu}{\lambda+2\mu}-\frac{2\mu}{\lambda+2\mu}\frac{V_0^2}{b^2}\right)\Big/\left(2-\frac{V_0^2}{b^2}\right)^2-\left(2-\frac{V_0^2}{b^2}\right)\right]$$
$$=-\frac{g}{fV_0^2}\left[\left(\frac{\lambda+3\mu}{\lambda+\mu}-\frac{\lambda+2\mu}{\lambda+\mu}\frac{V_0^2}{b^2}\right)\sqrt{\left(1-\frac{\mu}{\lambda+2\mu}\frac{V_0^2}{b^2}\right)}\right.$$
$$\left.-\left(\frac{\lambda+3\mu}{\lambda+\mu}-\frac{\mu}{\lambda+\mu}\frac{V_0^2}{b^2}\right)\sqrt{\left(1-\frac{V_0^2}{b^2}\right)}\right] \quad \text{...(31)}.$$

From (31) it appears that, to the first order in the small quantity g/fb^2, V is given by an equation of the form

$$V=V_0(1+\beta g/fb^2),$$

where β is a number which depends upon the ratio μ/λ, since the value of V_0^2/b^2 determined by (30) depends upon this ratio only. It is easy to see that, when μ/λ tends to zero as a limit, β is positive, that is to say, when the material is incompressible the wave-velocity is increased by gravity. Again it is not difficult to prove that, when $\lambda=\mu$, β vanishes, that is to say, when the Poisson's ratio of the material is $\frac{1}{4}$ the wave-velocity is not affected by gravity. The Table placed below shows some corresponding values of μ/λ, Poisson's ratio σ, V_0^2/b^2, and β, those for incompressible material being the values given by Bromwich. It appears that β is positive or negative according as σ is greater or less than $\frac{1}{4}$. Now in the application of the results to the transmission of waves over the surface of the earth the values of σ that come into consideration are such as belong to rocks near the surface. In the experimental research of Adams and Coker† eighteen different kinds of rocks were examined, and for all of them σ was found to lie between 1·9 and 2·9. For twelve of them it was found to be greater than $\frac{1}{4}$ and for the remaining six less. We may conclude that the wave-velocity of simple harmonic waves of the type under discussion is but little affected by gravity, but, on the whole, is likely to be increased slightly, the small increment being proportional to the wave-length. The result indicates a slight dispersion, and suggests that

* *Loc. cit.*, *ante* p. 145.

† F. D. Adams and E. G. Coker, "An investigation into the elastic constants of rocks......," Washington (Carnegie Institution), 1906.

the disturbance received at a place should be oscillatory, with gradually diminishing intervals between successive maxima.

μ/λ	0	$\frac{1}{2}$	1	$\frac{3}{2}$
σ	$\frac{1}{2}$	$\frac{1}{3}$	$\frac{1}{4}$	$\frac{1}{5}$
V_0^2/b^2	0·9126	0·8696	0·8543	0·8299
β	0·1089	0·0462	0	- 0·0309

175. If the earth could be treated as homogeneous, to a depth considerably greater than any of the wave-lengths that are involved, the large waves of earthquakes could be nothing but Rayleigh-waves modified by gravity. This is proved by Lamb's theory of tremors already cited. The modification necessitated by gravity is nothing more than a correction, which is trifling except in so far as it suggests an explanation of the observed fact that the movement is oscillatory. The velocity of Rayleigh-waves over the surface depends on the density and rigidity of surface-rocks, not on those of the substance at a great depth. Now the rigidities of many kinds of granite and marble were found by Adams and Coker to be roughly about $2{\cdot}5 \times 10^{11}$ dynes per square cm., and the average density of surface rocks is about 2·8, so that the velocity of Rayleigh-waves expressed by the formula $0{\cdot}9 \times \sqrt{(\mu/\rho)}$ would be about 3 km. per second. By slight changes in the assumed values of the rigidity and density we could easily fit any of the results found by observation in regard to the rate of transmission of the large waves. But we have seen that the theory needs some extension in order to account for the preponderance of transverse horizontal movements in the earlier phases of the main shock. The desired extension must introduce heterogeneity of the material.

Transverse waves in superficial layer.

176. It has already been stated that one way by which it has been attempted to explain the transverse movement in the earlier phases of the large waves is by taking them to be waves that travel through the crust of the earth, without penetrating deeply into the interior. By the "crust" we may understand a superficial layer of which the density and elasticity differ from those of the substance beneath it. If the layer is thin, and if such waves can be transmitted through it, the effects that could be observed at the surface would be nearly the same as if the waves diverged in two dimensions only. Accordingly our third problem will be to investigate the transmission of transverse waves in a superficial layer, on the understanding that such waves do not penetrate deeply into the subjacent material.

177. We shall take an origin on the lower boundary of the layer, and draw the axis of z vertically upwards. Then the lower boundary is the plane $z=0$, and the upper boundary will be taken to be the plane $z=T$, so that T denotes the thickness of the layer. Waves of the type we are seeking are not affected by gravity. We shall suppose the waves to travel in the negative direction of the axis of x, and shall take the displacement v to be parallel to the axis of y. We shall denote by μ and ρ the rigidity and density of the layer, and by μ' and ρ' those of the subjacent material. We shall take the wave-length and period to be $2\pi/f$ and $2\pi/p$. In both regions v is proportional to a simple harmonic function of

$$pt+fx.$$

Since t only occurs in simple harmonic functions of period $2\pi/p$, the equations of motion of the layer reduce to the single equation

$$(\nabla^2+\kappa^2)\,v=0 \qquad \text{.............................(32)},$$

where

$$\kappa^2=p^2\rho/\mu \qquad \text{.............................(33)}.$$

We shall now suppose that $\kappa>f$. Then in the layer v is of the form

$$v=(A\cos sz+B\sin sz)\cos(pt+fx+\epsilon) \qquad \text{..............(34)},$$

where

$$s^2=\kappa^2-f^2 \qquad \text{.............................(35)}.$$

It should be noted that s is here used in a different sense from that in § 173. In like manner the equations of motion of the subjacent material reduce to the single equation

$$(\nabla^2+\kappa'^2)\,v=0 \qquad \text{.............................(36)},$$

where

$$\kappa'^2=p^2\rho'/\mu' \qquad \text{.............................(37)},$$

and v must have the form

$$v=Ce^{s'z}\cos(pt+fx+\epsilon) \qquad \text{......................(38)},$$

where

$$s'^2=f^2-\kappa'^2 \qquad \text{.............................(39)},$$

and, in order that the disturbance may not penetrate to a great depth, it is necessary that the quantity s' should be positive.

The conditions which hold at the lower boundary $z=0$ are that the displacement and the tangential traction must be continuous. Apart from the initial stress, which does not affect the problem, there is no normal traction. These conditions give the two equations

$$A=C, \quad \mu sB=\mu's'C.$$

The condition that the upper boundary $z=T$ is free from traction is

$$-A\sin sT+B\cos sT=0.$$

On eliminating the constants A, B, C we obtain the equation

$$\tan sT = \mu' s' / \mu s \quad \text{.............................(40).}$$

Now from equations (33), (35), (37) and (39) we find

$$s'^2 = f^2 \left(1 - \frac{b^2}{b'^2}\right) - s^2 \frac{b^2}{b'^2} \quad \text{.......................(41),}$$

where

$$b^2 = \mu/\rho, \quad b'^2 = \mu'/\rho' \quad \text{.........................(42),}$$

so that b and b' denote the velocities of simple distortional waves in the two substances. In order that s' may be real, it is necessary that the right-hand member of (41) should be positive. If this is so, equation (40) becomes an equation connecting s and f, viz.

$$\tan sT = \frac{\mu'}{\mu} \left\{ \frac{f^2}{s^2} \left(1 - \frac{b^2}{b'^2}\right) - \frac{b^2}{b'^2} \right\}^{\frac{1}{2}} \quad \text{.................(43),}$$

and then it is necessary that the value of s which corresponds to any value of f should be such as to make $\tan sT$ positive. The condition of reality cannot be satisfied unless $b' > b$, but, if this inequality holds, there is always a value of s corresponding to any given value of f, as may be seen by writing equation (43) in the form

$$fT = sT \left\{ \frac{b^2}{b'^2 - b^2} + \frac{\mu^2}{\mu'^2} \frac{b'^2}{b'^2 - b^2} \tan^2 sT \right\}^{\frac{1}{2}} \quad \text{.............(44).}$$

We see that, as sT increases from 0 to $\frac{1}{2}\pi$, fT increases from 0 to ∞.

When the value of s corresponding to any given f is known, the corresponding value of κ given by equation (35) is real, and equation (41) shows that the corresponding real positive value of s' is less than f, so that the value of κ' given by equation (39) is also real.

178. In order that the solutions expressed by equations (34) and (38) may represent a motion which does not penetrate deeply into the material beneath the layer, the quantity denoted by $s'T$ must be rather large. In passing downwards from the under surface of the layer to a depth equal to the thickness of the layer, the amplitude of the motion diminishes in the ratio $e^{-s'T} : 1$. If this ratio is very small for any given wave-length, waves of that length are practically confined to the layer, otherwise they penetrate deeply into the subjacent material, and do not appear to diverge in two dimensions from the source. It can be seen beforehand that the conditions which are favourable for securing the smallness of $e^{-s'T}$ are (1) that the ratio b^2/b'^2 should be decidedly less than unity, (2) that the wave-length should be short compared with the thickness of the layer. These conditions are illustrated in the following table, in which approximate values of $e^{-s'T}$ are given for the three values 4, 1 and $\frac{1}{4}$ of the ratio of the wave-length L to the thickness T, and the three values $\frac{9}{10}$, $\frac{1}{2}$ and $\frac{1}{3}$ of the ratio μ/μ', the ratio ρ/ρ' being taken to be unity:—

μ/μ' \ L/T	4	1	$\frac{1}{4}$
$\frac{9}{10}$	·805	·180	·0004
$\frac{1}{2}$	·431	·013	2×10^{-8}
$\frac{1}{3}$	·341	·006	1×10^{-9}

179. The wave-velocity corresponding to the wave-length $2\pi/f$ is $b\kappa/f$, or, what is the same thing,

$$b\sqrt{(1+s^2/f^2)}.$$

Now equation (44) shows that f/s increases as s increases, that is to say as f increases. Hence κ/f diminishes as f increases; and therefore the wave-velocity increases as the wave-length increases. If f tends to zero as a limit, s^2/f^2 tends to (b'^2/b^2-1), and so the wave-velocity tends to b' as a limit. If s tends to $\frac{1}{2}\pi$ as a limit, so that f tends to ∞, s/f tends to zero and so the wave-velocity tends to b as a limit.

The equations and conditions obtained in § 177 show that, if

$$fT > \pi b/(b'^2-b^2)^{\frac{1}{2}},$$

there may be waves of length $2\pi/f$ which are transmitted with a higher velocity than any of those already considered. The corresponding types of motion involve the existence of one or more horizontal nodal planes within the layer. Since the values of s for motions of these types are greater than the corresponding values of s for motions of the type considered in §§ 177, 178, in which there are no horizontal nodal planes within the layer, equation (41) shows that the corresponding values of s' are smaller than those belonging to the type considered in those Sections, and therefore, for any given wave-length, such waves penetrate more freely into the interior than waves of the same length belonging to the previous type. We may therefore regard the waves already discussed as being the most important type of transverse waves in the layer from the point of view of seismological theory.

180. In all seismic records the recorded motion is oscillatory; and, although this feature may be partly due to vibratory motion set up in the recording instrument, there can be little doubt that the actual motion of the ground, both in the preliminary tremors and in the main shock, is also oscillatory. The explanation which I wish to suggest is that the oscillations are due to dispersion. If this explanation is correct, and if the analogy of waves on deep water is a safe guide, there should not be, at least in the earlier stages of the main shock, a movement resembling the passage, over the surface, of a long train of approximately simple harmonic waves, having a nearly constant wave-length and period. The actual motion may, of course, be analysed into an aggregate of co-existent standing simple harmonic waves, or, what comes to the same thing, an aggregate of simple harmonic wave-trains, each travelling with the wave-velocity appropriate to its wave-length, but these wave-trains have no separate physical existence. The "periods" observed at different stages are simply intervals of time separating successive instants at which the motion in some definite direction attains a maximum. Further, the main shock being transmitted by means of waves which diverge practically in two dimensions from the initially disturbed region, we should expect that the disturbance would not terminate after the time required to travel from the furthest part of the region with the minimum value of the wave-velocity, if the wave-velocities corresponding to waves of different lengths have such a minimum, but that it would be indefinitely prolonged, the amounts of the maxima gradually diminishing, and the intervals of time between successive maxima gradually changing. All this is quite in accordance with observation. In particular, Omori's diagram of the earlier phases of a typical seismic record* is strikingly like Lamb's figure† of the first few waves received at a place on the surface of deep water, over which waves are travelling from an initially disturbed region.

181. We have worked out the problem of § 177 on the supposition that $\kappa > f$. It is necessary also to consider the alternative supposition, viz. $\kappa < f$. If this inequality holds, equations (34) and (35) must be replaced by

$$v = (A \cosh sz + B \sinh sz) \cos (pt + fx + \epsilon) \quad \text{............(45)}$$

and

$$s^2 = f^2 - \kappa^2 \quad \text{..................................(46)},$$

while equations (38) and (39) are unaltered. Just as before we find the equations

$$A = C, \quad \mu s B = \mu' s' C$$

and

$$A \sinh sT + B \cosh sT = 0,$$

from which it follows that

$$\mu s \tanh sT + \mu' s' = 0.$$

Since it is necessary that s' should be positive, there is no relevant solution of this equation. From this result, and that found in § 177, it follows that it is not possible for transverse waves to be transmitted through the layer without penetrating far into the subjacent material, unless $b' > b$.

* See p. 200 of Knott's treatise already cited.

† H. Lamb, *Hydrodynamics* (3rd edition), p. 367.

This result has some bearing on Wiechert's suggestion (p. 148 *ante*) that the crust of the earth may rest on a sheet of magma in such a way as to be practically free. Apparently, the purpose for which the hypothetical sheet of magma is introduced is to furnish a reason why the waves should not penetrate deeply into the material beneath the layer, or, what comes to the same thing, to secure that the waves shall diverge practically in two dimensions. The simplest way of investigating the effects produced by such a sheet would seem to be to regard it as having a smaller rigidity than the crust. We have seen that, if it can be treated in this way, it must be ineffective for the purpose of confining the waves to the crust.

Effect of a superficial layer on Rayleigh-waves.

182. The hypothesis of a discontinuity of structure in the earth, at a depth which is small compared with the radius, has been shown to lead to important results in regard to the earlier phases of the main shock—the phases which are characterized by a preponderance of horizontal movement at right angles to the direction of propagation. We have now to consider the effect of such a layer upon the transmission of superficial waves which involve at the same time vertical displacement and horizontal displacement parallel to the direction of propagation. Our fourth problem will therefore be to investigate the transmission of waves analogous to Rayleigh-waves over the surface of a body which is covered by a superficial layer. It will be sufficient to consider the problem under the simplifying assumption of incompressibility, and to neglect gravity*.

183. Just as before we shall take the origin on the under surface of the layer, and draw the axis of z vertically upwards, and the axis of x in the direction of propagation of the waves. We shall denote by u, w the components of displacement in the directions of the axes of x and z, and we shall retain the notations T, f, p, μ, ρ, μ', ρ', κ, κ', s' of § 177, but we shall use s in a different sense, as in § 173. The condition of incompressibility is

$$\frac{\partial u}{\partial x} + \frac{\partial w}{\partial z} = 0 \qquad \text{.............................(47).}$$

The equations of vibratory motion of the layer are

$$\left.\begin{aligned} \rho \frac{\partial^2 u}{\partial t^2} &= -\frac{\partial \Pi}{\partial x} + \mu \nabla^2 u \\ \rho \frac{\partial^2 w}{\partial t^2} &= -\frac{\partial \Pi}{\partial z} + \mu \nabla^2 w \end{aligned}\right\} \qquad \text{.......................(48),}$$

* The problem was discussed by Bromwich, *loc. cit.*, *ante* p. 126, in the case where the thickness of the layer is small compared with the wave-length; but the case where the wave-length is comparable with, or small compared with, the thickness seems to be more important.

where Π denotes a hydrostatic pressure. The equations of vibratory motion of the subjacent material are obtained by replacing ρ and μ by ρ' and μ'.

We seek a solution in which Π, u and w, as functions of x and t, are simple harmonic functions of $pt+fx$. We see that, if we put

$$u=\frac{\partial\phi}{\partial x}+\frac{\partial\chi}{\partial z},\quad w=\frac{\partial\phi}{\partial z}-\frac{\partial\chi}{\partial x},\quad \Pi=-\rho\frac{\partial^2\phi}{\partial t^2}\quad\text{.........(49)},$$

equations (47) and (48) are satisfied, provided ϕ and χ satisfy the equations

$$\frac{\partial^2\phi}{\partial z^2}-f^2\phi=0,\qquad \frac{\partial^2\chi}{\partial z^2}-s^2\chi=0,$$

where

$$s^2=f^2-\kappa^2\quad\text{..............................(50)}.$$

Also Π is given by the equation

$$\Pi=\rho p^2\phi=\mu\kappa^2\phi\quad\text{........................(51)}.$$

Similar formulae hold in the subjacent material.

The solutions of the equations are of the form

$$\left.\begin{aligned}\phi&=(P\cosh fz+Q\sinh fz)\cos(pt+fx+\epsilon)\\ \chi&=(A\cosh sz+B\sinh sz)\sin(pt+fx+\epsilon)\end{aligned}\right\}\text{...........(52)},$$

where P, Q, A, B, ϵ are constants. This solution holds for the layer. In the material beneath the layer we should find in the same way

$$\left.\begin{aligned}\phi&=P'e^{fz}\cos(pt+fx+\epsilon)\\ \chi&=A'e^{s'z}\sin(pt+fx+\epsilon)\end{aligned}\right\}\quad\text{...................(53)},$$

where s' is given by (39) of p. 161. Then by (49) we have in the layer

$$\left.\begin{aligned}u&=\{-f(P\cosh fz+Q\sinh fz)+s(A\sinh sz+B\cosh sz)\}\sin(pt+fx+\epsilon)\\ w&=\{f(P\sinh fz+Q\cosh fz)-f(A\cosh sz+B\sinh sz)\}\cos(pt+fx+\epsilon)\end{aligned}\right\}$$
$$\text{......(54)},$$

and in the subjacent material we have

$$\left.\begin{aligned}u&=(-fP'e^{fz}+s'A'e^{s'z})\sin(pt+fx+\epsilon)\\ w&=(fP'e^{fz}-fA'e^{s'z})\cos(pt+fx+\epsilon)\end{aligned}\right\}\text{..............(55)}.$$

Now the normal and tangential components of the traction across any plane $z=$const. in the layer are expressed by the formulae

$$Z_z=-\Pi+2\mu\frac{\partial w}{\partial z}=\mu\left(-\kappa^2\phi+2\frac{\partial w}{\partial z}\right),$$

$$X_z=\mu\left(\frac{\partial u}{\partial z}+\frac{\partial w}{\partial x}\right),$$

and we find

$$Z_z = \mu \{(2f^2 - \kappa^2)(P \cosh fz + Q \sinh fz) \\ - 2sf(A \sinh sz + B \cosh sz)\} \cos(pt + fx + \epsilon),$$

$$X_z = \mu \{-2f^2(P \sinh fz + Q \cosh fz) \\ + (2f^2 - \kappa^2)(A \cosh sz + B \sinh sz)\} \sin(pt + fx + \epsilon),$$

in the second of which use has been made of (50). In like manner we find in the subjacent material

$$Z_z = \mu' \{(2f^2 - \kappa'^2) P' e^{fz} - 2s' f A' e^{s'z}\} \cos(pt + fx + \epsilon),$$
$$X_z = \mu' \{-2f^2 P' e^{fz} + (2f^2 - \kappa'^2) A' e^{s'z}\} \sin(pt + fx + \epsilon).$$

We can now write down the conditions of continuity of stress at the lower boundary of the layer. They are

$$\mu \{(2f^2 - \kappa^2) P - 2sfB\} = \mu' \{(2f^2 - \kappa'^2) P' - 2s'fA'\},$$
$$\mu \{(2f^2 - \kappa^2) A - 2f^2 Q\} = \mu' \{(2f^2 - \kappa'^2) A' - 2f^2 P'\}.$$

The conditions of continuity of displacement are

$$-fP + sB = -fP' + s'A',$$
$$Q - A = P' - A'.$$

On solving these equations we find

$$\left.\begin{aligned} \frac{\kappa^2}{f^2} P &= XP' + \frac{s'}{f} WA' \\ \frac{\kappa^2}{f^2} Q &= YP' + ZA' \\ \frac{\kappa^2}{f^2} A &= WP' + XA' \\ \frac{\kappa^2 s}{f^3} B &= ZP' + \frac{s'}{f} YA' \end{aligned}\right\} \quad \text{.........................(56)}$$

where, for shortness, the following notation has been introduced:—

$$\left.\begin{aligned} X &= \frac{\mu'}{\mu}\frac{\kappa'^2}{f^2} - 2\left(\frac{\mu'}{\mu} - 1\right), & Y &= \frac{\kappa^2}{f^2} + 2\left(\frac{\mu'}{\mu} - 1\right) \\ Z &= \frac{\mu'}{\mu}\frac{\kappa'^2}{f^2} - \frac{\kappa^2}{f^2} - 2\left(\frac{\mu'}{\mu} - 1\right), & W &= 2\left(\frac{\mu'}{\mu} - 1\right) \end{aligned}\right\} \quad \text{.........(57).}$$

The conditions that the plane $z = T$ may be free from traction are

$$\left(2 - \frac{\kappa^2}{f^2}\right)\left\{\left(XP' + \frac{s'}{f} WA'\right) \cosh fT + (YP' + ZA') \sinh fT\right\} \\ - 2\frac{s}{f}\left\{\frac{f}{s}\left(ZP' + \frac{s'}{f} YA'\right) \cosh sT + (WP' + XA') \sinh sT\right\} = 0 \text{...(58),}$$

and

$$-2\left\{\left(XP'+\frac{s'}{f}WA'\right)\sinh fT+(YP'+ZA')\cosh fT\right\}$$
$$+\left(2-\frac{\kappa^2}{f^2}\right)\left\{\frac{f}{s}\left(ZP'+\frac{s'}{f}YA'\right)\sinh sT+(WP'+XA')\cosh sT\right\}=0 \quad \text{...(59).}$$

If we write for shortness

$$\left.\begin{aligned}
\xi&=\left(2-\frac{\kappa^2}{f^2}\right)(X\cosh fT+Y\sinh fT)-2\left(Z\cosh sT+\frac{s}{f}W\sinh sT\right)\\
\eta&=\left(2-\frac{\kappa^2}{f^2}\right)\left(Z\sinh sT+\frac{s}{f}W\cosh sT\right)-2\frac{s}{f}(X\sinh fT+Y\cosh fT)\\
\xi'&=\left(2-\frac{\kappa^2}{f^2}\right)\left(Z\sinh fT+\frac{s'}{f}W\cosh fT\right)-2\left(\frac{s}{f}X\sinh sT+\frac{s'}{f}Y\cosh sT\right)\\
\eta'&=\left(2-\frac{\kappa^2}{f^2}\right)\left(\frac{s}{f}X\cosh sT+\frac{s'}{f}Y\sinh sT\right)-2\frac{s}{f}\left(Z\cosh fT+\frac{s'}{f}W\sinh fT\right)
\end{aligned}\right\} \quad \text{......(60),}$$

equations (58) and (59) become

$$\xi P'+\xi'A'=0, \qquad \eta P'+\eta'A'=0 \quad \text{..................(61),}$$

and, on eliminating P' and A', we obtain the equation

$$\xi\eta'-\xi'\eta=0 \quad \text{..............................(62).}$$

By this equation the wave-velocity is determined in terms of the wave-length.

184. To interpret this equation we begin by supposing that fT and sT are very great. Then we have approximately

$$2\xi=\left(2-\frac{\kappa^2}{f^2}\right)(X+Y)\,e^{fT}-2\left(Z+\frac{s}{f}W\right)e^{sT},$$

$$2\eta=\left(2-\frac{\kappa^2}{f^2}\right)\left(Z+\frac{s}{f}W\right)e^{sT}-2\frac{s}{f}(X+Y)\,e^{fT},$$

$$2\xi'=\left(2-\frac{\kappa^2}{f^2}\right)\left(Z+\frac{s'}{f}W\right)e^{fT}-2\left(\frac{s}{f}X+\frac{s'}{f}Y\right)e^{sT},$$

$$2\eta'=\left(2-\frac{\kappa^2}{f^2}\right)\left(\frac{s}{f}X+\frac{s'}{f}Y\right)e^{sT}-2\frac{s}{f}\left(Z+\frac{s'}{f}W\right)e^{fT},$$

and equation (62) becomes

$$e^{(s+f)T}\left\{\left(2-\frac{\kappa^2}{f^2}\right)^2-4\frac{s}{f}\right\}\left[(X+Y)\left(\frac{s}{f}X+\frac{s'}{f}Y\right)-\left(Z+\frac{s}{f}W\right)\left(Z+\frac{s'}{f}W\right)\right]=0 \quad \text{......(63).}$$

Equation (63) is satisfied if either the factor in { } or the factor in [ ] vanishes. The first factor is the same as the left-hand member of equation (28) on p. 158, so that the wave-velocity given by equating this factor to zero is the velocity of simple Rayleigh-waves. We shall omit for the present the consideration of the second factor, and attend to the results that can be obtained by retaining the equation (62), and supposing the wave-velocity to vary continuously with the wave-length in such a way that, for very short waves, it approaches the velocity of simple Rayleigh-waves as a limit.

185. The first step is to determine the sense of the variation of κ/f when e^{fT} is large. We re-write equations (60) in the forms

$$\left.\begin{aligned}
2\xi e^{-fT} &= \left(2-\frac{\kappa^2}{f^2}\right)\{(X+Y)+(X-Y)e^{-2fT}\}\\
&\quad -2e^{-(f-s)T}\left\{\left(Z+\frac{s}{f}W\right)+\left(Z-\frac{s}{f}W\right)e^{-2sT}\right\}\\
2\eta e^{-fT} &= \left(2-\frac{\kappa^2}{f^2}\right)e^{-(f-s)T}\left\{\left(Z+\frac{s}{f}W\right)-\left(Z-\frac{s}{f}W\right)e^{-2sT}\right\}\\
&\quad -2\frac{s}{f}\{(X+Y)-(X-Y)e^{-2fT}\}\\
2\xi' e^{-fT} &= \left(2-\frac{\kappa^2}{f^2}\right)\left\{\left(Z+\frac{s'}{f}W\right)-\left(Z-\frac{s'}{f}W\right)e^{-2fT}\right\}\\
&\quad -2e^{-(f-s)T}\left\{\left(\frac{s}{f}X+\frac{s'}{f}Y\right)-\left(\frac{s}{f}X-\frac{s'}{f}Y\right)e^{-2sT}\right\}\\
2\eta' e^{-fT} &= \left(2-\frac{\kappa^2}{f^2}\right)e^{-(f-s)T}\left\{\left(\frac{s}{f}X+\frac{s'}{f}Y\right)+\left(\frac{s}{f}X-\frac{s'}{f}Y\right)e^{-2sT}\right\}\\
&\quad -2\frac{s}{f}\left\{\left(Z+\frac{s'}{f}W\right)+\left(Z-\frac{s'}{f}W\right)e^{-2fT}\right\}
\end{aligned}\right\}\quad\ldots(64).$$

Now when fT is very great, s^2/f^2 approximates to the value 0·08738*, so that e^{-fT} is much smaller than e^{-sT}, and therefore a second approximation to the complete form of (62) gives

$$\begin{aligned}
&\left\{\left(2-\frac{\kappa^2}{f^2}\right)^2-\frac{4s}{f}\right\}\left[(X+Y)\left(X\frac{s}{f}+Y\frac{s'}{f}\right)-\left(Z+\frac{s}{f}W\right)\left(Z+\frac{s'}{f}W\right)\right]\\
&+\left\{\left(2-\frac{\kappa^2}{f^2}\right)^2+\frac{4s}{f}\right\}\left[(X+Y)\left(X\frac{s}{f}-Y\frac{s'}{f}\right)+\left(Z-\frac{s}{f}W\right)\left(Z+\frac{s'}{f}W\right)\right]e^{-2sT}=0
\end{aligned}$$

$$\ldots\ldots(65).$$

Now we observe that

$$\left(2-\frac{\kappa^2}{f^2}\right)^2-4\frac{s}{f}=\left(1+\frac{s^2}{f^2}\right)^2-4\frac{s}{f}=\left(1-\frac{s}{f}\right)\left(1-3\frac{s}{f}-\frac{s^2}{f^2}-\frac{s^3}{f^3}\right)\ldots(66).$$

Let $s/f=s_0/f+\delta(s/f)$, where s_0 corresponds to simple Rayleigh-waves, so that

$$(1+s_0^2/f^2)^2-4s_0/f=0,$$

* A slight correction, made by Bromwich, of Lord Rayleigh's value 0·08725 is here introduced.

then

$$\left(2-\frac{\kappa^2}{f^2}\right)^2-4\frac{s}{f}=4\left\{\frac{s_0}{f}\left(1+\frac{s_0^2}{f^2}\right)-1\right\}\delta\frac{s}{f}=-4\left\{1-2\left(\frac{s_0}{f}\right)^{\frac{3}{2}}\right\}\delta\frac{s}{f},$$

and so equation (65) becomes with sufficient approximation

$$\left\{1-2\left(\frac{s_0}{f}\right)^{\frac{3}{2}}\right\}\delta\frac{s}{f}\left[(X+Y)\left(X\frac{s}{f}+Y\frac{s'}{f}\right)-\left(Z+\frac{s}{f}W\right)\left(Z+\frac{s'}{f}W\right)\right]$$
$$=2\frac{s_0}{f}\left[(X+Y)\left(X\frac{s}{f}-Y\frac{s'}{f}\right)+\left(Z-\frac{s}{f}W\right)\left(Z+\frac{s'}{f}W\right)\right]e^{-2sT}\ldots(67),$$

where all the quantities in the square brackets are to have the same values as they would have if the waves were simple Rayleigh-waves. With the value of s_0/f stated above the first factor of the left-hand member of (67) is positive. Owing to the number of quantities involved, it seems to be rather difficult to give a perfectly general determination of the signs of the factors in square brackets in the two members; but this can be effected in two classes of cases, which, taken together, seem to include all that are of much interest.

186. In the first of these classes of cases $\mu'>\mu$, while $\rho'=\rho$. We have then

$$\mu'\kappa'^2=\mu\kappa^2,$$

and so we find

$$X=1-\frac{s_0^2}{f^2}-2\left(\frac{\mu'}{\mu}-1\right),\qquad Y=1-\frac{s_0^2}{f^2}+2\left(\frac{\mu'}{\mu}-1\right),$$
$$-Z=W=2\left(\frac{\mu'}{\mu}-1\right);$$

we have also
$$1-\frac{s_0'^2}{f^2}=\frac{\kappa'^2}{f^2}=\frac{\mu}{\mu'}\frac{\kappa^2}{f^2}=\frac{\mu}{\mu'}\left(1-\frac{s_0^2}{f^2}\right),$$

where s_0' is the value of s' that corresponds to the value s_0 of s. We use the last relation to express μ'/μ in terms of s_0 and s_0'. We find

$$(X+Y)\left(X\frac{s}{f}+Y\frac{s'}{f}\right)-\left(Z+\frac{s}{f}W\right)\left(Z+\frac{s'}{f}W\right)$$
$$=2\left(1-\frac{s_0^2}{f^2}\right)^2\left(\frac{s_0}{f}+\frac{s_0'}{f}\right)$$
$$+4\frac{s_0'^2/f^2-s_0^2/f^2}{1-s_0'^2/f^2}\left(1-\frac{s_0^2}{f^2}\right)\left(\frac{s_0'}{f}-\frac{s_0}{f}\right)-4\left(\frac{s_0'^2/f^2-s_0^2/f^2}{1-s_0'^2/f^2}\right)^2\left(1-\frac{s_0}{f}\right)\left(1-\frac{s_0'}{f}\right).$$

The sum of the two last terms is positive if

$$\left(1+\frac{s_0}{f}\right)\left(1+\frac{s_0'}{f}\right)>\frac{s_0}{f}+\frac{s_0'}{f},$$

which is the case; and therefore the whole expression is positive. Again we find

$$(X+Y)\left(X\frac{s}{f}-Y\frac{s'}{f}\right)+\left(Z-\frac{s}{f}W\right)\left(Z+\frac{s'}{f}W\right)$$
$$=-2\left(1-\frac{s_0^2}{f^2}\right)^2\left(\frac{s_0'}{f}-\frac{s_0}{f}\right)$$
$$-4\frac{s_0'^2/f^2-s_0^2/f^2}{1-s_0'^2/f^2}\left(1-\frac{s_0^2}{f^2}\right)\left(\frac{s_0'}{f}+\frac{s_0}{f}\right)+4\left(\frac{s_0'^2/f^2-s_0^2/f^2}{1-s_0'^2/f^2}\right)^2\left(1+\frac{s_0}{f}\right)\left(1-\frac{s_0'}{f}\right).$$

The sum of the last two terms is negative if

$$\left(1+\frac{s_0'}{f}\right)\left(1-\frac{s_0}{f}\right)>\frac{s_0'}{f}-\frac{s_0}{f},$$

that is to say if

$$s_0 s_0' < f^2,$$

which is true. Hence the whole expression is negative, and the value of $\delta(s/f)$ given by (67) is negative.

In the second class of cases referred to at the end of § 185, $\mu' > \mu$, and $\rho' > \rho$, but $\mu'/\mu = \rho'/\rho$. In these cases $\kappa' = \kappa$, and $s' = s$. Then, remembering equation (28), we find

$$X=2\left(1-\frac{\mu'}{\mu}\sqrt{\frac{s_0}{f}}\right),\qquad Y=2\left(\frac{\mu'}{\mu}-\sqrt{\frac{s_0}{f}}\right),\qquad Z=-2\left(\frac{\mu'}{\mu}-1\right)\sqrt{\frac{s_0}{f}},$$

and W is the same as before. Hence we find

$$(X+Y)\left(X\frac{s}{f}+Y\frac{s'}{f}\right)-\left(Z+\frac{s}{f}W\right)\left(Z+\frac{s'}{f}W\right)=16\frac{\mu'}{\mu}\frac{s_0}{f}\left(1-\sqrt{\frac{s_0}{f}}\right)^2,$$

which is positive; and we also find

$$(X+Y)\left(X\frac{s}{f}-Y\frac{s'}{f}\right)+\left(Z-\frac{s}{f}W\right)\left(Z+\frac{s'}{f}W\right)=-8\left(\frac{\mu'}{\mu}-1\right)\frac{s_0}{f}\left(1-\frac{s_0}{f}\right),$$

which is negative. Here again the value of $\delta(s/f)$ given by (67) is negative.

187. We shall now take it for granted that, as fT diminishes from very great values, s/f diminishes. This being so, κ/f increases. This means that the wave-velocity increases as the wave-length increases. It seems to be rather difficult to determine the wave-velocity which corresponds to a particular wave-length when μ'/μ and ρ'/ρ are given. It is easier to assume some smaller value than s_0/f for s/f and to deduce corresponding values for μ'/μ, or ρ'/ρ. Now the value of s_0/f, corresponding to the case where fT tends to ∞, is 0·2956*; and we may illustrate the theory by working out a numerical example in which

$$fT=6,\quad s/f=0{\cdot}25,\quad \rho'=\rho.$$

The corresponding value of the wave-velocity is $(0{\cdot}9682)\,b$, where b stands, as usual, for $\sqrt{(\mu/\rho)}$, so that it is a little greater than the value $(0{\cdot}9553)\,b$ of simple Rayleigh-waves. Then we have

$$X=0{\cdot}9375-W,\quad Y=0{\cdot}9375+W,\quad Z=-W.$$

* Here again use has been made of Bromwich's correction noted on p. 169 *ante*.

We have also to put

$$sT = 1{\cdot}5, \quad s'^2/f^2 = (W + 0{\cdot}125)/(W + 2).$$

When these substitutions are made in ξ, ξ', η, η', as given by equations (60), equation (62) becomes an equation for W, which is found to be approximately

$$46{\cdot}6 - (48{\cdot}7)\, W + (15{\cdot}3)\, W^2 + \frac{s'}{f}\{18{\cdot}2 + (21{\cdot}5)\, W - (15{\cdot}3)\, W^2\} = 0,$$

and the single positive root is approximately 2·65, so that we find

$$\mu'/\mu = 2{\cdot}325.$$

In our special numerical example, therefore, the rigidity of the lower medium is a little more than twice that of the superficial layer, and the wave-length is a little greater than the thickness of the layer. The wave-velocity is greater than that of simple Rayleigh-waves by about 1 per cent.

188. It is a matter of some interest to determine the ratio of amplitudes of the horizontal and vertical displacements in a wave of the type now under discussion. Going back to the formulae (54) of p. 166 and substituting from (56), we find that the displacement can be expressed by the formulae

$$u = \bar{u}(z) \sin(pt + fx + \epsilon),$$
$$w = \bar{w}(z) \cos(pt + fx + \epsilon),$$

where $\bar{u}(z)$ and $\bar{w}(z)$ are functions of z expressed by the equations

$$\left.\begin{aligned} \bar{u}(z) &= \frac{f^3}{\kappa^2}\left[P'\left\{(X\cosh fz + Y\sinh fz) - \left(Z\cosh sz + \frac{s}{f}W\sinh sz\right)\right\}\right. \\ &\qquad \left. + A'\left\{\left(Z\sinh fz + \frac{s'}{f}W\cosh fz\right) - \left(\frac{s}{f}X\sinh sz + \frac{s'}{f}Y\cosh sz\right)\right\}\right] \\ \bar{w}(z) &= \frac{f^4}{s\kappa^2}\left[P'\left\{\frac{s}{f}(X\sinh fz + Y\cosh fz) - \left(Z\sinh sz + \frac{s}{f}W\cosh sz\right)\right\}\right. \\ &\qquad \left. + A'\left\{\frac{s}{f}\left(Z\cosh fz + \frac{s'}{f}W\sinh fz\right) - \left(\frac{s}{f}X\cosh sz + \frac{s'}{f}Y\sinh sz\right)\right\}\right] \end{aligned}\right\} \quad \text{......(68).}$$

On substituting from equations (58) and (59) we find

$$\frac{\kappa^2}{f^3}\bar{u}(T) = \frac{\kappa^2}{2f^2}\left\{P'(X\cosh fT + Y\sinh fT) + A'\left(Z\sinh fT + \frac{s'}{f}W\cosh fT\right)\right\},$$

$$\frac{\kappa^2}{f^3}\bar{w}(T) = \frac{-\kappa^2}{2f^2 - \kappa^2}\left\{P'(X\sinh fT + Y\cosh fT) + A'\left(Z\cosh fT + \frac{s'}{f}W\sinh fT\right)\right\}.$$

Even if fT is as small as 6, $\cosh fT$ differs from $\sinh fT$ by less than one part in 100,000, and both of them are over 200. We see therefore that the absolute value of the ratio $\overline{w}(T)/\overline{u}(T)$ is nearly equal to $2f^2/(2f^2-\kappa^2)$. In all the waves that we have been considering κ^2/f^2 differs but little from unity, and therefore the ratio of amplitudes of the vertical and horizontal displacements is nearly equal to 2 as Lord Rayleigh found.

189. The motion consequent on any displacement and velocity, initially confined to a limited region, is to be obtained by superposing systems of standing simple harmonic waves, as in Cauchy and Poisson's solution of the problem of waves on deep water. The components of displacement in a standing simple harmonic wave are expressed by formulae of the type

$$u = \overline{u}(z)\cos pt \cos(fx+\epsilon'),$$
$$\overline{w} = -\overline{w}(z)\cos pt \sin(fx+\epsilon'),$$

and the corresponding formulae for the displacement in an aggregate of such waves would appear to be

$$u = \int_0^\infty \overline{u}(z)\cos pt\, df \int_{-\infty}^{\infty} F(\alpha)\cos f(x-\alpha)\, d\alpha + \int_0^\infty \overline{u}(z)\cos pt\, df \int_{-\infty}^{\infty} G(\alpha)\sin f(x-\alpha)\, d\alpha,$$

$$w = -\int_0^\infty \overline{w}(z)\cos pt\, df \int_{-\infty}^{\infty} F(\alpha)\sin f(x-\alpha)\, d\alpha + \int_0^\infty \overline{w}(z)\cos pt\, df \int_{-\infty}^{\infty} G(\alpha)\cos f(x-\alpha)\, d\alpha,$$

where F and G denote functions determined by the values of the initial displacement at various points; and we could add to these expressions similar ones containing $\sin pt$, instead of $\cos pt$, and two functions determined by the values of the initial velocity at various points. Now it by no means follows from the result that $-\overline{w}(T)$ is about twice as great as $\overline{u}(T)$ that the maximum of w is nearly twice that of u. It may very well happen that the amplitudes of the simple harmonic constituents of the vertical displacement at $z=T$ are larger than the amplitudes of the corresponding constituents of the horizontal displacement, and yet that the maxima of an aggregate of the former are less than those of an aggregate of the latter. This can happen because p is a function of f.

190. In §§ 185—187 we traced some of the consequences of supposing that the wave-velocity for very short waves is to be found by equating to zero the factor placed in { } in the left-hand member of equation (63) on p. 168. The equation can also be satisfied if there is any pair of corresponding values of s and s' which make the factor placed in [ ] vanish. We have, therefore, to consider the possibility of satisfying the equation

$$(X+Y)\left(\frac{s}{f}X+\frac{s'}{f}Y\right)-\left(Z+\frac{s}{f}W\right)\left(Z+\frac{s'}{f}W\right)=0.$$

This equation is

$$\left(\frac{\mu'}{\mu}\frac{\kappa'^2}{f^2}+\frac{\kappa^2}{f^2}\right)\left[\left\{2\left(\frac{\mu'}{\mu}-1\right)+\frac{\kappa^2}{f^2}\right\}\frac{s'}{f}-\left\{2\left(\frac{\mu'}{\mu}-1\right)-\frac{\mu'}{\mu}\frac{\kappa'^2}{f^2}\right\}\frac{s}{f}\right]$$
$$-\left\{2\left(\frac{\mu'}{\mu}-1\right)\left(1-\frac{s}{f}\right)+\frac{\kappa^2}{f^2}-\frac{\mu'}{\mu}\frac{\kappa'^2}{f^2}\right\}\left\{2\left(\frac{\mu'}{\mu}-1\right)\left(1-\frac{s'}{f}\right)+\frac{\kappa^2}{f^2}-\frac{\mu'}{\mu}\frac{\kappa'^2}{f^2}\right\}=0 \qquad \text{......(69).}$$

Before attempting any general discussion of this equation we consider the particular class of cases in which $\rho'=\rho$. Then

$$\mu'\kappa'^2=\mu\kappa^2, \quad \frac{s'^2}{f^2}=1-\frac{\mu}{\mu'}\frac{\kappa^2}{f^2}, \quad \frac{\kappa^2}{f^2}=1-\frac{s^2}{f^2},$$

and equation (69) becomes, after omission of the factor $(1-s/f)$,

$$2\left(1+\frac{s}{f}\right)\left\{2\left(\frac{\mu'}{\mu}-1\right)\left(\frac{s'}{f}-\frac{s}{f}\right)+\left(1-\frac{s^2}{f^2}\right)\left(\frac{s'}{f}+\frac{s}{f}\right)\right\}-4\left(\frac{\mu'}{\mu}-1\right)^2\left(1-\frac{s'}{f}\right)=0.$$

We write for shortness $\qquad \dfrac{\mu'}{\mu}=1+\alpha, \quad \dfrac{s}{f}=x,$

arrange the equation in the form

$$\{(1+x)(1-x^2)+2\alpha(1+x)+2\alpha^2\}\frac{s'}{f}=-x(1+x)(1-x^2)+2\alpha x(1+x)+2\alpha^2,$$

and rationalize it by squaring both members. We get

$$\{(1+x)(1-x^2)+2\alpha(1+x)+2\alpha^2\}^2\{1-(1-x^2)/(1+\alpha)\}$$
$$=\{x(1+x)(1-x^2)-2\alpha x(1+x)-2\alpha^2\}^2,$$

or

$$(\alpha+x^2)\{(1+x)(1-x^2)+2\alpha(1+x)+2\alpha^2\}^2$$
$$-(\alpha+1)\{x(1+x)(1-x^2)-2\alpha x(1+x)-2\alpha^2\}^2=0.$$

Clearly α and $(1-x^2)$ are factors of the left-hand member, and, on removing them, we find the equation

$$4\alpha^3+\{8\alpha^2+4\alpha(1+x)^2\}(1+x+x^2)+(1+x)^2(1+6x^2+x^4)=0 \quad \text{...(70).}$$

Hence, if α is positive, or $\mu'>\mu$, the equation cannot be satisfied by any value of x between 0 and 1. It follows that, if $\mu'>\mu$ and $\rho'=\rho$, there cannot be any simple harmonic waves of which the wave-velocities are given by equation (69).

191. Again we consider the particular class of cases in which $\mu'/\mu = \rho'/\rho$. In these cases $s' = s$, $\kappa' = \kappa$, and the equation becomes

$$(\alpha + 2)^2 x (1 - x^2)^2 - \alpha^2 (1 - x)^4 = 0.$$

On removing the factor $(1 - x)^2$ this becomes

$$\alpha^2 (x^3 + x^2 + 3x - 1) + 4\alpha x (1 + x)^2 + 4x (1 + x)^2 = 0 \quad \text{......(71)}.$$

This equation has a root between 0 and 1, and, in fact, the root is less than the positive root of the equation

$$x^3 + x^2 + 3x - 1 = 0.$$

Hence if the rigidities and densities are different in the two media, but the velocities of simple distortional waves are the same, there can be a wave-motion with a wave-velocity intermediate between that of simple Rayleigh-waves and that of simple distortional waves. This discussion applies, of course, only to waves of a length very short compared with the thickness of the superficial layer, for the equation (69) was obtained on this supposition as to the wave-length.

192. For a more general discussion of equation (69) we put

$$\mu'/\mu = 1 + \alpha, \quad \rho'/\rho = 1 + \beta, \quad s/f = x, \quad s'/f = x'.$$

The equation becomes

$$(\beta + 2)(1 - x^2)[\{2\alpha + (1 - x^2)\} x' - \{2\alpha - (\beta + 1)(1 - x^2)\} x]$$
$$- \{2\alpha (1 - x) - \beta (1 - x^2)\} \{2\alpha (1 - x') - \beta (1 - x^2)\} = 0.$$

Removing the factor $(1 - x)$, and rearranging the equation, we find

$$x' [2\alpha \{2\alpha - \beta (1 + x)\} + \{2\alpha + (1 - x^2)\} (\beta + 2)(1 + x)]$$
$$= \{2\alpha - \beta (1 + x)\} \{2\alpha - \beta (1 - x^2)\} + \{2\alpha - (\beta + 1)(1 - x^2)\} (\beta + 2) x (1 + x).$$

Now we have
$$x'^2 = \frac{\alpha + x^2 - \beta (1 - x^2)}{\alpha + 1},$$

and therefore the rationalized equation becomes

$$\{\alpha + x^2 - \beta (1 - x^2)\} \{4\alpha^2 + 4\alpha (1 + x) + (\beta + 2)(1 + x)(1 - x^2)\}^2$$
$$- (\alpha + 1) \{4\alpha^2 + 4\alpha x (1 + x) - 4\alpha\beta (1 - x^2) - (3\beta + 2) x (1 + x)(1 - x^2)$$
$$+ \beta^2 (1 - x^2)^2\}^2 = 0.$$

On removing the factor $(1 - x^2)$, we find, after some reduction, that the equation becomes

$$16\alpha^2 \{\alpha (\alpha + 1 + x^2) - \beta (\alpha + 1 + x)^2\}$$
$$+ \{\alpha + x^2 - \beta (1 - x^2)\} \{8\alpha (\beta + 2)(\alpha + 1 + x)(1 + x) + (\beta + 2)^2 (1 + x)^2 (1 - x^2)\}$$
$$+ (\alpha + 1) [8\alpha \{\alpha + x (1 + x)\} \{4\alpha\beta + (3\beta + 2) x (1 + x) - \beta^2 (1 - x^2)\}$$
$$- \{4\alpha\beta + (3\beta + 2) x (1 + x) - \beta^2 (1 - x^2)\}^2 (1 - x^2)] = 0 \quad \text{......(72)}.$$

If in the left-hand member we substitute 0 for x, it becomes

$$(\alpha-\beta)\{4\alpha(\alpha+1)+(\beta+2)\}^2-(\alpha+1)(2\alpha-\beta)^4,$$

but, if we substitute 1 for x, it becomes

$$16\alpha(\alpha+2)(\alpha^2\beta+\alpha^2+4\alpha\beta+4\alpha+4\beta+2).$$

In all interesting cases α and β are positive, and we see that, if $(\alpha-\beta)$ is sufficiently small, the equation has a root between 0 and 1. The condition stated in the form that $(\alpha-\beta)$ must be small is the same as the condition that the velocities of simple distortional waves in the two media should be nearly equal. We see that, when this condition holds, there exists a wave-motion such that the velocity of short waves is given by equation (69), provided, as was shown in § 190, that the densities in the two media are different.

193. It is a result of some theoretical interest that, under suitable conditions, there can exist a type of superficial waves differing from that investigated by Lord Rayleigh, but having in common with it the property that the tangential displacement is parallel to the direction of propagation. The suitable conditions are (1) that the body must be covered over by a superficial layer of different density and rigidity from those of the rest of the body, (2) that the velocity of simple distortional waves in the layer must be nearly equal to that of such waves in the rest of the body. It seems however to be unlikely that this result can be of any practical importance in relation to the transmission of seismic waves. Whether the large waves of the main shock are identified with Rayleigh-waves or not, their velocities cannot differ much from the velocity of simple distortional waves in the superficial portions of the earth, and it is probable that there is a decided difference between this velocity and the velocity of simple distortional waves in the subjacent material. The velocity of the large waves is variously estimated at from 3 to $3\frac{1}{2}$ km. per second, while the velocity of the second phase preliminary tremors is generally estimated at from 5 to 6 km. per second. In order that the second phase preliminary tremors may be transmitted with a velocity practically identical with that of distortional waves in the material beneath the crust, it is necessary that their paths should be mainly beneath the crust, so that observations made at stations very near to the source of disturbance are not available for determining this velocity. It is probable that the velocity of distortional waves which pass below the crust is different at different depths, and several investigations have been made of the law of variation. According to the memoir by Wiechert and Zöppritz cited on p. 148, the velocity in question increases uniformly from 4 km. per second at relatively small depths to more than $6\frac{1}{2}$ km. per second at a depth of 1500 km. It seems, therefore, to be agreed that the velocity of distortional waves in the crust is decidedly smaller than that of such waves in the material beneath the crust. Further we found that such a decided difference was necessary for the development of transverse waves propagated over the surface of the layer, and we saw that such waves are shown in seismic records. It seems therefore that we are justified in concluding that the actual conditions exclude the development of waves of the special type examined in §§ 190—192. It may be observed that, if waves of this type are developed, they have in common with Rayleigh-waves the property that the vertical displacement of any simple harmonic constituent is larger than the horizontal displacement, for in the investigation given in § 188 no use is made of any property of Rayleigh-waves other than that expressed by the statement that κ^2/f^2 is nearly equal to unity, and this property belongs also to the waves considered in §§ 190—192.

194. We have now to combine the results obtained in the solutions of our second, third and fourth problems. We have seen that, if the earth is covered over with a superficial layer of moderate thickness, and if the velocity of simple distortional waves in the layer is decidedly less than that in the subjacent material, two classes of waves can be transmitted over the surface without penetrating far beneath the layer. The first class are characterized by a horizontal displacement at right angles to the direction of propagation, the second class by a vertical displacement combined with a horizontal displacement parallel to the direction of propagation. The wave-velocity of any simple harmonic constituent of the waves of the first class exceeds the velocity of simple distortional waves in the layer, but is less than the velocity of such waves in the subjacent material; and, since, as we have seen, short waves must predominate, the important wave-velocities, although they do exceed the velocity of simple distortional waves in the layer, do not exceed it very much. The wave-velocity of any simple harmonic constituent of the waves of the second class is less than the velocity of simple distortional waves in the layer, although it does not fall far short of this velocity. These simple harmonic constituents of the waves of the second class can be nothing but Rayleigh-waves, modified by gravity and by the discontinuity of structure which occurs at the under surface of the layer. Both classes of waves are subject to dispersion, and the wave-velocity increases with the wave-length. Both diverge practically in two dimensions from a source of disturbance, and therefore both may be expected to be indefinitely prolonged with gradually diminishing amplitudes. In both classes we should expect the observed motion to be oscillatory, with intervals between successive maxima which gradually diminish as time goes on. We should also expect that a decided change of type should occur after the time required to travel over the surface from the source to the place of observation with the velocity of simple distortional waves in the superficial layer. Observation shows that there is a very definite change of type in the main shock, that the transverse waves arrive first, that the intervals between their maxima diminish, that when these waves become less prominent, and waves with horizontal displacement parallel to the direction of propagation begin to predominate, the intervals between successive maxima again diminish, and that the disturbance is prolonged in a gradual oscillatory subsidence. All the general features of the large waves of earthquakes are represented in the theory suggested by the analogous theory of waves on deep water, except the observed comparative smallness of the vertical motion. Now if the oscillatory waves which appear to be transmitted over the surface were physically existing simple harmonic wave-trains, this difficulty could only be met by the supposition that adequate instruments for separating the vertical motion from the horizontal, and recording it faithfully, have not so far been devised*. But the suggestion which has been made already (p. 173 *ante*) that these observed oscillations are the result of superposing an infinite number of standing simple harmonic waves, may perhaps furnish a different explanation. Such waves can combine to form progressive oscillatory waves, but we have seen that there is no reason why the ratio of amplitudes of the vertical and horizontal component displacements which is characteristic of the constituent standing waves should be maintained in the maxima of the aggregates. The difficulty may therefore perhaps be regarded as less serious than it has been thought to be.

* In regard to this suggestion reference may be made to the discussion in chapter V of Knott's treatise already cited.

INDEX

(The numbers refer to the pages)

CATALOGUE OF DOVER BOOKS

BOOKS EXPLAINING SCIENCE AND MATHEMATICS

General

WHAT IS SCIENCE?, Norman Campbell. This excellent introduction explains scientific method, role of mathematics, types of scientific laws. Contents: 2 aspects of science, science & nature, laws of science, discovery of laws, explanation of laws, measurement & numerical laws, applications of science. 192pp. 5⅜ x 8. S43 Paperbound **$1.25**

THE COMMON SENSE OF THE EXACT SCIENCES, W. K. Clifford. Introduction by James Newman, edited by Karl Pearson. For 70 years this has been a guide to classical scientific and mathematical thought. Explains with unusual clarity basic concepts, such as extension of meaning of symbols, characteristics of surface boundaries, properties of plane figures, vectors, Cartesian method of determining position, etc. Long preface by Bertrand Russell. Bibliography of Clifford. Corrected, 130 diagrams redrawn. 249pp. 5⅜ x 8. T61 Paperbound **$1.60**

SCIENCE THEORY AND MAN, Erwin Schrödinger. This is a complete and unabridged reissue of SCIENCE AND THE HUMAN TEMPERAMENT plus an additional essay: "What is an Elementary Particle?" Nobel laureate Schrödinger discusses such topics as nature of scientific method, the nature of science, chance and determinism, science and society, conceptual models for physical entities, elementary particles and wave mechanics. Presentation is popular and may be followed by most people with little or no scientific training. "Fine practical preparation for a time when laws of nature, human institutions . . . are undergoing a critical examination without parallel," Waldemar Kaempffert, N. Y. TIMES. 192pp. 5⅜ x 8. T428 Paperbound **$1.35**

FADS AND FALLACIES IN THE NAME OF SCIENCE, Martin Gardner. Examines various cults, quack systems, frauds, delusions which at various times have masqueraded as science. Accounts of hollow-earth fanatics like Symmes; Velikovsky and wandering planets; Hoerbiger; Bellamy and the theory of multiple moons; Charles Fort; dowsing, pseudoscientific methods for finding water, ores, oil. Sections on naturopathy, iridiagnosis, zone therapy, food fads, etc. Analytical accounts of Wilhelm Reich and orgone sex energy; L. Ron Hubbard and Dianetics; A. Korzybski and General Semantics; many others. Brought up to date to include Bridey Murphy, others. Not just a collection of anecdotes, but a fair, reasoned appraisal of eccentric theory. Formerly titled IN THE NAME OF SCIENCE. Preface. Index. x + 384pp. 5⅜ x 8. T394 Paperbound **$1.50**

A DOVER SCIENCE SAMPLER, edited by George Barkin. 64-page book, sturdily bound, containing excerpts from over 20 Dover books, explaining science. Edwin Hubble, George Sarton, Ernst Mach, A. d'Abro, Galileo, Newton, others, discussing island universes, scientific truth, biological phenomena, stability in bridges, etc. Copies limited; no more than 1 to a customer, FREE

POPULAR SCIENTIFIC LECTURES, Hermann von Helmholtz. Helmholtz was a superb expositor as well as a scientist of genius in many areas. The seven essays in this volume are models of clarity, and even today they rank among the best general descriptions of their subjects ever written. "The Physiological Causes of Harmony in Music" was the first significant physiological explanation of musical consonance and dissonance. Two essays, "On the Interaction of Natural Forces" and "On the Conservation of Force," were of great importance in the history of science, for they firmly established the principle of the conservation of energy. Other lectures include "On the Relation of Optics to Painting," "On Recent Progress in the Theory of Vision," "On Goethe's Scientific Researches," and "On the Origin and Significance of Geometrical Axioms." Selected and edited with an introduction by Professor Morris Kline. xii + 286pp. 5⅜ x 8½. T799 Paperbound **$1.45**

BOOKS EXPLAINING SCIENCE AND MATHEMATICS

Physics

CONCERNING THE NATURE OF THINGS, Sir William Bragg. Christmas lectures delivered at the Royal Society by Nobel laureate. Why a spinning ball travels in a curved track; how uranium is transmuted to lead, etc. Partial contents: atoms, gases, liquids, crystals, metals, etc. No scientific background needed; wonderful for intelligent child. 32pp. of photos, 57 figures. xii + 232pp. 5⅜ x 8. T31 Paperbound **$1.50**

THE RESTLESS UNIVERSE, Max Born. New enlarged version of this remarkably readable account by a Nobel laureate. Moving from sub-atomic particles to universe, the author explains in very simple terms the latest theories of wave mechanics. Partial contents: air and its relatives, electrons & ions, waves & particles, electronic structure of the atom, nuclear physics. Nearly 1000 illustrations, including 7 animated sequences. 325pp. 6 x 9. T412 Paperbound **$2.00**

FROM EUCLID TO EDDINGTON: A STUDY OF THE CONCEPTIONS OF THE EXTERNAL WORLD, Sir Edmund Whittaker. A foremost British scientist traces the development of theories of natural philosophy from the western rediscovery of Euclid to Eddington, Einstein, Dirac, etc. The inadequacy of classical physics is contrasted with present day attempts to understand the physical world through relativity, non-Euclidean geometry, space curvature, wave mechanics, etc. 5 major divisions of examination: Space; Time and Movement; the Concepts of Classical Physics; the Concepts of Quantum Mechanics; the Eddington Universe. 212pp. 5⅜ x 8. T491 Paperbound **$1.35**

PHYSICS, THE PIONEER SCIENCE, L. W. Taylor. First thorough text to place all important physical phenomena in cultural-historical framework; remains best work of its kind. Exposition of physical laws, theories developed chronologically, with great historical, illustrative experiments diagrammed, described, worked out mathematically. Excellent physics text for self-study as well as class work. Vol. 1: Heat, Sound: motion, acceleration, gravitation, conservation of energy, heat engines, rotation, heat, mechanical energy, etc. 211 illus. 407pp. 5⅜ x 8. Vol. 2: Light, Electricity: images, lenses, prisms, magnetism, Ohm's law, dynamos, telegraph, quantum theory, decline of mechanical view of nature, etc. Bibliography. 13 table appendix. Index. 551 illus. 2 color plates. 508pp. 5⅜ x 8.
Vol. 1 S565 Paperbound **$2.25**
Vol. 2 S566 Paperbound **$2.25**
The set **$4.50**

A SURVEY OF PHYSICAL THEORY, Max Planck. One of the greatest scientists of all time, creator of the quantum revolution in physics, writes in non-technical terms of his own discoveries and those of other outstanding creators of modern physics. Planck wrote this book when science had just crossed the threshold of the new physics, and he communicates the excitement felt then as he discusses electromagnetic theories, statistical methods, evolution of the concept of light, a step-by-step description of how he developed his own momentous theory, and many more of the basic ideas behind modern physics. Formerly "A Survey of Physics." Bibliography. Index. 128pp. 5⅜ x 8. S650 Paperbound **$1.15**

THE ATOMIC NUCLEUS, M. Korsunsky. The only non-technical comprehensive account of the atomic nucleus in English. For college physics students, etc. Chapters cover: Radioactivity, the Nuclear Model of the Atom, the Mass of Atomic Nuclei, the Disintegration of Atomic Nuclei, the Discovery of the Positron, the Artificial Transformation of Atomic Nuclei, Artificial Radioactivity, Mesons, the Neutrino, the Structure of Atomic Nuclei and Forces Acting Between Nuclear Particles, Nuclear Fission, Chain Reaction, Peaceful Uses, Thermoculear Reactions. Slightly abridged edition. Translated by G. Yankovsky. 65 figures. Appendix includes 45 photographic illustrations. 413 pp. 5⅜ x 8. S1052 Paperbound **$2.00**

PRINCIPLES OF MECHANICS SIMPLY EXPLAINED, Morton Mott-Smith. Excellent, highly readable introduction to the theories and discoveries of classical physics. Ideal for the layman who desires a foundation which will enable him to understand and appreciate contemporary developments in the physical sciences. Discusses: Density, The Law of Gravitation, Mass and Weight, Action and Reaction, Kinetic and Potential Energy, The Law of Inertia, Effects of Acceleration, The Independence of Motions, Galileo and the New Science of Dynamics, Newton and the New Cosmos, The Conservation of Momentum, and other topics. Revised edition of "This Mechanical World." Illustrated by E. Kosa, Jr. Bibliography and Chronology. Index. xiv + 171pp. 5⅜ x 8½. T1067 Paperbound **$1.35**

THE CONCEPT OF ENERGY SIMPLY EXPLAINED, Morton Mott-Smith. Elementary, non-technical exposition which traces the story of man's conquest of energy, with particular emphasis on the developments during the nineteenth century and the first three decades of our own century. Discusses man's earlier efforts to harness energy, more recent experiments and discoveries relating to the steam engine, the engine indicator, the motive power of heat, the principle of excluded perpetual motion, the bases of the conservation of energy, the concept of entropy, the internal combustion engine, mechanical refrigeration, and many other related topics. Also much biographical material. Index. Bibliography. 33 illustrations. ix + 215pp. 5⅜ x 8½. T1071 Paperbound **$1.25**

HEAT AND ITS WORKINGS, Morton Mott-Smith. One of the best elementary introductions to the theory and attributes of heat, covering such matters as the laws governing the effect of heat on solids, liquids and gases, the methods by which heat is measured, the conversion of a substance from one form to another through heating and cooling, evaporation, the effects of pressure on boiling and freezing points, and the three ways in which heat is transmitted (conduction, convection, radiation). Also brief notes on major experiments and discoveries. Concise, but complete, it presents all the essential facts about the subject in readable style. Will give the layman and beginning student a first-rate background in this major topic in physics. Index. Bibliography. 50 illustrations. x + 165pp. 5⅜ x 8½. T978 Paperbound **$1.15**

THE STORY OF ATOMIC THEORY AND ATOMIC ENERGY, J. G. Feinberg. Wider range of facts on physical theory, cultural implications, than any other similar source. Completely non-technical. Begins with first atomic theory, 600 B.C., goes through A-bomb, developments to 1959. Avogadro, Rutherford, Bohr, Einstein, radioactive decay, binding energy, radiation danger, future benefits of nuclear power, dozens of other topics, told in lively, related, informal manner. Particular stress on European atomic research. "Deserves special mention . . . authoritative," Saturday Review. Formerly "The Atom Story." New chapter to 1959. Index. 34 illustrations. 251pp. 5⅜ x 8. T625 Paperbound **$1.60**

THE STRANGE STORY OF THE QUANTUM, AN ACCOUNT FOR THE GENERAL READER OF THE GROWTH OF IDEAS UNDERLYING OUR PRESENT ATOMIC KNOWLEDGE, B. Hoffmann. Presents lucidly and expertly, with barest amount of mathematics, the problems and theories which led to modern quantum physics. Dr. Hoffmann begins with the closing years of the 19th century, when certain trifling discrepancies were noticed, and with illuminating analogies and examples takes you through the brilliant concepts of Planck, Einstein, Pauli, de Broglie, Bohr, Schroedinger, Heisenberg, Dirac, Sommerfeld, Feynman, etc. This edition includes a new, long postscript carrying the story through 1958. "Of the books attempting an account of the history and contents of our modern atomic physics which have come to my attention, this is the best," H. Margenau, Yale University, in "American Journal of Physics." 32 tables and line illustrations. Index. 275pp. 5⅜ x 8. T518 Paperbound **$1.75**

THE EVOLUTION OF SCIENTIFIC THOUGHT FROM NEWTON TO EINSTEIN, A. d'Abro. Einstein's special and general theories of relativity, with their historical implications, are analyzed in non-technical terms. Excellent accounts of the contributions of Newton, Riemann, Weyl, Planck, Eddington, Maxwell, Lorentz and others are treated in terms of space and time, equations of electromagnetics, finiteness of the universe, methodology of science. 21 diagrams. 482pp. 5⅜ x 8. T2 Paperound **$2.25**

THE RISE OF THE NEW PHYSICS, A. d'Abro. A half-million word exposition, formerly titled THE DECLINE OF MECHANISM, for readers not versed in higher mathematics. The only thorough explanation, in everyday language, of the central core of modern mathematical physical theory, treating both classical and modern theoretical physics, and presenting in terms almost anyone can understand the equivalent of 5 years of study of mathematical physics. Scientifically impeccable coverage of mathematical-physical thought from the Newtonian system up through the electronic theories of Dirac and Heisenberg and Fermi's statistics. Combines both history and exposition; provides a broad yet unified and detailed view, with constant comparison of classical and modern views on phenomena and theories. "A must for anyone doing serious study in the physical sciences," JOURNAL OF THE FRANKLIN INSTITUTE. "Extraordinary faculty . . . to explain ideas and theories of theoretical physics in the language of daily life," ISIS. First part of set covers philosophy of science, drawing upon the practice of Newton, Maxwell, Poincaré, Einstein, others, discussing modes of thought, experiment, interpretations of causality, etc. In the second part, 100 pages explain grammar and vocabulary of mathematics, with discussions of functions, groups, series, Fourier series, etc. The remainder is devoted to concrete, detailed coverage of both classical and quantum physics, explaining such topics as analytic mechanics, Hamilton's principle, wave theory of light, electromagnetic waves, groups of transformations, thermodynamics, phase rule, Brownian movement, kinetics, special relativity, Planck's original quantum theory, Bohr's atom, Zeeman effect, Broglie's wave mechanics, Heisenberg's uncertainty, Eigen-values, matrices, scores of other important topics. Discoveries and theories are covered for such men as Alembert, Born, Cantor, Debye, Euler, Foucault, Galois, Gauss, Hadamard, Kelvin, Kepler, Laplace, Maxwell, Pauli, Rayleigh, Volterra, Weyl, Young, more than 180 others. Indexed. 97 illustrations. ix + 982pp. 5⅜ x 8.
T3 Volume 1, Paperbound **$2.25**
T4 Volume 2, Paperbound **$2.25**

SPINNING TOPS AND GYROSCOPIC MOTION, John Perry. Well-known classic of science still unsurpassed for lucid, accurate, delightful exposition. How quasi-rigidity is induced in flexible and fluid bodies by rapid motions; why gyrostat falls, top rises; nature and effect on climatic conditions of earth's precessional movement; effect of internal fluidity on rotating bodies, etc. Appendixes describe practical uses to which gyroscopes have been put in ships, compasses, monorail transportation. 62 figures. 128pp. 5⅜ x 8. T416 Paperbound **$1.25**

THE UNIVERSE OF LIGHT, Sir William Bragg. No scientific training needed to read Nobel Prize winner's expansion of his Royal Institute Christmas Lectures. Insight into nature of light, methods and philosophy of science. Explains lenses, reflection, color, resonance, polarization, x-rays, the spectrum, Newton's work with prisms, Huygens' with polarization, Crookes' with cathode ray, etc. Leads into clear statement of 2 major historical theories of light, corpuscle and wave. Dozens of experiments you can do. 199 illus., including 2 full-page color plates. 293pp. 5⅜ x 8. S538 Paperbound **$1.85**

THE STORY OF X-RAYS FROM RÖNTGEN TO ISOTOPES, A. R. Bleich. Non-technical history of x-rays, their scientific explanation, their applications in medicine, industry, research, and art, and their effect on the individual and his descendants. Includes amusing early reactions to Röntgen's discovery, cancer therapy, detections of art and stamp forgeries, potential risks to patient and operator, etc. Illustrations show x-rays of flower structure, the gall bladder, gears with hidden defects, etc. Original Dover publication. Glossary. Bibliography. Index. 55 photos and figures. xiv + 186pp. 5⅜ x 8. T662 Paperbound **$1.50**

ELECTRONS, ATOMS, METALS AND ALLOYS, Wm. Hume-Rothery. An introductory-level explanation of the application of the electronic theory to the structure and properties of metals and alloys, taking into account the new theoretical work done by mathematical physicists. Material presented in dialogue-form between an "Old Metallurgist" and a "Young Scientist." Their discussion falls into 4 main parts: the nature of an atom, the nature of a metal, the nature of an alloy, and the structure of the nucleus. They cover such topics as the hydrogen atom, electron waves, wave mechanics, Brillouin zones, co-valent bonds, radioactivity and natural disintegration, fundamental particles, structure and fission of the nucleus,etc. Revised, enlarged edition. 177 illustrations. Subject and name indexes. 407pp. 5⅜ x 8½. S1046 Paperbound **$2.25**

PHYSICS, HISTORIES AND CLASSICS

A HISTORY OF PHYSICS: IN ITS ELEMENTARY BRANCHES (THROUGH 1925), INCLUDING THE EVOLUTION OF PHYSICAL LABORATORIES, Florian Cajori. Revised and enlarged edition. The only first-rate brief history of physics. Still the best entry for a student or teacher into the antecedents of modern theories of physics. A clear, non-mathematical, handy reference work which traces in critical fashion the developments of ideas, theories, techniques, and apparatus from the Greeks to the 1920's. Within each period he analyzes the basic topics of mechanics, light, electricity and magnetism, sound, atomic theory and structure of matter, radioactivity, etc. A chapter on modern research: Curie, Kelvin, Planck's quantum theory, thermodynamics, Fitzgerald and Lorentz, special and general relativity, J. J. Thomson's model of an atom, Bohr's discoveries and later results, wave mechanics, and many other matters. Much bibliographic detail in footnotes. Index. 16 figures. xv + 424pp. 5⅜ x 8. T970 Paperbound **$2.00**

A HISTORY OF THE MATHEMATICAL THEORIES OF ATTRACTION AND THE FIGURE OF THE EARTH: FROM THE TIME OF NEWTON TO THAT OF LAPLACE, I. Todhunter. A technical and detailed review of the theories concerning the shape of the earth and its gravitational pull, from the earliest investigations in the seventeenth century up to the middle of the nineteenth. Some of the greatest mathematicians and scientists in history applied themselves to these questions: Newton ("Principia Mathematica"), Huygens, Maupertuis, Simpson, d'Alembert, etc. Others discussed are Poisson, Gauss, Plana, Lagrange, Boit, and many more. Particular emphasis is placed on the theories of Laplace and Legendre, several chapters being devoted to Laplace's "Mécanique Céleste" and his memoirs, and several others to the memoirs of Legendre. Important to historians of science and mathematics and to the specialist who desires background information in the field. 2 volumes bound as 1. Index. xxxvi + 984pp. 5⅜ x 8.
S148 Clothbound **$7.50**

OPTICKS, Sir Isaac Newton. In its discussions of light, reflection, color, refraction, theories of wave and corpuscular theories of light, this work is packed with scores of insights and discoveries. In its precise and practical discussion of construction of optical apparatus, contemporary understandings of phenomena it is truly fascinating to modern physicists, astronomers, mathematicians. Foreword by Albert Einstein. Preface by I. B. Cohen of Harvard University. 7 pages of portraits, facsimile pages, letters, etc. cxvi + 414pp. 5⅜ x 8.
S205 Paperbound **$2.25**

TREATISE ON LIGHT, Christiaan Huygens. The famous original formulation of the wave theory of light, this readable book is one of the two decisive and definitive works in the field of light (Newton's "Optics" is the other). A scientific giant whose researches ranged over mathematics, astronomy, and physics, Huygens, in this historic work, covers such topics as rays propagated in straight lines, reflection and refraction, the spreading and velocity of light, the nature of opaque bodies, the non-spherical nature of light in the atmosphere, properties of Iceland Crystal, and other related matters. Unabridged republication of original (1912) English edition. Translated and introduced by Silvanus P. Thompson. 52 illustrations. xii + 129pp. 5⅜ x 8. S179 Paperbound **$1.50**

FARADAY'S EXPERIMENTAL RESEARCHES IN ELECTRICITY. Faraday's historic series of papers containing the fruits of years of original experimentation in electrical theory and electrochemistry. Covers his findings in a variety of areas: Induction of electric currents, Evolution of electricity from magnetism, New electrical state or condition of matter, Explication of Arago's magnetic phenomena, New law of electric conduction, Electro-chemical decomposition, Electricity of the Voltaic Pile, Static Induction, Nature of the electric force or forces, Nature of electric current, The character and direction of the electric force of the Gymnotus, Magneto-electric spark, The magnetization of light and the illumination of magnetic lines of force, The possible relation of gravity to electricity, Sub-terraneous electro-telegraph wires, Some points of magnetic philosophy, The diamagnetic conditions of flame and gases, and many other matters. Complete and unabridged republication. 3 vols. bound as 2. Originally reprinted from the Philosophical Transactions of 1831-8. Indices. Illustrations. Total of 1463pp. 5⅜ x 8. S783-4, Clothbound **$17.50** (tentative)

REFLECTIONS ON THE MOTIVE POWER OF FIRE, Sadi Carnot, and other papers on the 2nd law of thermodynamics by E. Clapeyron and R. Clausius. Carnot's "Reflections" laid the groundwork of modern thermodynamics. Its non-technical, mostly verbal statements examine the relations between heat and the work done by heat in engines, establishing conditions for the economical working of these engines. The papers by Clapeyron and Clausius here reprinted added further refinements to Carnot's work, and led to its final acceptance by physicists. Selections from posthumous manuscripts of Carnot are also included. All papers in English. New introduction by E. Mendoza. 12 illustrations. xxii + 152pp. 5⅜ x 8.
S661 Paperbound **$1.50**

DIALOGUES CONCERNING TWO NEW SCIENCES, Galileo Galilei. This classic of experimental science, mechanics, engineering, is as enjoyable as it is important. A great historical document giving insights into one of the world's most original thinkers, it is based on 30 years' experimentation. It offers a lively exposition of dynamics, elasticity, sound, ballistics, strength of materials, the scientific method. "Superior to everything else of mine," Galileo. Trans. by H. Crew, A. Salvio. 126 diagrams. Index. xxi + 288pp. 5⅜ x 8.
S99 Paperbound **$1.75**

TREATISE ON ELECTRICITY AND MAGNETISM, James Clerk Maxwell. For more than 80 years a seemingly inexhaustible source of leads for physicists, mathematicians, engineers. Total of 1082pp. on such topics as Measurement of Quantities, Electrostatics, Elementary Mathematical Theory of Electricity, Electrical Work and Energy in a System of Conductors, General Theorems, Theory of Electrical Images, Electrolysis, Conduction, Polarization, Dielectrics, Resistance, etc. "The greatest mathematical physicist since Newton," Sir James Jeans. 3rd edition. 107 figures, 21 plates. 1082pp. 5⅜ x 8. S636-7, 2 volume set, paperbound **$4.00**

A HISTORY OF THE THEORY OF ELASTICITY AND THE STRENGTH OF MATERIALS, I. Todhunter and K. Pearson. For over 60 years a basic reference, unsurpassed in scope or authority. Both a history of the mathematical theory of elasticity from Galileo, Hooke, and Mariotte to Saint Venant, Kirchhoff, Clebsch, and Lord Kelvin and a detailed presentation of every important mathematical contribution during this period. Presents proofs of thousands of theorems and laws, summarizes every relevant treatise, many unavailable elsewhere. Practically a book apiece is devoted to modern founders: Saint Venant, Lamé, Boussinesq, Rankine, Lord Kelvin, F. Neumann, Kirchhoff, Clebsch. Hundreds of pages of technical and physical treatises on specific applications of elasticity to particular materials. Indispensable for the mathematician, physicist, or engineer working with elasticity. Unabridged, corrected reprint of original 3-volume 1886-1893 edition. Three volume set. Two indexes. Appendix to Vol. I. Total of 2344pp. 5⅜ x 8⅜. S914–916 The set, Clothbound **$15.00**

DE MAGNETE, William Gilbert. This classic work on magnetism founded a new science. Gilbert was the first to use the word "electricity", to recognize mass as distinct from weight, to discover the effect of heat on magnetic bodies; invent an electroscope, differentiate between static electricity and magnetism, conceive of the earth as a magnet. Written by the first great experimental scientist, this lively work is valuable not only as an historical landmark, but as the delightfully easy to follow record of a perpetually searching, ingenious mind. Translated by P. F. Mottelay. 25-page biographical memoir. 90 figures. lix +368pp. 5⅜ x 8. S470 Paperbound **$2.00**

ASTRONOMY

THE INTERNAL CONSTITUTION OF THE STARS, Sir A. S. Eddington. Influence of this has been enormous; first detailed exposition of theory of radiative equilibrium for stellar interiors, of all available evidence for existence of diffuse matter in interstellar space. Studies quantum theory, polytropic gas spheres, mass-luminosity relations, variable stars, etc. Discussions of equations paralleled with informal exposition of intimate relationship of astrophysics with great discoveries in atomic physics, radiation. Introduction. Appendix. Index. 421pp. 5⅜ x 8. S563 Paperbound **$2.75**

PLANETARY THEORY, E. W. Brown and C. A. Shook. Provides a clear presentation of basic methods for calculating planetary orbits for today's astronomer. Begins with a careful exposition of specialized mathematical topics essential for handling perturbation theory and then goes on to indicate how most of the previous methods reduce ultimately to two general calculation methods: obtaining expressions either for the coordinates of planetary positions or for the elements which determine the perturbed paths. An example of each is given and worked in detail. Corrected edition. Preface. Appendix. Index. xii + 302pp. 5⅜ x 8½. S1133 Paperbound **$2.25**

CANON OF ECLIPSES (CANON DER FINSTERNISSE), Prof. Theodor Ritter von Oppolzer. Since its original publication in 1887, this has been the standard reference and the most extensive single volume of data on the calculation of solar and lunar eclipses, past and future. A comprehensive introduction gives a full explanation of the use of the tables for the calculations of the exact dates of eclipses, etc. Data furnished for the calculation of 8,000 solar and 5,200 lunar eclipses, going back as far as 1200 B.C. and giving predictions up to the year 2161. Information is also given for partial and ring eclipses. All calculations based on Universal (Greenwich) Time. An unsurpassed reference work for astronomers, scientists engaged in space research and developments, historians, etc. Unabridged republication, with corrections. Preface to this edition by Donald Menzel and Owen Gingerich of the Harvard College Observatory. Translated by Owen Gingerich. 160 charts. lxx + 538pp. 8⅜ x 11¼. S114 Clothbound **$10.00**

THEORY OF THE MOTION OF THE HEAVENLY BODIES MOVING ABOUT THE SUN IN CONIC SECTIONS, Karl Friedrich Gauss. A landmark of theoretical astronomy by the great German scientist. Still authoritative and invaluable to the practicing astronomer. Part I develops the relations between the quantities on which the motion about the sun of the heavenly bodies depends—relations pertaining simply to position in the orbit, simply to position in space, between several places in orbit, and between several places in space. The calculation methods of Part II based on the groundwork of Part I include: determination of an orbit from 3 complete observations, from 4 observations (of which only two are complete), determination of an orbit satisfying as nearly as possible any number of observations whatever, and determination of orbits, taking into account the perturbations. Translation of "Theoria Motus" and with an appendix by C. H. Davis. Unabridged republication. Appendices and tables. 13 figures. xviii + 376pp. 6½ x 9¼. S1056 Paperbound **$2.95**

THE GALACTIC NOVAE, C. Payne-Gaposchkin, Prof. of Astronomy, Harvard Univ. A work that will be the standard reference source for years to come. Gathers together all the pertinent data, results recorded by countless observers of galactic novae over the centuries, in order to formulate a valid starting point for an interpretation of the nova process. Covers information and statistics on known novae, their variations in luminosity, distribution in the sky, spectral changes, etc.; symbiotic novae; frequently-recurring variables of the U Geminorum and Z Camelopardis class; supernovae; comparison of spectral changes; theories and interpretations of these phenomena, etc. "A comprehensive summary of everything that is now known about these stars," SCIENCE. Bibliographical references. Preface. Indices. 49 figures. 6 plates. 101 tables. x + 336pp. 5⅜ x 8⅜. S1170 Paperbound **$2.45**

BINARY STARS, R. G. Aitken. Still the definitive work in the field of double star astronomy. Written by the director of the Lick Observatory (considered the father of the modern study of binary star systems), this book sums up the results of 40 years of experience in the field, plus the work of centuries of research. Includes historical survey of major discoveries and contributions of the past, observational methods for visual binary stars, the radial velocity of a star (by Dr. J. H. Moore), eclipsing binary stars, known orbits of binary stars, some binary systems of special interest, the origin of binary stars. Much information on methods of spectrum analysis, orbit plotting, use of the telescope, and other practical matters. Useful for classroom study and advanced hobbyists, etc. Revised edition, corrected and with additional notes by Prof. J. T. Kent. New preface. 50 tables, 13 figures, 4 full-page plates. Bibliographies. Appendix. Indices. xii + 309pp. 5⅜ x 8½.
S1102 Paperbound **$2.00**

THE NATURE OF COMETS, N. B. Richter. An authority on comets presents a concise, but thorough survey of the state of our present-day knowledge of comets and cometary activity. Based on over 20 years of research, this is a middle-level account that even the layman can appreciate, providing a fund of information on historical theories (from 1700 to the present); statistical research on total number of comets, orbital forms, perturbations caused by Jupiter, comet groups, etc.; the structure of a comet; comets as processes of cosmic decay; origin and formation of comets; etc. Also: a lengthy introduction on modern theories by Dr. R. A. Lyttleton, much technical data and observational material of specific comets, supplementary tables, and the like. Revised (1963) edition. Translated and revised by Arthur Beer. 69 illustrations, including 54 photographs of comets, tails, spectra. 41 tables. Bibliography. Index. xli + 221pp. S1111 Clothbound **$10.00**

CELESTIAL OBJECTS FOR COMMON TELESCOPES, Rev. T. W. Webb. Classic handbook for the use and pleasure of the amateur astronomer. Of inestimable aid in locating and identifying thousands of celestial objects. Vol. I, The Solar System: discussions of the principle and operation of the telescope, procedures of observations and telescope-photography, spectroscopy, etc., precise location information of sun, moon, planets, meteors. Vol. II, The Stars: alphabetical listing of constellations, information on double stars, clusters, stars with unusual spectra, variables, and nebulae, etc. Nearly 4,000 objects noted. Edited and extensively revised by Margaret W. Mayall, director of the American Assn. of Variable Star Observers. New Index by Mrs. Mayall giving the location of all objects mentioned in the text for Epoch 2000. New Precession Table added. New appendices on the planetary satellites, constellation names and abbreviations, and solar system data. Total of 46 illustrations. Total of xxxix + 606pp. 5⅜ x 8. Vol. I: T917 Paperbound **$2.25**
Vol. II: T918 Paperbound **$2.25**
Two Volume Set Paperbound **$4.50**

ASTRONOMY AND COSMOGONY, Sir James Jeans. A modern classic which is still of enormous value to everyone in astronomy, etc., this is Jean's last and most famous exposition. The summation of a lifetime's devotion to science, it presents his final conclusions on a host of problems ranging over the whole of descriptive astronomy, astrophysics, stellar dynamics, and cosmology. Contents: The Light from the Stars, Gaseous Stars, the Source of Stellar Energy, Liquid Stars, The Evolution of the Stars, The Configuration of Rotating Masses, The Evolution of Binary Systems, The Ages of the Stars, The Great Nebulae, The Galactic Systems, Variable Stars, etc. New preface by L. Motz, Columbia U. 16 full-page photographic illustrations. xv + 428pp. 5⅝ x 8⅜. S923 Paperbound **$2.45**

ASTRONOMY OF STELLAR ENERGY AND DECAY, Martin Johnson. Middle level treatment of astronomy as interpreted by modern atomic physics. Part One is non-technical, examines physical properties, source of energy, spectroscopy, fluctuating stars, various models and theories, etc. Part Two parallels these topics, providing their mathematical foundation. "Clear, concise, and readily understandable," American Library Assoc. Bibliography. 3 indexes. 29 illustrations. 216pp. 5⅜ x 8. S537 Paperbound **$1.50**

MATHEMATICAL THEORIES OF PLANETARY MOTIONS, Otto Dziobek. Translated by Mark W. Harrington and William J. Hussey. Lucid account of the principles of mathematical astronomy. It examines that part of celestial mechanics which deals with the motions of heavenly bodies considered as material points. Contents: Solution of the Problem of Two Bodies; Formation of the General Integrals for Problem of **n** Bodies . . . including discussions of elliptic, parabolic, and hyperbolic orbits, the solution of Kepler's equation, etc.; and sections headed The General Properties of the Integrals and The Theory of Perturbations . . . which deals with the theory of absolute perturbations, analytical development of the perturbing function, the variation of the elements, the secular variation of the mean longitude, etc. vi + 294pp. 5⅜ x 8½. S129 Paperbound **$2.00**

GEOLOGY, GEOGRAPHY, METEOROLOGY

PRINCIPLES OF STRATIGRAPHY, A. W. Grabau. Classic of 20th century geology, unmatched in scope and comprehensiveness. Nearly 600 pages cover the structure and origins of every kind of sedimentary, hydrogenic, oceanic, pyroclastic, atmoclastic, hydroclastic, marine hydroclastic, and bioclastic rock; metamorphism; erosion; etc. Includes also the constitution of the atmosphere; morphology of oceans, rivers, glaciers; volcanic activities; faults and earthquakes; and fundamental principles of paleontology (nearly 200 pages). New introduction by Prof. M. Kay, Columbia U. 1277 bibliographical entries. 264 diagrams. Tables, maps, etc. Two volume set. Total of xxxii + 1185pp. 5⅜ x 8.
S686 Vol I Paperbound **$2.50**
S687 Vol II Paperbound **$2.50**
The set **$5.00**

TREATISE ON SEDIMENTATION, William H. Twenhofel. A milestone in the history of geology, this two-volume work, prepared under the auspices of the United States Research Council, contains practically everything known about sedimentation up to 1932. Brings together all the findings of leading American and foreign geologists and geographers and has never been surpassed for completeness, thoroughness of description, or accuracy of detail. Vol. 1 discusses the sources and production of sediments, their transportation, deposition, diagenesis, and lithification. Also modification of sediments by organisms and topographical, climatic, etc. conditions which contribute to the alteration of sedimentary processes. 220 pages deal with products of sedimentation: minerals, limestones, dolomites, coals, etc. Vol. 2 continues the examination of products such as gypsum and saline residues, silica, strontium, manganese, etc. An extensive exposition of structures, textures and colors of sediments: stratification, cross-lamination, ripple mark, oolitic and pisolitic textures, etc. Chapters on environments or realms of sedimentation and field and laboratory techniques are also included. Indispensable to modern-day geologists and students. Index. List of authors cited. 1733-item bibliography. 121 diagrams. Total of xxxiii + 926pp. 5⅜ x 8½.
Vol. I: S950 Paperbound **$2.50**
Vol. II: S951 Paperbound **$2.50**
Two volume set Paperbound **$5.00**

THE EVOLUTION OF THE IGNEOUS ROCKS, N. L. Bowen. Invaluable serious introduction applies techniques of physics and chemistry to explain igneous rock diversity in terms of chemical composition and fractional crystallization. Discusses liquid immiscibility in silicate magmas, crystal sorting, liquid lines of descent, fractional resorption of complex minerals, petrogenesis, etc. Of prime importance to geologists & mining engineers, also to physicists, chemists working with high temperatures and pressures. "Most important," TIMES, London. 3 indexes. 263 bibliographic notes. 82 figures. xviii + 334pp. 5⅜ x 8. S311 Paperbound **$2.25**

INTERNAL CONSTITUTION OF THE EARTH, edited by **Beno Gutenberg.** Completely revised. Brought up-to-date, reset. Prepared for the National Research Council this is a complete & thorough coverage of such topics as earth origins, continent formation, nature & behavior of the earth's core, petrology of the crust, cooling forces in the core, seismic & earthquake material, gravity, elastic constants, strain characteristics and similar topics. "One is filled with admiration . . . a high standard . . . there is no reader who will not learn something from this book," London, Edinburgh, Dublin, Philosophic Magazine. Largest bibliography in print: 1127 classified items. Indexes. Tables of constants. 43 diagrams. 439pp. 6⅛ x 9¼.
S414 Paperbound **$3.00**

HYDROLOGY, edited by **Oscar E. Meinzer.** Prepared for the National Research Council. Detailed complete reference library on precipitation, evaporation, snow, snow surveying, glaciers, lakes, infiltration, soil moisture, ground water, runoff, drought, physical changes produced by water, hydrology of limestone terranes, etc. Practical in application, especially valuable for engineers. 24 experts have created "the most up-to-date, most complete treatment of the subject," AM. ASSOC. of PETROLEUM GEOLOGISTS. Bibliography. Index. 165 illustrations. xi + 712pp. 6⅛ x 9¼. S191 Paperbound **$3.50**

SNOW CRYSTALS, W. A. Bentley and W. J. Humphreys. Over 200 pages of Bentley's famous microphotographs of snow flakes—the product of painstaking, methodical work at his Jericho, Vermont studio. The pictures, which also include plates of frost, glaze and dew on vegetation, spider webs, windowpanes; sleet; graupel or soft hail, were chosen both for their scientific interest and their aesthetic qualities. The wonder of nature's diversity is exhibited in the intricate, beautiful patterns of the snow flakes. Introductory text by W. J. Humphreys. Selected bibliography. 2,453 illustrations. 224pp. 8 x 10¼. T287 Paperbound **$2.95**

PHYSICS OF THE AIR, W. J. Humphreys. A very thorough coverage of classical materials and theories in meteorology . . . written by one of this century's most highly respected physical meteorologists. Contains the standard account in English of atmospheric optics. 5 main sections: Mechanics and Thermodynamics of the Atmosphere, Atmospheric Electricity and Auroras, Meteorological Acoustics, Atmospheric Optics, and Factors of Climatic Control. Under these headings, topics covered are: theoretical relations between temperature, pressure, and volume in the atmosphere; composition, pressure, and density; circulation; evaporation and condensation; fog, clouds, thunderstorms, lightning; aurora polaris; principal ice-age theories; etc. New preface by Prof. Julius London. 226 illustrations. Index. xviii + 676pp. 5⅜ x 8½. S1044 Paperbound **$3.00**

URANIUM PROSPECTING, H. L. Barnes. For immediate practical use, professional geologist considers uranium ores, geological occurrences, field conditions, all aspects of highly profitable occupation. Index. Bibliography. x + 117pp. 5⅜ x 8. T309 Paperbound **$1.00**

SELECTED PAPERS IN THE THEORY OF THERMAL CONVECTION: WITH SPECIAL APPLICATION TO THE EARTH'S PLANETARY ATMOSPHERE, Edited by Barry Saltzman. An indispensable volume for anyone interested in the motions of the earth's atmosphere. 25 basic theoretical papers on thermal convection by major scientists, past and present: Helmholtz, Overbeck, Jeffreys, Rayleigh, G. I. Taylor, Chandrasekhar, A. R. Low, Rossby, Davies, Charney, Eady, Phillips, Pellew and Southwell, Elbert, Fjortoft, and H.-L. Kuo. Bibliography. x + 461pp. 6⅛ x 9¼. S171 Paperbound **$3.00**

THE FOUNDERS OF GEOLOGY, Sir Archibald Geikie. Survey of the high moments and the work of the major figures of the period in which the main foundations of modern geology were laid—the latter half of the 18th century to the first half of the 19th. The developments in the science during this era centering around the lives and accomplishments of the great contributors: Palissy, Guettard, Demarest, Pallas, Lehmann, Füchsel, Werner, Hutton, Playfair, Sir James Hall, Cuvier, Lyell, Logan, Darwin, Agassiz, Nicol, and others. Comprehensive and readable. Index. xi + 486pp. 5⅜ x 8½. T352 Paperbound **$2.25**

THE BIRTH AND DEVELOPMENT OF THE GEOLOGICAL SCIENCES, F. D. Adams. Most thorough history of the earth sciences ever written. Geological thought from earliest times to the end of the 19th century, covering over 300 early thinkers & systems: fossils & their explanation, vulcanists vs. neptunists, figured stones & paleontology, generation of stones, dozens of similar topics. 91 illustrations, including medieval, renaissance woodcuts, etc. Index. 632 footnotes, mostly bibliographical. 511pp. 5⅜ x 8. T5 Paperbound **$2.25**

A HISTORY OF ANCIENT GEOGRAPHY, E. H. Bunbury. Standard study, in English, of ancient geography; never equalled for scope, detail. First full account of history of geography from Greeks' first world picture based on mariners, through Ptolemy. Discusses every important map, discovery, figure, travel, expedition, war, conjecture, narrative, bearing on subject. Chapters on Homeric geography, Herodotus, Alexander expedition, Strabo, Pliny, Ptolemy, would stand alone as exhaustive monographs. Includes minor geographers, men not usually regarded in this context: Hecataeus, Pythea, Hipparchus, Artemidorus, Marinus of Tyre, etc. Uses information gleaned from military campaigns such as Punic wars, Hannibal's passage of Alps, campaigns of Lucullus, Pompey, Caesar's wars, the Trojan war. New introduction by W. H. Stahl, Brooklyn College. Bibliography. Index. 20 maps. 1426pp. 5⅜ x 8.
T570-1, clothbound, 2 volume set **$12.50**

DE RE METALLICA, Georgius Agricola. 400-year old classic translated, annotated by former President Herbert Hoover. The first scientific study of mineralogy and mining, for over 200 years after its appearance in 1556, it was the standard treatise. 12 books, exhaustively annotated, discuss the history of mining, selection of sites, types of deposits, making pits, shafts, ventilating, pumps, crushing machinery; assaying, smelting, refining metals; also salt, alum, nitre, glass making. Definitive edition, with all 289 16th century woodcuts of the original. Biographical, historical introductions, bibliography, survey of ancient authors. Indexes. A fascinating book for anyone interested in art, history of science, geology, etc. Deluxe edition. 289 illustrations. 672pp. 6¾ x 10¾. Library cloth. S6 Clothbound **$10.00**

GEOGRAPHICAL ESSAYS, William Morris Davis. Modern geography & geomorphology rest on the fundamental work of this scientist. 26 famous essays presenting most important theories, field researches. Partial contents: Geographical Cycle, Plains of Marine and Subaerial Denudation, The Peneplain, Rivers and Valleys of Pennsylvania, Outline of Cape Cod, Sculpture of Mountains by Glaciers, etc. "Long the leader & guide," ECONOMIC GEOGRAPHY. "Part of the very texture of geography . . . models of clear thought," GEOGRAPHIC REVIEW. Index. 130 figures. vi + 777pp. 5⅜ x 8. S383 Paperbound **$2.95**

Prices subject to change without notice.

Dover publishes books on art, music, philosophy, literature, languages, history, social sciences, psychology, handcrafts, orientalia, puzzles and entertainments, chess, pets and gardens, books explaining science, intermediate and higher mathematics, mathematical physics, engineering, biological sciences, earth sciences, classics of science, etc. Write to:

Dept. catrr.
Dover Publications, Inc.
180 Varick Street, N.Y. 14, N.Y.